science and theology join together to form a
new understanding of the image of man.

"We must seize the initiative and force out
a merger of the naturalistic emphasis on determinism and the humanistic emphasis on
freedom," states the author. "It is my hope
that this book will contribute to such an initiative."

THE AUTHOR

HAROLD E. HATT is professor of theology
and philosophy at the Graduate Seminary,
Phillips University, Enid, Oklahoma.

Author of *Encountering Truth*, a study of
the theological concept of revelation, Dr. Hatt
is a member of the American Academy of Religion and the American Philosophical Association. He is a frequent participant and
consultant in conferences, workshops, and lectures on cybernetics and technological change.

He is a graduate of the University of British
Columbia (B.A.), Southwestern Baptist Theo-
logical Seminary (B.D.), Baylor University
(M.A.), and Vanderbilt University (Ph.D.),
where he studied on a Rockefeller Doctoral
Fellowship.

Cybernetics
and the
Image of Man

Cybernetics
and the
Image of Man

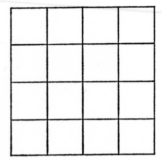

a study of freedom and responsibility in man and machine

HAROLD E. HATT

ABINGDON PRESS—Nashville and New York

CYBERNETICS AND THE IMAGE OF MAN

Copyright © 1968 by Abingdon Press

Library of Congress Catalog Card Number: 68-28827

The quotation from *The Power Elite* by C. Wright Mills, copyright 1957, is used by permission of Oxford University Press. Material from "The Case for Determinism," by Brand Blanshard, and "Determinism and Novelty," by William Barrett is from *Determinism and Freedom*, Sidney Hook, ed., copyright 1958, and is used by permission of New York University Press. Quotations from *The Freedom of the Will* by Austin Farrer, copyright 1958 by Adam & Charles Black, Ltd. of London, are used by permission of the publishers. Quotation from *Hardness of Heart* by E. La B. Cherbonnier, copyright © 1955 by E. La B. Cherbonnier; reprinted by permission of Doubleday & Company, Inc. Material from *Philosophical Papers* by John Austin, copyright 1961, is used by permission of the Clarendon Press, Oxford. Selections from Richard L. Gregory, "The Logic of the Localization of Function in the Central Nervous System," and M. C. Goodall, "Induction and Logical Types," are from *Biological Prototypes and Synthetic Systems*, Vol. I, Eugene E. Bernard and Morley R. Kare, eds., copyright 1961, and are used by permission of Plenum Press. Material from Hilary Putnam, "Robots: Machines or Artificially Created Life?" is from *The Journal of Philosophy*, Vol. LXI, no. 21 (Nov. 12, 1964), and is used by permission of The Journal of Philosophy and the author. Quotations from Robert Theobald, "Cybernetics and the Problems of Social Reorganization"; Hyman Rickover, "A Humanistic Technology"; and Marshall McLuhan, "Cybernetics and Culture," are from *The Social Impact of Cybernetics*, Charles E. Dechert, ed., copyright 1966, and are used by permission of the University of Notre Dame Press. Selections reprinted from *Cybernetics: Or Control and Communication in the Animal and the Machine* by Norbert Wiener are used by permission of The M.I.T. Press, Cambridge, Massachusetts. Copyright © 1948 and 1961 by the Massachusetts Institute of Technology. The quotation from "The Historical Roots of Our Ecological Crisis," Lynn White, Jr., *Science*, Vol. 155, pp. 1203-1207, 10 March 1967, copyright 1967 by the American Association for the Advancement of Science, is used by permission of the American Association for the Advancement of Science. The poem on p. 230 is reprinted by permission of G. P. Putnam's Sons from *Deaths for the Ladies (and Other Disasters)* by Norman Mailer. Copyright © 1962 by Norman Mailer. The quotation from Roger L. Shinn, "The Moral Meaning of Transportation," is reprinted from *Christianity and Crisis*, October 3, 1966. Copyright by Christianity and Crisis, Inc., 1966.

SET UP, PRINTED, AND BOUND BY THE
PARTHENON PRESS, AT NASHVILLE,
TENNESSEE, UNITED STATES OF AMERICA

To my parents, Mr. and Mrs. Fred Hatt

Contents

Contents

Introduction

Communication and control are becoming increasingly significant as we move through the final third of the twentieth century toward the twenty-first century. Cybernetics involves the comparative study of communication and control in the brain and nervous system of organisms and in mechanical-electrical systems. Study of the brain and nervous system has yielded insights that are valuable in the development of mechanical-electrical control systems, and, conversely, the study of such systems has yielded insights into the physiology and neurology of organisms. Man was nudged from the center of the universe by Copernicus; Darwin drew man's physical nature within the natural evolutionary process; man's unique claim to rationality was greatly reduced by Freud; and now, it seems, man is nothing but a highly complex communication-control system. Indeed, man is already excelled by the machine in some of the simpler, more routine tasks. What does the future hold?

Application of the term "cybernetics" to automation has given us the term "cybernation." We are fast moving into the age of automated factories, computerized teaching and date-making services, programmed space flights, automatic data-processing and information retrieval systems, and so forth. These are no longer curiosities, and will soon be a part of the gear of everyday life. It is hard for us to realize that the space age began with the launch of Sputnik on October 4, 1957, that the

9

first computer (already a museum piece) was not in operation until World War II, and that computers did not become commercially available until the early 1950's.

Although the influence of mathematics and physics is a major one in cybernetics, these two disciplines are not dominating the scientific scene as they did earlier in the century. Biology is making a strong resurgence. Molecular biology, which deals with such things as DNA and RNA, has been especially significant. DNA is the "computer tape" which "programs" heredity. We can already read the code, and we expect to be able to write it before long. It seems that we will be able to feed in characteristics that we consider desirable and to eliminate features that we want to reject. Even these few intimations of the changes in store explain the strong sense of hope and expectation, and the occasional pangs of fear and apprehension, with which we view the future.

The image of man can provide a helpful focus for seeing the relation between theological and other disciplines. Moreover, the relation is not a one-way street, as indicated by this statement of Walter Lippmann on the relation of political science to the Christian understanding of man.

Though the political government is concerned primarily with the affairs of the existential world, though the churches are primarily committed to the realm of the spirit, they meet whenever and wherever there are issues of right and wrong, issues of what is the nature of man, of what is his true image, his place in the scheme of things, and his destiny.[1]

It is very important that science and theology clarify their understanding of the image of man, because we live in what Albert T. Rasmussen aptly calls a "sea of influence"[2] that tries to make us into the image that is desired by interested parties in our culture. If we do not take the trouble to clarify

[1] *The Public Philosophy* (Boston: Little, Brown & Co., 1955), p. 154.
[2] *Christian Social Ethics* (Englewood Cliffs, N. J.: Prentice-Hall, 1956), chap. 2.

our image, there are others who will do it for us. C. Wright Mills has a very succinct, powerful, and disturbing analysis of the influence of the mass media upon the very image of man.

> The media have not only filtered into our experience of external realities, they have also entered into our very experience of our own selves. They have provided us with new identities and new aspirations of what we should like to be, and what we should like to appear to be. They have provided in the models of conduct they hold out to us a new and larger and more flexible set of appraisals of our very selves. In terms of the modern theory of the self, we may say that the media bring the reader, listener, viewer into the sight of larger, higher reference groups— groups, real or imagined, up-close or vicarious, personally known or distractedly glimpsed—which are looking glasses for his self-image. They have multiplied the groups to which we look for confirmation of our self-image.
>
> More than that: (1) the media tell the man in the mass who he is— they give him identity; (2) they tell him what he wants to be—they give him aspirations; (3) they tell him how to get that way—they give him technique; and (4) they tell him how to feel that he is that way even when he is not—they give him escape. The gaps between the identity and aspiration lead to technique and/or to escape. That is probably the basic psychological formula of the mass media today. But, as a formula, it is not attuned to the development of the human being. It is the formula of a pseudo-world which the media invent and sustain.[3]

The problem that is of particular concern in this study is the nature of human freedom and responsibility in the light of cybernetics. Man is a product of environment and heredity. With the rapid growth of cybernetics and molecular biology, these factors are both becoming increasingly subject to manipulation and control. If causally determined machines continue to make inroads into activities that were formerly unique to man, can we continue to think of man as free? If we can condition man to function in whatever kind of environment we desire to create,

---

[3] *The Power Elite* (New York: Oxford University Press, 1957), p. 314.

can we say that man is freely choosing his own destiny? If manipulation of DNA molecules can create a different man and perhaps even transfer learning from one man to another, can we deny that man is determined? And if man is determined in such ways as these, then is there any possible sense in which we can speak of man as responsible? This sort of question has already been faced in a serious way by our recognition of the influence of environment. If such factors as slum conditions and broken families create social misfits, then how can we hold the individual responsible? But now this question comes at us in a much more fundamental form and with a universal application. We are no longer dealing solely with the influence of certain factors upon a portion of society. We are now talking about the basic foundation of life for all people.

In my book *Encountering Truth,* I argued that the I-Thou encounter with God can never be completely free of I-It elements, and I proposed an emended form of encounter theology that incorporated I-It elements from metaphysics and science as essential and legitimate components of theological reflection within the framework of encounter theology. This book will apply such a methodology to the problem of the relation of human freedom and responsibility (I-Thou relation) and scientific understanding of man (I-It connection). Since my own stance is more in the tradition of existential than of analytic philosophy, and since my concern is to develop a form of existentialism that is more appreciative of the scientific enterprise than is characteristic of earlier forms of existentialism, I am especially interested in showing how scientific insights can be incorporated within an existential view of human freedom and responsibility.

Emil Brunner's attitude toward technology is typical of those theologians who wanted to be appreciative of the achievements of civilization, but who were primarily concerned with the threats to civilization. Two world wars and the advent of the atomic bomb provided the context within which they thought.

It is because of such destructive manifestations of technology, or "technics" as Brunner calls it, that he writes:

Modern technics is the product of the man who wants to redeem himself by rising above nature, who wants to gather life into his hand, who wants to owe his existence to nobody but himself, who wants to create a world after his own image, an artificial world which is entirely his creation. Behind the terrifying, crazy tempo of the technical evolution, there is all the insatiability of secularized man who, not believing in God or eternal life, wants to snatch as much of this world within his lifetime as he can. Modern technics is, to put it crudely, the expression of the world-voracity of modern man, and the tempo of its development is the expression of his inward unrest, the disquiet of the man who is destined for God's eternity, but has himself rejected this destiny. The hypertrophy of technical interest, resulting in a hyperdynamism of technical evolution, is the necessary consequence of man's abandonment to the world of things, which follows his emancipation from God. . . . When . . . a country rejoices over the growth of a city of millions of inhabitants, this is as stupid as if someone were to rejoice over the growth of a cancer. Giant cities are merely symptoms, but they are obvious symptoms of autonomous technical growth which finally leads to destruction.[4]

The last two sentences quoted from Brunner are in sharp contrast to the attitude of Harvey Cox in *The Secular City*. Whereas the city is demonic for Brunner, it is messianic for Cox. Recognition of the possibilities and values of life in our large cities was long overdue. But recent violence in our cities suggests a reappraisal. As Christians accept and affirm life in the contemporary technological era, it may prove necessary to retain more of the neo-orthodox theological tradition than we first thought. True, this theological tradition is very closely related to the social

---

[4] *Christianity and Civilization* (New York: Charles Scribner's Sons, 1949), II, 4-5, 13. In a similar context, Brunner says: "How impotent is human reason in construction, how almighty in destruction! With a few bombs man destroys in a few seconds the work of centuries, and no one knows whether the next war will sweep away, in a few days, the culture of thousands of years, for ever."— *Man in Revolt*, trans. Olive Wyon (Philadelphia: The Westminster Press, 1947), pp. 184-85.

conditions of its day and cannot be appropriated without modification. However, it may be more viable in the technological era than we have been inclined to recognize. On the other hand, there are some who predict that the trend toward concentration in cities will be reversed by the development of media of communication in the cybernetic revolution. Be that as it may, Brunner is fully aware of the biblical injunction to subdue the earth and of technology as one of the means to this end. His complaint, we must be careful to note, is not against technology as such. Brunner feels that the organic forms of technology that enrich the human spirit have given way to "highly abstract mechanical and therefore inhuman technics." [5] Here are still some valuable insights for us, in spite of some distortions occasioned by Brunner's close identification of technology with the destructiveness of war.

There is no disputing the fact, even by the most ardent advocates of the creative possibilities opened up by cybernetics, that the concern for automatic weapons systems in World War II was the impetus that gave birth to control theory. (World War II may also have had considerable influence on birth control theory, but that is another subject.) England was reeling under the blitz from the *Luftwaffe,* and antiaircraft weapons were crucial. It was necessary to locate airplanes, plot their flight, and shoot them down. These functions, formerly done entirely by men, were assigned to machines, and engineers became adept at communication with machines and at establishing lines of communication within machines.[6] The combination of nuclear energy and cybernetic systems for controlling its delivery has unleashed an unprecedented destructive potential.

---

[5] *Christianity and Civilization*, p. 6.

[6] Fred S. Grodins, *Control Theory and Biological Systems* (New York: Columbia University Press, 1963), p. 100; Norbert Wiener, *The Human Use of Human Beings: Cybernetics and Society* (New York: Avon, 1967), p. 148. For a chart showing the carry-over from military projects to commercial use, see John Diebold, *Beyond Automation: Managerial Problems of an Exploding Technology* (New York: McGraw-Hill, 1964), p. 37.

The situation of war is an important factor in understanding the attitude of men like Brunner. Indeed, the problem of technology is still frequently set in this context. But the sinister element of technology has certainly receded, even if it has not entirely disappeared. Consequently, the problem of war no longer seems appropriate as the paramount viewpoint from which to appraise technology, even if it is still legitimate as one perspective on the problem. There are at least two reasons why the issue of war, though it is still a significant issue, is no longer as crucial to the understanding and appraisal of technology as it once was.

In the first place, the control of modern communications media may be a much more serious threat than the possession of modern weapons.[7] It is propaganda that prepares men for the use of these weapons. Propaganda need not be blatant and oppressive. In fact, people in democratic societies who are intellectually convinced that they are impervious to propaganda are thereby rendered much more susceptible to certain subtle forms of propaganda than are less sophisticated people.[8] Whereas propaganda in the past has been important as a means to manipulate people to wage war, the cybernetic revolution is increasingly making communications important as an end in itself. Perhaps it will even become a substitute for war.

In the second place, although the development of cybernetics has been motivated by its usefulness in war, it may create a frame of mind which no longer first thinks of war as a solution. We are living in the transition between the industrial revolution and the cybernetic revolution. The industrial revolution emphasized the magnification of man's muscle power. Competition was settled by a display of power. But the cybernetic revolution emphasizes the magnification of man's exercise of communication

---

[7] C. F. von Weizsäcker, in *The Relevance of Science* (New York: Harper & Row, 1964), pp. 20-21, mentions his twelve years under a dictatorship in support of this contention.

[8] Aldous Huxley, *Brave New World Revisited* (New York: Harper & Row, 1958), chap. 4. Propaganda under a dictatorship is discussed in chap. 5.

and control. Competition may now switch from the manifestation of power to the display of ability to overcome the natural trend toward the increase of disorder. And so, cybernetics may be used for war, but its implications are for order. There are perhaps no signs yet of a decrease in the amount of warfare, but there is definitely a marked change in attitude toward war. In addition to the disillusionment concerning war, we can see also an upsurge of interest in competition over the exercise of control, such as the race for space.

Perhap those such as Robert Ardrey, who argues in *African Genesis* and *Territorial Imperative* that war is inevitable because of man's natural inheritance, are correct. Nonetheless, it seems to me that our traditional concern with war will be at least partially redirected toward the attack upon disequilibrium in society.

An alternative theory of war bases it on technology rather than on biology. Kenneth E. Boulding [9] defends the thesis that war is essentially a phenomenon of civilization, dating approximately from 3000 B.C. to A.D. 2000. War is not appropriate either to precivilized or to postcivilized societies. Prerequisite to war is the forceful gathering of a food supply in the cities, and an army is understood as a movable city. Boulding recognizes that there was conflict in precivilized society and that there will be conflict in postcivilized society, but he insists that only in the interlude of civilized society does conflict take the form of organized warfare. For Boulding the excitement of living in the twentieth century is in the prospect that we will either eliminate war and enter into postcivilized society, or we will become extinct. There will still be conflict in postcivilized society, but the primary emphasis will be upon means of controlling it.

An example of this new deployment of our energies may

---

[9] *The Meaning of the Twentieth Century* (New York: Harper & Row, 1964), chap. 4.

be the war on poverty. In the past, social betterment was viewed as the road to utopia, but we now find that this kind of effort is beset with many difficulties, such as the black power declaration of impatience. Indeed, this can be seen as a declaration of war on the part of those who recognize the widening gap between the technological advance of our society and their own situation. The refusal of the black power leaders to make any concession in word or deed to the white liberals who support the civil rights movement and the war on poverty can be understood as a refusal to give aid and comfort to the enemy. While the cybernetic revolution does have implications for order, it has also intensified the alienation of the disinherited from the rest of society.

If Christianity is to be a reconciling force in the present age, it must overcome its own hostility to technology. Karl Heim commented in the introduction to his *Christian Faith and Natural Science* that the question of the relation of these two fields is not the central question of faith, but neither is it peripheral.[10] This question is preliminary, but nonetheless fundamental. The importance of the relation of science to faith has increased tremendously since Heim wrote, because science plays a much more significant role in everyone's life. One reason for the growing impact is that science has become so closely identified with technology that there is little basis for distinguishing between them. This merging of science and technology is being catalyzed by resource grants from government and industry.

In an article entitled "Conditions and Limits of Man's Mastery Over Nature" contributed to the *Festschrift* for Brunner's sixtieth birthday,[11] Walter Marshall Horton asks how Christianity and technology could have become so hostile to one another. Recognizing the issue to be complex, Horton

---

[10] (New York: Harper & Bros., 1953) , p. 31.
[11] *Das Menschenbild im Lichte des Evangeliums* (Zurich: Zwingli-Verlag, 1950) , pp. 89-103.

suggests that the key is "the fact that the Bible lays down moral conditions and acknowledges metaphysical limits to man's mastery over nature, while modern culture increasingly has ignored these conditions and limits, with disastrous consequences." In the age of modern technology Horton contends that man has neglected the moral values, except those which make him a good scientist or technician, and that with his success in overcoming what other cultures have accepted as natural limitations, technological man has ignored his finitude. But he insists that when man fights his duel with nature in such a frame of mind, it is nature that triumphs. The reason is that man's mind is divided and is driven to contradictory conclusions. " 'Nature is everything and I am nothing.'—'Nature is a mere appearance, and I am one with the Mind that holds the appearance.' The first conclusion is naturalistic, deterministic, materialistic; the second is humanistic, libertarian, idealistic." Horton points out that both of these conclusions are logically defensible, and the battle between adherents of one or the other is evenly matched. Kant, Hegel, and the idealist tradition focus on the creative power of the human mind to impose human purpose upon nature. Feuerbach, Marx, Darwin, and the naturalistic tradition focus on the mechanical sequence of natural phenomena that yields understanding and control. He cites Bertrand Russell as an example of one who wavers between seeing man as nothing but a machine subject to the processes of nature, and seeing man as a Titan who brings nature under his domination.

Horton reflects that Christianity's task has been to proclaim judgment in times of prosperity, and hope of redemption in times of adversity. Noting that naturalistic pessimism seems to be overpowering modern man in his search for salvation through technology, Horton asserts that the mission of the church is to proclaim the Christian hope of cosmic redemption. If man will recognize his dependence upon God and the primacy of humane values, God may use the secular order of saints known as scientists and technicians to help construct a "new heaven and a new earth." The Christian's hope, however, unlike historical utopianism, is tempered by a realization that sin will persist and will continue to require forgiveness to the end of history.

The church, however, should be more than simply a reactor to culture. Although the church ought to speak a word of hope to those who despair and a word of judgment to those who are at ease, we ought not to be content with this role. It is important to seek to restore balance when it is lost, but we must further attempt to eliminate the source of imbalance. We must seize the initiative and forge out a merger of the naturalistic emphasis on determinism and the humanistic emphasis on freedom. It is my hope that this book will contribute to such an initiative.

The purpose of Part One is to set the stage for a consideration of this problem, various facets of which will be discussed in the subsequent parts. Part One is concerned with two images of man—*imago machinae* and *imago dei*. We will first sketch the development of science from its emergence to the present age of cybernetics. In examining this development, we will be especially interested in those factors which have helped to shape the concept of man in the image of the machine. Then we will turn to the concept of the *imago dei*, developing Brunner's interpretation of this phrase. The general problem that we have indicated can then be focused in the question concerning the compatibility of these two images. The remainder of the book will seek to explore the problem as it becomes joined in this way.

Part One

Two Images of Man

1 | The Imago Machinae

The way in which we so easily came to speak of computers as electronic brains indicates the power of the *imago machinae* for speaking of man. I am not intending to imply that all people thought of the development of "thinking machines" as the first step across the threshold to man's creation of "man." Indeed, many people, when confronted with the astounding feats performed by machines, responded: "Yes, but it can't think for itself. It can only carry out what man programs for it." With subsequent developments, some of which will be considered in part two, this kind of statement needs considerable qualification. "Electronic brain" may still be a metaphor, but it is not nearly so stretched as when the phrase first became current.

When I say that there is a pervasive *imago machinae* for speaking of man, I am referring not only to the affinity between the human brain and the electronic brain, but also to the development of the electronic brain from the mechanical computer, to the relation between the mechanical computer and the machine model of the entire universe, and to the development of the machine model from the displacement of teleological by mechanical explanation in the sixteenth century. In short, I am speaking not only of a particular logical connection, but of a nexus of thought that has influenced the thinking of Western man for centuries. Even though the machine model of the universe has been found inadequate, the mechanical meta-

phor has not been completely supplanted. It does not provide
a complete explanation, but it is a component in our contemporary understanding of nature and of man, even when we are
not conscious of its influence. In setting the problem that is to
engage our attention in this study, our first task is to sketch the
development of man's understanding of nature and himself,
with special emphasis on the *imago machinae* and the cybernetic revolution.

Preliterate Society

Communication and control are the key elements of cybernetics.
Our task in these first two chapters is to sketch the development
of the *imago machinae* and then of the *imago dei,* so that later
chapters can deal with the issues raised by the attempt to interrelate these two images. But even so, we must begin our brief
sketch with preliterate society, for here too communication and
control are significant concerns. It may be a long road from the
rain dance of preliterate society to the computerization of
weather data in our own technological age, but nonetheless
there is a common concern for communication and control relating one to the other. And there may be a link between the
voodoo doll and the android used for medical education.

It is sometimes held that the people of preliterate society
are quite different from us, especially in the way they think.
They are described as living in a "primitive" society, this term
being used not simply in the literal sense of "earliest," but in
the pejorative sense of "crude." They are described as prelogical.[1] But it seems more accurate to say that the people of
preliterate society are different from moderns, not by virtue of
underdeveloped powers of reasoning, but by virtue of a different

---

[1] Cf. Claude Lévi-Strauss, *La Pensée sauvage* (Paris: Librairie Plon, 1962),
chap. 9, which seeks to refute Sartre's view in *Critique de la raison dialectique,*
that there is a dichotomy between "civilized" thought, which is dialectical (historical), and "primitive" thought, which is nonhistorical and prelogical.

framework within which they conduct their reasoning. What seems logically inconsistent from our perspective may be consistent within their framework of thought. This framework does contain some limitations compared with our own, and this is what gives some strength to the spurious notion that their powers of reasoning are underdeveloped.

The most significant limitation is indicated in the term "preliterate." As McLuhan would put it, they employ a different medium, and "the medium is the message." But McLuhan further notes that we are gaining new affinities with tribal societies. Our electronic media of communication are rendering us postliterate and are establishing us as inhabitants of a global village. But there is a difference between the situations of preliterate and postliterate men, because the former are restricted to memory and oral transmission and cannot enrich their thinking with the contribution of other cultures.

Another limitation is the precariousness of life in preliterate society. Starvation and disease are constant specters, and threat and distress diminish the powers of discrimination. In contemporary society, this condition can be induced experimentally through drugs or extreme fatigue, and it can also be observed in situations of social disorder, such as wars and rioting. But in preliterate society threat is inescapable.

With his limited scope of observation, primitive man might not notice the relationship between pregnancy and the act of sexual intercourse; and he might attribute a successful hunt to a dance which immediately preceded it. Nonetheless, we can discern categories of cause and effect at work in such explanation. Distinctions between emotions and physical objects, which may seem obvious to us, are not recognized in preliterate society, and this is why its members think of trees and rocks as alive and capable of being flattered or insulted. But within their framework they proceed logically. The same holds true for their lack of discrimination between dreamed experiences and those of the wakened state.

Claude Lévi-Strauss has argued in *La Pensée sauvage* that the mythical thinking of preliterate society is as intellectually rigorous as scientific thinking. Bronislaw Malinowski has pointed out in his essay "Magic, Science and Religion," that science is present, albeit in rudimentary form, in preliterate society. Efforts at communication and control are not restricted to magic and religion, and preliterate man knows that it is not enough to dance, chant, and offer sacrifices in order to secure a good crop. He knows that there is a certain time for planting, and that his plants must be watered as they are growing, and so forth. But he also knows that taking every scientific precaution does not guarantee a good crop; therefore other powers must be involved, and man must seek to communicate with these mysterious forces and control them for his benefit. Paul Radin argues that out of their reflection upon the limitations of life, men of preliterate cultures develop advanced philosophical doctrines.[2]

Ancient Greece

As man develops, the many spirits become many gods and the mysterious power becomes localized. In the developing national religions there is still a multiplicity of gods, who may work at cross purposes, but nonetheless there is some development toward order and control. In Greece, for example, we have the Homeric pantheon with its home base on Mt. Olympus. Homer used to be taken at face value as giving a factual account of the religious beliefs of the day. But now he is recognized as more creative than descriptive. His account is not a narrative, but is stylized with a view to bringing about a unification of the pantheon. Later Greek poets intensify his drive toward unification.

---

[2] See esp. Paul Radin, *Primitive Man as Philosopher*, 2nd rev. ed. (New York: Dover, 1957); and *The World of Primitive Man* (New York: Henry Schuman, 1953), chaps. 11-13.

The first known Western philosopher, Thales of Miletus, takes another major step in man's attempt to understand and control his world. Thales is commonly recognized as the father of philosophy, and it is appropriate to consider him as the father of science also. He discounts supernatural explanation of natural events and looks for one primordial element which underlies the diversity of the world around us. His concern for a naturalistic and orderly explanation of phenomena is an early expression of scientific approach. Not all philosophers were to concur in Thales' naturalistic orientation nor in his monism, but he did inaugurate a quest for an understanding of the world which emphasized simplicity and uniformity. The Pythagoreans contribute an opposing emphasis upon harmonization. The major expressions of harmony observed by the Pythagoreans are music, mathematics, and health. In their understanding of mathematics they point to the division between odd and even numbers and hold the view that all things are numbers. Their contribution is enforced by Plato. Modern science combines elements of both the naturalist concern for the observation of nature and the rationalist concern for mathematical analysis. It is man's quest for the order and regularity that underlie the diversity and complexity of the world which makes the pre-Socratic era such an exciting period; and if this factor is overlooked, the fascination of this period is largely, if not wholly, lost. Unfortunately, we cannot pursue in detail inquiry into what the world is made of (*Weltstoff*) and how it operates. But it was this pursuit, and the insights and frustrations it engendered, that opened up the whole gamut of classical philosophy. Although philosophy began as a purely naturalistic pursuit, the frustrations of the attempt to explain the constitution and operations of the cosmos raised questions about the nature of man and his powers of knowledge and the proper use of his powers. In Wilhelm Windelband's terms, there is a progression from the cosmological to the anthropological to the systematic period in Greek thought.

The Cosmos as Organism (Classical and Medieval Thought)

Although our concern is focused on the image of the machine as the basis for the understanding of man, we need to see this understanding against the background of the major models for understanding the cosmos.[3] One of the important facets of the development of science and of its impact on other areas has been the changing models of the world in science. We may tend to separate science and metaphor, but these world models are more influential than is often recognized.

It is a matter of historical record that there are fashions in the preferences scientists exhibit for various kinds of models, whether substantive or purely formal ones. Theories based on unfamiliar models frequently encounter strong resistance until the novel ideas have lost their strangeness, so that a new generation will often accept as a matter of course a type of model which to a preceding generation was unsatisfactory because it was unfamiliar. What is nevertheless beyond doubt is that models of some sort, whether substantive or formal, have played and continue to play a capital role in the development of scientific theory.[4]

Even one who argues that a theory should be judged on the basis of its adequacy for handling experimental problems, rather than on the basis of the availability of a model or analogy, may still express a sense of discomfort over the loss of a satisfactory model, as in modern quantum theory, for example.[5] Even in contemporary science we can discern an influential model,

---

[3] Our concern is only to sketch these models as a background for our study. For an elaboration of these images, see the work of the philosopher R. G. Collingwood, *The Idea of Nature* (New York: Oxford University Press, 1945), or the work of the theologian-physicist Stanley L. Jaki, *The Relevance of Physics* (Chicago: University of Chicago Press, 1966), Part I, pp. 1-137.

[4] Ernest Nagel, *The Structure of Science* (New York: Harcourt, Brace & World, 1961), pp. 114 f., quoted in Israel Scheffler, *The Anatomy of Inquiry* (New York: Alfred A. Knopf, 1963), pp. 322-23.

[5] Cf. P. W. Bridgman, *The Nature of Physical Theory* (Princeton, N.J.: Princeton University Press, 1936), p. 63.

though it is formal rather than substantial and consequently not as vivid as earlier models. As background to our study we will sketch the development from the classical view, which employed the model of an organism, through the model of a machine employed by modern science, to the model of a pattern of numbers employed in contemporary science.

The Greeks thought of the cosmos on the model of a vast organism, extended in space and moving in time. There are two significant implications of this analogy. First, there is a basic unity to the entire universe, and second, the universe is moved by an inherent force or principle. In order to understand the world, one seeks to discover the goal or purpose toward which it is striving. The basic question is *why* a thing acts as it does.

This emphasis on teleological explanation continued through the medieval period, and it is often felt that this was a stagnant period because man's attention was drawn away from the world and toward God. It is true that the medieval orientation was primarily, though not exclusively, theological. (Consider the development of guilds for example.) Moreover, human affairs were not only attended to directly, but were also considered in the light of the contemplation of God.

In connection with the aims of this study, we are particularly concerned with the contribution of Christian theology to the Greek legacy in the growth of modern science.[6] Langdon Gilkey succinctly points out the Christian contribution to the development of science.

The Greek viewpoint provided no basis for the two central characteristics of modern science that have made it a fruitful form of inquiry. These two convictions are: (1) that the intelligibility and order of the natural world are to be found within its physical and material relations, rather than in its qualitative and purposive forms; and, (2) that this order is not deduci-

---

[6] Cf. *Encountering Truth* (Nashville: Abingdon Press, 1966), pp. 113-14, for a discussion of how Christianity fosters science.

ble from ideas or forms in our minds, but is "contingent," and therefore discoverable only by sensory experience, and by the manipulation and study of the material aspects of natural events.[7]

The scientists' presumption of an intelligible order in the world and their evaluation of it as worthy of study rest upon a perspective bequeathed to our modern world by the Christian understanding of God, and especially the doctrine of God as creator. In a section headed "From Nicaea to the Atom Bomb," Denis De Rougemont writes:

That the fundamental options exercised by the Council of Nicaea should also have settled the kind of science which Christianized Europe would produce seems indisputable; the contrary is what would be surprising. How could we account for the unmistakable fact that science is bound up with the West, if the starting point were made once more the old conflict between science and religion, in the guise it assumed as the predominant conflict of the nineteenth century? Would they have been opposed to one another anywhere else than in a civilization which had deliberately pushed up the value of matter and body—together the subject matter of science— at the same time as liberty, the subject of conflict.[8]

He says that the doctrine of the incarnation "implicitly invests the phenomenal world of matter and flesh—that is to say, what was going to be the subject matter of our natural and physical sciences—with a *dignity* and a *reality* denied to them on principle in the East." He notes further "that *faith* put an end to the magic, myths, and natural religion which served ancient human societies in lieu of science." [9] If it is true that Christianity made a positive contribution to the development of science, then it is all the more desirable that the contemporary fruits of scientific

---

[7] Langdon Gilkey, *Maker of Heaven and Earth* (Garden City, N.Y.: Doubleday, 1959) , p. 112.

[8] *Man's Western Quest,* trans. Montgomery Belgion (New York: Harper & Bros., 1957) , p. 114.

[9] *Ibid.,* p. 115.

endeavor be incorporated within our theological reflection, and not merely from a discreet distance.

The Renaissance was marked by a conscious turning away from medievalism to a neoclassicism. The Renaissance deserves a more positive appreciation by modern Christianity than the Renaissance was willing to give to medieval Christianity. It may be as genuine a development and flowering of Christian thought as were the Reformation and Counter-Reformation. Renaissance men, it is true, often thought that they were repudiating Christianity and recovering classicism. But even the Italian Renaissance, which was more anticlerical than its Northern counterparts, saw the classical culture through the eyes of Christian tradition. Thus, for example, they had a stronger emphasis on individualism than could be found in classical thought, which was interested in universals rather than in particulars. The contemplative-speculative mood of classical thought was not the temper of Renaissance thought. Although logical deduction was not subordinated to experimentation until the eighteenth century, the turn toward observation and experimentation started at this time and seems to have been strongly influenced by the Christian doctrines of creation and incarnation and their implications concerning the worth and significance of the material order. Even the religion of the Renaissance—for chivalry was a religion of woman—combined both pagan and Christian sources (for example, Tristan and Isolde, and the Virgin Mary). This religion of woman, however, gradually gave way to a religion of science. The mystery of woman yielded to the mystery of the universe. The desire for woman, grounded in curiosity, gave way to a general curiosity. Unamuno notes that both religions were prompted by the desire to save life and achieve immortality.[10]

---

[10] Miguel de Unamuno, *The Tragic Sense of Life*, trans. J. E. Crawford Flitch (New York: Macmillan, 1921), pp. 220-21.

The Cosmos as Machine (Modern Science)

In the sixteenth century modern science was born, and it was elaborated in the seventeenth century, which Whitehead calls "the century of genius" [11] although he is sharply critical of it. He says that the seventeenth-century scientists systematized the ideas fermented in the sixteenth-century revolt and thereby provided the intellectual capital for, and bequeathed the vexing problems to, the next two and a half centuries.

The basic model for understanding the cosmos is now that of a machine. The concern of modern science is not with *what* a thing is nor *why* it behaves as it does. The question is *how* it acts. Instead of being interested in the goal or purpose toward which the cosmos is striving, men now try to understand events by discovering the mechanical forces that impel them. These forces operate externally, like one billiard ball hitting another. Life is understood in terms of past forces rather than of future goals. These past forces are external and measurable. Moreover, they are capable of being expressed in universal laws. In the pre-Galilean period, nature was thought of as lawful, in the sense that each thing obeyed its unique laws as determined by its own qualitative nature and purpose. After Galileo nature is thought of as composed of quantitative units, all of which are subject to the same laws. The earliest examination of nature in the modern period had an accompanying awareness of nature as the handiwork of God. It was quite common for scientists to express praise and gratitude to God as Lord and Creator. Kepler and Galileo felt that they were examining and explaining portions of God's work.

By Newton's time the vastness of the natural world had destroyed the ideal of studying nature's parts in relation to the comprehensive totality of the divine work of creation. Consequently, nature was beginning to be thought of independently

---

[11] Alfred North Whitehead, *Science and the Modern World* (New York: Macmillan, 1925), chap. 3.

of God. The scientist might believe in God as a person, but this had no bearing on his scientific investigations. The scientist's task was completed when he achieved a mechanical-mathematical explanation of phenomena. Newton applied this method to a wide range of problems and set the style for subsequent scientific procedure. The influence of mathematics is apparent from a glance at almost any page of Isaac Newton's *The Mathematical Principles of Natural Philosophy*. It is often said that Newton's contribution is the discovery of the law of gravity when the fabled apple fell on his head. But more accurately, Newton's contribution is his suggestion that the law of gravity is universally applicable. Everyone knew that apples fell to the ground and landed on any heads that were in the way. But it was Newton who related this knowledge to the movement of the planets, to the tides of the ocean, and so forth. Newton successfully predicted occurrences on the basis that the universe operates according to mechanical laws that are operative throughout nature. The discovery of mechanical laws expressible in mathematical formulas took all limits off the scope of scientific explanation. What happens in stellar space and what happens right under our noses is governed by and explicable in terms of the same laws. This influences the meaning of "nature" and "natural." Originally, these terms referred to what came to man directly; now they refer to what man can study by means of mathematical and mechanical principles. This also means a change in "the nature of nature." Originally it referred to something lively and colorful; now it is much more abstract and lifeless. In Whitehead's description of this outlook, "Nature is a dull affair, soundless, scentless, colourless; merely the hurrying of material, endlessly, meaninglessly."[12] This is illustrated in the change from the direct perceiving of a color to the understanding of it as a certain wave length. Nature evokes quite a different picture in the two instances. In one case, the difference in color is qualitative; in the

---

[12] *Ibid.*, p. 77.

other it is quantitative—a difference of 1/120,000, to be more specific.

In the eighteenth century, the deists applied the machine model of thought to the heavenly machine, *Machina Coelestis,* and spoke of God as being like a great watchmaker who put the universe together and wound it up but then let it tick away. As Loren Eiseley put it, the result was that "the machine reigned. God, who had set the clocks to ticking, was now an anomaly in his own universe." [13]

The machine picture of the universe was the accepted view when the United States was established, and the American system of checks and balances is an application of the clock theory to politics. Also related to this concept is the economic theory of Adam Smith, especially the notion of an "invisible hand" that keeps everything in line. Like a good machine, the nation will run well, and we need government only for occasional repairs.

Darwin's theory of evolution interpreted man's physical nature as the product of such orderly forces. The analogy of God as a watchmaker could lead to a deistic removal of God from all but the initiation of human affairs, but it could also lead to a theistic adoration of God as the master-workman, as in Joseph Butler's *Analogy of Religion* (1736) and William Paley's *Natural Theology* (1802). Such arguments from the mechanically regulated watch to the designer who planned its order were scuttled by Darwin.[14] Darwin explained the orderliness and purposefulness of nature (including the species man) in purely mechanical terms. Nature is marked by overproduction in the sense that millions of seeds are created in order to produce one plant or foetus. These organisms that are brought to life must then engage in a struggle for existence or, more accurately, for survival of the species, for nature cares little for individuals.

---

[13] *The Firmament of Time* (New York: Atheneum, 1960) , p. 15.

[14] For a study of the post-Darwinian reformulation of the teleological argument ("the wider argument") , see Peter Bertocci, *The Empirical Arguments for God in Late British Thought* (Cambridge: Harvard University Press, 1938) .

(Interestingly, laissez-faire economic theory, which is closely interrelated with Darwinism, did apply the economic struggle for the survival of the fittest to individuals, rather than species.) An important facet of this struggle of the species for survival is ramification, or the production of a great variety of forms within the species. The determination as to which of the great variety of forms will continue the species is a matter of natural selection, or survival of the fittest. The forms best adapted to survive perpetuate their own kind. Whereas Butler and Paley, assuming the fixed nature of species, spoke of a Creator who adapted all animals to their environment at the very beginning of the universe, Darwin spoke of change and development of species. Instead of a cosmos efficiently carrying out the master plan of a skilled master craftsman, Darwin spoke of a wasteful and ruthless nature. Nonetheless, it is orderly and purposeful—not because it is guided by the purpose of a Divine Mind but because of the mechanical operation of the principle of natural selection.

The Freudian analysis of man shifts the focus from man's body to his psyche, but it also is influenced by the mechanistic orientation of Enlightenment rationalism, although Freud also manifests major influences from the Romantic tradition,[15] which I will touch upon in a moment. The various activities of man are qualitatively different in appearance only. In man, as in nature, qualitative difference is only superficial. For adequate understanding, we must penetrate to the basic units of force. Human behavior is the result of sexual energy, which Freud termed "libido." People are born with a set amount of libido, and differences in behavior result from the different ways in which the energy is expended or repressed. Freud's formula, "Where the id is, there let the ego be," can serve as the motto of psychoanalysis. The aim of therapy is the strengthening of the

---

[15] For example, the influence of Enlightenment rationalism is seen in his numerous references to "our God Logos" in *The Future of an Illusion;* and the influence of Romanticism is seen in his interpretation of society as productive of an intolerable increase of pressures in *Civilization and Its Discontents.*

ego so that it can take over the id, redirecting libidinal forces
into acceptable channels rather than trying to repress them into
the unconscious where pressure builds up until neuroses and
psychoses burst through all efforts to contain them. One of
Freud's analogies of psychoanalysis is appropriately taken from
engineering—namely, the reclamation of the Zuider Zee, winning fertile soil from the salt water of the sea.

Freud's understanding of man (like Darwin's) has often
been compared with the laissez-faire theory of economics that
prevailed in his day and that was also strongly influenced by the
mechanistic outlook. Freud gives us a psychological version of
laissez-faire capitalism, especially in his theory of culture. Libidi-
nous energy is like capital. It must not be spent freely. Rather,
man must curb his desire to spend until he accumulates capital.
The masses of men spend what they get—financially and psychologically—but the major advances, economic and cultural, are
made by those who will deprive themselves of momentary satis-
factions in favor of long term gains. Erich Fromm puts the parallel succinctly: "Just as wealth is the product of saving, culture is
the product of instinctual frustration." [16] Freud's emphasis on
the aggressiveness of human relations and the tensions of society
can also be understood in this light. Because the number of goods
is limited, men engage in fierce competition for them. The
ferocity of this competition is such that social cohesion is constantly threatened. Property and possessions are not so much the
cause of man's aggressive competition as they are the objects of it.
Man's possessiveness is particularly keen in his competition over
the available females, and the quest for property and possessions
may be a means to further this quest or an attempt to subli-
mate it.

Although there have been significant influences from other
traditions, the mechanical-magnitudinal approach has remained
prominent in psychological investigations. Even studies of man

---

[16] *Sigmund Freud's Mission* (New York: Harper & Row, 1959) , p. 96.

which employ qualitative terms may be based on a quantitative method of study. For example, a certain individual may be described as "hostile" or "aggressive." But these qualitative terms may be based on a quantitative measurement, such as a response of 85 percent to items on a questionnaire that is supposed to measure hostility or aggression. Even when talking about qualities, one may be using quantitative data. The tendency to employ such an approach is greatly heightened by the convenience of computer analysis of such data. The completed questionnaires can be fed into the machine, scored, averaged, translated into graphs, tables, and so forth. And the information thus gained can provide us with probabilities that make it possible to make accurate predictions. My own favorite statistical reports come from George Bernard Shaw and Marshall McLuhan. Shaw reports that one out of every one person will have to die; and McLuhan, that the typical Eskimo family consists of five persons—a father, a mother, two children, and an anthropologist. Because there is an element that is neglected by a magnitudinal approach, there are some who swim against the stream by employing a nonstatistical, nonmagnitudinal approach, which is concerned not only with the frequency with which something is done but also with the attitudes and feelings that accompany it.[17]

The Reaction to Mechanism

The Romantic movement in the nineteenth century reacted against the mechanical and lifeless understanding of man and of

---

[17] For two examples of nonmagnitudinal surveys from widely different areas, viz. sexual behavior among the affluent and seminary education in America, the reader is referred to John F. Cuber and Peggy B. Harroff, *The Significant Americans* (New York: Appleton-Century, 1965); see especially the "Foreword" by Morton M. Hunt, chap. 1, and pp. 172-73, 192; and Charles R. Feilding, with Thomas W. Klink, W. John Minter, and James D. Glasse, *Education for Ministry* (Dayton, Ohio: American Association of Theological Schools, 1966); see especially chap. 1.

nature that prevailed in the Enlightenment. The Romantics attempted to recapture the qualities and vitalities that had been neglected in man's preoccupation with science. They thought that the vital qualities of life and duty had been not merely neglected, but surrendered; and so they advocated not only a new direction for science, but moreover a departure from science. This, however, was impossible. Science had accomplished too much. And so it continued to develop, and Romanticism died. However, the Romantic protest against science was revived in the twentieth century by existentialism, and even in the nineteenth century science could not ignore its attack. In response to the Romanticist critique, scientists sought to explain the relation between the qualitative experience of phenomena and their quantitative description. In this effort, science had recourse to the ancient (fifth century B.C.) Greek philosophy of atomism. The essence of this view is that the combinations of atoms produce the qualitative world we experience, but that the configurations and movements of the individual atoms are explained in mechanical-mathematical terms. Qualitative differences result from varied arrangements of quantitatively identical units.

Electrical theory was a little troubling to this resolution of the problem, since it rendered the field of force primary over matter. But this could be brought in line by the supposition of a material ether that conveyed these forces.

Later, scientists discovered that they had applied the term "atom" too quickly. The atom could be split. This too was troubling, but not devastating, since it was simply a mistake about what was the final indivisible building block of reality. The necessary revision is achieved simply by explaining that the protons, neutrons, and electrons are the real atoms, and what we call "atoms" are the first level of combinations of the building blocks. Nor was this the end of peeling back to more fundamental particles. Later it was found that protons and neutrons could be smashed, and that all particles of matter could be converted into energy. Dr. John A. Wheeler, professor of physics at Princeton University, has urged physicists to probe far beyond what is now considered elementary. In an address to the American Physical Society, entitled "The End of Time," he developed his theoretical basis for dealing with elements that are on such a small scale that time can have no meaning.[18]

The real disruption occurred when it was discovered that these elementary particles cannot be known independently of the act of knowing them. They cannot be known objectively, because the act of knowing them is involved in their behavior. We cannot observe them without their being disturbed by the process. Thus nature has come to be relinked with man, at least in the sense that it is no longer possible to talk about the natural world as something separate from man.

A classic expression of the involvement of the scientist in his measurements is found in Heisenberg's principle of indeterminacy. This principle is based on the fact that our measurement of the position of a particle makes it impossible for us to measure its velocity, and vice versa. Consequently we cannot predict the future position of a particle, and the position of it cannot be said to be causally determined. Some have tried to apply this principle to the problem of freedom and determinism in human action, but it is generally held that it is not possible to extrapolate from the subatomic realm to human behavior. Others have held that the principle of indeterminacy is not applicable because it is a reflection of our limitations of measurement rather than of the state of nature. This second objection is often rejected, however, on the ground that the principle of indeterminacy does not deal with a limitation that man can overcome. With regard to this principle, Niels Bohr has investigated the methods of measuring and has enunciated the principle of complementarity. Since we cannot measure position and velocity simultaneously, we are forced to choose. If we choose to describe something in terms of space and time, we are unable to describe it in

---

[18] *The New York Times*, Feb. 5, 1967, p. 5E.

terms of causality. If we choose to describe it in terms of causality, we are unable to describe it in terms of space and time. We can employ either type of description, and we can alternate between them, but we cannot employ both at the same time. But because we cannot observe these subatomic particles without their being disturbed by the process, nature has come to be re-linked with man, at least in the sense that it is no longer possible to talk about the natural world as a machine, separate from man, which is a detached object of investigation. The involvement of the scientist in what he studies is captured in this apt turn of phrase: "Scientific observation does not consist, as many seem to believe, in sitting with your mouth open waiting for things to happen. It consists in going about and interfering with things." [19]

The participation of the scientist, as opposed to passive observation, is illustrated in the development of atomic theory. In the seventeenth and eighteenth centuries, there was actually little development in the ancient Greek theory of atomism. Atoms were the unobservable elementary building blocks which combined to make the world and the qualities with which we are familiar. Subsequently, techniques were developed for probing into the atomic world, and atoms were discovered to be quite different from the earlier conception of them as extremely tiny, solid, round, billiard-ball-like objects. The discovery of the nature of atoms did not force itself upon man, but yielded itself to the active search of man.

The Cosmos as Numerical Pattern
(Contemporary Science)

The numerical pattern as the model of the cosmos was developed in the twentieth century under the impact of the quantum theory

[19] A. D. Ritchie, *Essays in Philosophy* (New York: Longmans, Green & Co., 1948), p. 83.

and the theory of relativity.[20] Max Planck developed the quantum theory in 1900. Planck discovered that energy changes were characterized not by flow from one level to another, but by jumps.[21] The question as to whether radiant energy, such as light, heat, and X rays, is transmitted in the form of waves or in the form of discontinuous particles vexed physicists. Some phenomena seemed to demand one theory, and some seemed to demand the other. Heisenberg and Born resolved the dilemma by saying that it was not necessary to choose one or the other. Rather, one employed the theory which best served the investigation at hand. The rationale behind this is that the physicist is dealing with aggregates, and large numbers of electrons can act like either moving particles or waves. But this means the end of mechanical models of the structure of the universe.[22] The concern is no longer with how a machine operates, but with statistical probability.

Albert Einstein's theory of relativity led to the same position. Einstein destroyed the Newtonian concept of absolute time and absolute space. Time and space are not things that we can express with substantive models. They are relations. What do they relate? Not solid matter, but concentrations of energy. There is nothing in this idea that can be gotten hold of; it is all impalpable. Matter can no longer be understood as a tangible reality. It is simply a concentration of energy. It is this identification of matter and energy expressed in the formula $E = mc^2$

---

[20] Norbert Wiener credits Willard Gibbs, rather than Einstein, Heisenberg, or Planck with the change from Newtonian to probabilistic physics. See *The Human Use of Human Beings*, p. 10; also pp. 7-12; and *Cybernetics*, 2nd ed. (Cambridge: M. I. T. Press, 1961), chaps. 1-2.

[21] A similar development occurred in biology. Darwin's theory assumed flowing transitions. In 1900 the work of Mendel was rediscovered by de Vries, Correns, and Tschermok, and this led to de Vries's mutation theory. For interpretation of this in the light of the quantum theory, see Erwin Schrödinger, *What Is Life?* (Cambridge: Cambridge University Press, 1962), chaps. 3-5.

[22] For a discerning statement of the basic change in the understanding of reality that was implied in developments in modern physics, see Ernst Cassirer, *Determinism and Indeterminism in Modern Physics*, trans. O. Theodor Benfey (New Haven: Yale University Press, 1956).

that opened the possibility of man's use of atomic power. On the other hand, energy is also mass; so light can be affected by gravity and does not travel in a straight line as Newton thought; and the straight line is not the shortest distance between two points. Why retain such theories so far removed from what we consider reality? Because they work, and they work much better than theories correlated with the so-called real world. Mathematics has had to become increasingly abstract in order to deal with the concrete. Consider, for example, Albert Einstein's reply[23] to Samuel's argument that mental constructs, such as space, could have no effect on any natural process, and that mathematical models ought to be correlated with empirical data. Einstein's response argued that the so-called real world is not simply given to me by sense-perceptions, but is constructed by me on the basis of sense perceptions. For example, I do not perceive "a table," but rather, I combine a variety of perceptions and refer to this grouping by the word "table." Einstein's clinching argument is that the abstract concepts give us a better understanding of "reality" than do the more concrete data of perception.

Although mathematics is tremendously important in our contemporary world, it often assumes some forms that are not familiar. Let us consider, for example, the use of number systems with different bases.

Let us begin with the familiar decimal (base 10) system. This system is based on man's practice of counting things on his fingers. Man groups things in 10. Anything less than 10 is expressed in units, and anything over 10 we express in higher orders. For example, "14" expresses a group of 10 plus 4 more units. If we were to add 7 more units, we would group the first 6 with the 4 units, making a second group of 10, plus one unit remaining, i.e. "21."

[23] Herbert L. Samuel, *Essays in Physics* (New York: Harcourt, Brace & Co., 1952), pp. 157-62.

But a number system need not employ base 10. For example, the octal system employs base 8. In this case, the position of the digit represents a power of 8 rather than of 10. For example, 14 in the decimal system is short for 1×10^1 and 4 units. Its equivalent in the octal system is 16, i.e. 1×8^1 and 6 units. In the decimal system, 7 plus $14 = 21$, i.e. $(2 \times 10^1) + 1$. In the octal system, 7 plus $16 = 25$, i.e. $(2 \times 8^1) + 5$. There are similar differences in subtracting, multiplying, and dividing, due to the difference in the basic grouping.[24]

Why would we want another number system? For one thing, the base 8 number system would simplify fractions, for bisection proceeds, on this order—1/2, 1/4, 1/8, 1/16, 1/32, 1/64, etc. The base 8 system can handle these much more readily than the decimal system, and some mathematicians have lamented that man did not ignore his thumbs when first devising his numbering system on the basis of counting on his fingers. Multiplication in an octal system would require only half as much effort as that of the decimal system.

The advantages of other number systems can be further seen in a consideration of the binary system (base 2) which is in great use today. It is helpful to the telephone company, for example, since they are interested in a two-value system, viz. a closed circuit and an open circuit. Because it is used in electronic computers, it will be helpful to consider the binary system more fully. An electronic computer, even when its output is translated into the decimal system, operates on the binary system. It consists of a series of circuits, each of which is switched either on (1) or off (0) by means of a flip-flop. If a circuit is already on (1) and we add 1 to it, then it changes to 0 and carries over to the next circuit, changing it from 0 to 1, or from 1 to 0 with a carry-over to the next circuit. (In base 10, this is like the odometer going

---

[24] For a considerably more detailed introduction to operations in different number systems, see Donald G. Fink, *Computers and the Human Mind* (Garden City, N. Y.: Doubleday Anchor Books, 1966), chap. 2.

from 9 to 0 and advancing the next higher column, only in the binary system this happens when going from 1 to 0, rather than from 9 to 0). To represent 14, the electronic computer would have tube 0 on in circuit a, tube 1 in circuits b, c, and d—i.e., 14 would be represented by 1110 in the binary system. This means, starting from the left (though it is actually built up from the right), one group of 8 (2^3) —here we see the value of the octal system—one group of 4 (2^2), one group of 2 (2^1), and no units. Suppose we add 7 to 14. In order to see how it is built up, let us feed it in one at a time:

> 1 plus   1110 is   1111
> 1 plus   1111 is   10000 (analogous to "9999 plus 1 is
>   1,000" in the decimal system)
> 1 plus 10000 is   10001
> 1 plus 10001 is   10010
> 1 plus 10010 is   10011
> 1 plus 10011 is   10100
> 1 plus 10100 is   10101

In terms of groupings, 21 is one group of 16, plus no group of 8, plus one group of 4, plus no group of 2, plus one unit. So, in the binary system, 14   1110

$$7 \;=\; 111$$

$$21 \quad 10101$$

The column-by-column addition in the binary system is as follows:

> 0 plus 1 = 1
> 1 plus 1 = 0, and carry 1
> 1 carried, plus 1, plus 1 = 1 and carry 1
> 1 carried plus 1 = 0, and carry 1
> 1 carried plus 0 = 1

This may seem very slow and awkward, but it is more than compensated for by the tremendous speed of electronic computers. The difference between mechanical and electronic computers is one of speed, rather than principle of operation. A mechanical computer on the decimal system is quite fast enough for measuring the mileage of our cars. But other computations benefit from the electronic computers, which can work about a million times faster than the mechanical computers, since electrons move at almost the speed of light. And electronic computers have been further improved by such developments in circuitry as transistors, which are much more efficient and smaller than vacuum tubes. A current development in integrated circuitry is the development of a hair-thin wafer of silicon. A slice about the size of a half-dollar can be imprinted with 4,000 transistors and can do the work of about 64,000 vacuum tubes. And transistors are not the end of the road in microelectronics. Neuristors may soon replace transistors, resistors, and capacitors. This would make possible an even closer approximation of machines to living organisms. The neuristor acts like a nerve fiber. Electrical impulses can traverse an inch of neuristor in less than one millionth of a second, which is about 10,000 times faster than a similar impulse can travel through biological nerve cells.[25] It is no surprise that the nanosecond (one billionth of a second) is a unit of measurement in this field.

The multitude of steps taken by computers in solving a problem does raise a hazard. A malfunction at any point will result in a breakdown in communication. It takes only one malfunction to distort the communication of information. It may be only one thing in a million that went wrong, but this means that the final result is wrong. Consequently, it is important to check the work of these machines. It must be possible to check rapidly, or the high speed of the machines is nullified.

One way to verify with little or no loss of speed is to run the same program on two or three machines. If two machines are used, they are rigged so that any discrepancy sends a signal

[25] *Science News Letter,* June 19, 1965, p. 392.

to the operator. The data is stored, so that the operation can be resumed as soon as the cause of the malfunction is discerned, and the necessary correction, such as the replacement of a transistor, is effected.

If three machines are used, the computation need not stop if one of the machines shows a discrepancy. The computation can continue on the basis of the two agreeing reports while the operator locates the reason for the malfunction in one of the machines.

It is probable that the brain works on the principle of multiple transmission so that malfunctions can be overcome. As Norbert Wiener comments: "Like the computing machine, the brain probably works on a variant of the famous principle expounded by Lewis Carroll in The Hunting of the Snark: 'What I tell you three times is true.' "[26] The same principle seems to operate in the storage of material in the brain. It is estimated that the same information is stored in six to ten different places. If no more than thirty per cent of the cortex is removed in brain surgery, memory recall is unimpaired.[27]

The program interrupt device also increases the rapidity of computer operation. This device allows a computer to receive data for its memory while the calculating part of the machine continues operating on other data. With this device programmers who desire to add more data to the computer's memory after a program has begun can avoid the loss of operating time formerly resulting from manual interruption of the program.[28]

Another way in which the tremendous speed of computers is more efficiently employed is the technique of sharing.[29] Instead

---

[26] Wiener, Cybernetics, pp. 145-46.

[27] Science News Letter, Aug. 21, 1965, p. 120.

[28] Science News, May 27, 1967, p. 509.

[29] A series of four articles on various facets of time sharing was featured in Computers and Automation, XV (Oct., 1966), 18-40; and a series of five articles was featured in Datamation, X (Nov., 1964), 24-54. For a discussion of the distinction between and interrelation of time sharing and multiprocessing, see

of sitting idle until a certain person or company is ready to employ its services, a computer can now be made available, even at long distance, to a number of subscribers. For any one of them, the cost of a computer would exceed its value, but sharing a computer solves this problem. Even with, and indeed partly because of remote-control sharing, there has been a tremendous increase in the number of computers in use. Eventually, computers in the home will be as common as are typewriters and stereos at the present. However, time sharing will probably not disappear when computers are more readily available. Although it began as an economic convenience, time sharing has resulted in other advantages. It has especially enhanced the capacities of computers by making possible the sharing of data and programs. Information discovered by one user becomes available for other users of the system.[30]

But even more startling than the "population explosion" among computers is the development of the capacities of computers. We shall see more of this in Part Two, but we need to note certain developments that bear upon our discussion of the speed of computers. The original machines could solve mathematical problems in seconds that would take months or even years to work out on a slide rule or a mechanical calculator. However, much of the time gain was absorbed in the lengthy process of programming the problem so that the computer could handle it. Originally, the problem had to be translated into numerical terms. Computers can now receive information in verbal form if it is punched out on cards or tapes. Research is currently directed toward the oral transmission of information to a computer. Initial success has come with numbers, and the more complicated task of developing a computer capable of receiving

Ellsworth L. Johnson, "Computer Time Sharing in Perspective," *Automation*, XIV (Mar., 1967), 92-95.

[30] R. M. Fano and F. J. Corbato, "Time-Sharing on Computers," *Scientific American*, CCXV (Sept., 1966), 129-40.

and interpreting phonemes is proceeding more slowly, but success is on the horizon.[31]

Computers are an important, but far from exclusive, concern of the discipline known as "cybernetics." [32] Cybernetics is the comparative study of systems of communication and control in man and machine. A fundamental concept in cybernetics is that of "message." A message is any pattern which carries information and influences behavior. A regular pattern performs this task more efficiently, but is much less frequent than irregular patterns. To refer to the loss of order and organization in communication systems, the term "entropy" is employed. The term "noise" refers to elements which interfere with the process of communication. Cybernetics proceeds on the assumption that however man and machine may differ in construction, the process of communication and control is identical.

A control system has three phases. In the first phase there is an input of information. The second phase is the interpretation of this information. The resultant behavior, or output, is the third phase. This analysis of phases holds for both men and machines.

In the early stages, however, there was a marked difference between man and machine. Man was able to learn from his behavior. In other words, some of his output reentered as

---

[31] For a discussion of progress in the automatic recognition of speech made at the Acoustical and Electromechanical Research Laboratory of RCA, see Harry F. Olson and Herbert Belar, "Recognition of the Spoken Word by Machine," *Biological Prototypes and Synthetic Systems*, ed. Eugene E. Bernard and Morley R. Kare (New York: Plenum Press, 1962) , I, 110-18. See especially p. 113 on phonetic spelling and pp. 113-18 on different displays from different voicings. To indicate the difficulties encountered in this regard, one hundred voicings of "a" by the same speaker yielded fourteen different displays, and one hundred voicings of "I" by the same speaker yielded thirty different displays. Cf. also Charles Vossler and Leonard Uhr, "A Computer Simulation of Pattern Perception and Concept Formation," *ibid.*, pp. 233-43, for a discussion of the recognition of spoken words in the larger context of the recognition of sensory patterns by machines.

[32] See the warning against the popular tendency to confine cybernetics to communication and control in computers in G. T. Guilbaud, *What Is Cybernetics?* (New York: Grove Press, 1960) , p. 3.

input. This process is known as "feedback." In defining the term
Wiener gives a clear statement of its significance: "This control
of a machine on the basis of its *actual* performance rather than
its *expected* performance is known as feedback." [33] Feedback
can result in changes as minute as slight variations of movement
or as broad as changes of policy in light of past experience. It is
by means of feedback that a system adapts to its environment
and learns from its own experience. This capacity was not present in the earliest machines. They were dependent solely upon
the programmer. He programmed a machine on the basis of
what he expected it to do. If his prediction was faulty, the
operation was affected accordingly. Eventually, however, it was
possible to achieve feedback in machines. We will examine this
development in Chapter Five, but enough has been said to indicate that this development greatly narrowed the gap between
man and machine. Contemporary work in cybernetics is seeking
to develop further the capacity of machines for self-adjustment
on the basis of what they learn from feedback and from communication with other systems, and it is this activity which gives
point to our question concerning the nature of human freedom
and responsibility in the light of cybernetics.

By virtue of such developments, we have entered the age of
androids. Androids are automatons in human form. They were
once encountered only in science fiction, but at the time of
writing the first actual android has been demonstrated. It took
three years to develop, and was underwritten by the U. S. Office
of Education at a cost of $272,130. It will be used to teach anes-
thesiology, and subsequent androids will be available for teaching the entire gamut of health services. The first android is 6' 2",
weighs 195 pounds, and is covered with skin-colored and skin-
textured plastic. But the important thing about it is that it

---

[33] *The Human Use of Human Beings*, p. 24. With an interesting word play
I. A. Richards emphasizes the significance of "feedforward," which is the conscious
or unconscious expectation with which we begin any activity.—"The Secret of
'Feedforward,' " *Saturday Review*, Feb. 3, 1968, pp. 14-17.

breathes and opens its mouth so that it can receive anesthetic gases in its plastic bronchial tubes or drugs injected by catheter, and it reacts to these drugs as a man would. Its eyes blink, and it has a heartbeat and pulse. Although this first android is animated only in the head and chest area, it is expected that a fully functional android is only a few years distant. The second android is even expected to be able to sweat and to shed tears and bleed at the mouth, and possibly to groan if the student treats it too roughly.

As machines become more and more like man, there is more and more tendency to think of man as being in the image of the machine, and as a creator who can make the machine in his own image. But there is another important image of man, and we turn our attention now from the *imago machinae* to the *imago dei,* and after that to the problems of the compatibility of these two images.

2 | The Imago Dei

In examining the concept of the *imago dei,* we will follow the development of this theological category in the work of one man—Emil Brunner.[1] As I noted in *Encountering Truth,*[2] Brunner is rather indifferent to science, although he relies on scientific truth in his theological work to a greater extent than he realizes. It is a major concern of this study to combine encounter theology and science more consciously and more fully as we seek to explore the nature of human freedom and responsibility in the light of cybernetics. The methodology developed from the examination of the nature of revelation in *Encountering Truth* will here be tested by an attempt to apply it to a specific area of the Christian understanding of man.

The understanding of man is a concern which arises early and remains central in the theological work of Emil Brunner. It is most appropriate that the *Festschrift* for his sixtieth birthday centered on the theme *Das Menschenbild im Lichte des Evangeliums.* A crucial element in the understanding of the nature of man is the concept of the *imago dei.* This concept has received

---

[1] For a historical survey of the concept of the *imago dei* in the Bible and in the history of Christian thought, see Brunner, Appendix I of *Man in Revolt,* and Appendix A to chap. 2 of *Dogmatics,* Vol. II. For a more elaborate historical survey of this concept from a Brunnerian perspective see David Cairns, *The Image of God in Man* (New York: Philosophical Library, 1953).

[2] Pp. 111-13.

widely varying definitions in the course of the history of Christian thought, and it is an issue that has divided not only the generations but also contemporary theologians. However, the opening essay in the *Festschrift* for Brunner contends that the intention, at least, of this theological concept is quite clear. However one may define the *imago dei,* its purpose is to indicate that which comprises the specific character of man and his special relation to his Creator.[3] Moreover, as a creature of God man is to be understood in relation to God, not merely in relation to the created order, both animal and natural or animate and inanimate. For his contribution to the *Festschrift* Helmut Thielicke chose a section from the manuscript of *Theologischen ethik* dealing with the doctrine of the *imago dei.*[4]

For Brunner the concept of the *imago dei* deals with man's relation to God, especially with regard to the problem of man's knowledge of God. In particular, Brunner's understanding of the *imago dei* is developed by his defense of the concept of general revelation, especially in controversy with Karl Barth.

The Imago and Divine Self-disclosure

In *Gott und Mensch* (1930), a collection of four essays concerning personal being, Brunner engages in a discussion of revelation as the self-disclosure of God which is the sole means of man's relation to the word of God. Man's need for the revelatory word of God is not simply a need for the disclosure of knowledge about God but is an expression of man's need for relation with God. The word of God is not simply the impartation of knowledge but is the personal address which calls man to respond and which establishes his human nature as specifically "existence in responsibility." All creation is brought into being

---

[3] Franz J. Leenhardt, "La situation de l'homme d'après la Genèse," *Das Menschenbild,* p. 2.

[4] "Die Subjekthaftigkeit des Menchen. Eine Studie zu einem Hauptproblem der Imago-Dei-Lehre," *Das Menschenbild,* pp. 65-79.

by means of the word of God, but in the case of man it is further true that the word of God is an addressing as well as a creating word. Man's unwillingness to respond to the word of God which addresses him does not silence the word of God but distorts it. When the word of God is not truly heard by man he does not cease to be a personal being, but he does forfeit the true personal being which was intended by God. The *imago dei* in man is not annihilated or destroyed by sin but is perverted or corrupted; and because man has perverted the word of God that comes through creation, God has given a second revelation to sinful men through the incarnation. The intent of this second revelation is to restore the personal communion of God and man which was intended in creation. In this second revelation God adapts his speech to the sinful condition of man and the consequent distortion of man's hearing of the word of God. God descends from his level to enter into the sphere of sinful human existence in order that man might know the true nature of God as love. By this communication of himself God makes possible a relation of communion or fellowship between God and man. This act of God means that man must relate himself similarly to his fellow creatures. By virtue of entering into communion with God, man is by this very token turned toward his neighbor, so that the will to fellowship with his neighbor is one with the recognition of God's will to fellowship with man. The perversion of man's relation to God is also a perversion of his relation to his neighbor, and consequently the act of turning to God is likewise an act of turning to our neighbor.

In the course of this discussion Brunner has a long footnote in which he argues that Karl Barth is extreme in his critique of Augustine's understanding of the *imago dei*. Barth repudiates any provision whatsoever for natural knowledge of God. In response, Brunner appeals to Paul and to the Reformers for a less exaggerated position which acknowledges a measure of general revelation and a consequent possibility of some natural knowledge of God. Brunner does concur with Barth's under-

standing of the *imago dei* as an expression of divine grace and
not an achievement of man. But Brunner argues that Barth has
overlooked the significance of the word of God for man as
sinner. The ability to sin is specifically human and expresses
man's relationship (albeit a distorted one) with God, so that the
very possibility of sin necessitates man's continuing to exist in the
imago dei. But if one is to speak of the continuing *imago dei* in
the sinner, then it is necessary to distinguish the general revelation in creation and the special revelation in Christ. And
Brunner further insists that it is only on this basis that one can
profitably discuss the quest (albeit a misguided one) for God in
philosophy and the non-Christian religions.

However, in this book Brunner's major use of the concept
of the *imago dei* is found in his essay, "The Specifically Biblical
Contribution to Psychology." In speaking of a biblical or Christian contribution to psychology Brunner disavows any intention
of questioning the development of empirical psychology on the
model of the natural sciences, although he does challenge the
assumption that it has thereby avoided making any philosophical
or metaphysical presuppositions. Brunner argues that far from
being presuppositionless, psychology is profoundly influenced
by its understanding of the relation between subject and object.
Naturalistic realism subordinates the subject to the object; idealism subordinates the object to the subject; and romanticism
identifies the subject and object as two modes of an ultimate but
hidden unity. These three metaphysical options underlie the
three basic options in psychology, though not necessarily of
specific psychologists, who may be quite eclectic.

Naturalistic psychologies study perceptible objects in relation to other objects and ignore or deny the subject. In this approach the *imago machinae* is a powerful model, and the basic
aim is to understand the mechanics of behavior in terms of
causal laws. Brunner feels that this approach is helpful for the
understanding of atomic components but that it is unable to
deal with a whole as more than the sum of its parts.

Recognition of this limitation inherent in naturalistic psychology led to the revival of idealistic psychology. Its emphasis on the subject is an emphasis on unity or comprehensiveness. The emphasis upon spirit in this approach enables it to deal with the meaning of the whole process. But it is weak in its appreciation of individuality and in its understanding of that which is nonrational.

The nonrational elements come into prominence in romantic psychology. It avoids the objectivist reductionism of naturalistic psychology and the subjectivist reductionism of idealist psychology. Its aim is to seek neither mechanical laws of causation nor the system of meaning which explains the whole. It is concerned, rather, with the vitality and creativity of the expression of the individual spirit. But the emphasis on vitality makes it impossible for romantic psychology to discern the specifically human, i.e. that which differentiates man from other living creatures; and its repudiation of mechanical and rational laws of explanation renders it vulnerable to serious distortions.

Despite their difference of opinion as to whether the one principle should be mechanism, rationalism, or vitalism, the three types of psychology are all of one mind in their conviction that psychological understanding can be gained on the basis of one principle. It is here that Brunner places the specific contribution of Christian psychology which sees recognition of contradiction as necessary to an understanding of man. The contradiction in man that is perceived in the Christian understanding is that man is created by God for fellowship with God, but man has perverted the divine word so that he lives in enmity with God rather than in fellowship with him. This state of sinful existence is exactly opposed to what God intended when he created man in his own image, and yet only a creature fashioned in the image of God is able to become a sinner. If the contradiction in man were peripheral we could safely ignore it and still secure an adequate interpretation in terms of a single principle. It is the failure to recognize that the contradiction is central that has led to confusion as to whether the "real" man is the one who is a causally determined mechanism or the one who is a free rational spirit. The specifically Christian insight that man is a sinner and that contradiction is an inescapable characteristic of man is what enables us to understand why man can interpret himself only in ways that give partial insights but that themselves stand in need of correction by other perspectives. Christianity does not give us a system to replace the partial systems developed in the different schools of psychology, but it does give us a rationale for understanding why all of them must be taken into account, even though none of them is a fully adequate interpretation.

The naturalist understands man as a mechanical object; the idealist, as a spiritual being; and the romanticist, as an expression of the unity of nature and spirit so that man is partly natural and partly spiritual but not fully either. In contrast, a Christian understanding of man does not identify him with nature or with spirit or partly with both. Rather it sees man as a creature made in the image of God and therefore related to the Spirit of God and to the creatureliness of nature. The Christian understanding of man agrees with naturalism and romanticism against idealism that man *is* body, and is thus properly understood as a finite creature. But the Christian view also says that man is unlike the rest of creation in that he is created in the image of God. In this sense it agrees with the idealist emphasis on spirit, but it insists that spirit is something which man has only by virtue of his being addressed by God so that he can respond to the divine word. Consequently the Christian view recognizes human spirituality, but it emphasizes that this is a finite spirituality, in contrast with the idealist tendency to see it as unconditioned and autonomous. Naturalism sees the finitude of man and his dependence on the body and consequent involvement in the world of objects. Since freedom and spirituality are not discoverable in the object-world, naturalism denies these. Idealism on the other hand affirms the spirituality and freedom of man but

fails to recognize man's dependence on his body and the consequent limitation of human freedom and spirituality. Romanticism recognizes the unity of the physical and the spiritual aspects
of man, but it fails to recognize the freedom and responsibility of self-determination and the bondage of guilt.
Moreover, the Christian view insists that man becomes human
only in terms of his responsibility to or communion with his
fellow creatures. He becomes himself only in relation to his
fellow creatures. Even more significantly, human personality is
dependent upon the divine-human encounter. So in the Christian view, not only recognition of the contradiction in man but
also recognition of his need for fellowship or communion is
necessary to an adequate understanding of man. However, because man as sinner is in contradiction with his true nature,
this element of community is distorted into an individualism
which egotistically asserts its independence of others, and into a
collectivism which forces fellowship and thus crushes the freedom of one's neighbors. The word of God addresses man, invit-
ing him to respond in fellowship with God who is the source of
his being and whose image is truly reflected when man is in
fellowship with his creator and with his fellow creature.

Brunner's later writings have not made any essential changes
in this basic position, but they have elaborated some aspects of it
and have looked at various issues from this basic perspective.

The Imago and the Good Life

In *Das Gebot und die Ordnungen* (1932), translated into
English as *The Divine Imperative*, 1947), Brunner offered his
first major treatment of Christian ethics. In Book One Brunner
states the problem, dealing with natural morality and the relation of the Christian message to it. In Book Two he deals with
the divine command (*das Gebot*). In Book Three he looks at
the orders of creation (*die Ordnungen*).

Brunner agrees with the Reformers' movement from the

Aristotelian-Thomist understanding of the Good as that which fulfills human nature, back to the biblical truth that the Good is solely that which God wills. Consequently the sole Good is union with God. This is a truly "religious" ethic, but there is a "secularity" in this view because God's will is that man should serve him in and through the world in general and the community of mankind in particular. Unlike the secularity of the Enlightenment, this secularity calls for theonomy rather than autonomy, and it calls for union with God rather than emancipation of the individual, because there is no human good which is not based on the free gift of a transcendent God. In this development we see Brunner's conviction that man is human by virtue of his response to the claim which God makes upon him. For Brunner everything revolves around the encounter of man with God. In this regard he distinguishes Christian ethics from forms of ethics which include the divine but which are essentially centered around man himself. For example the Stoic does the Good which is the expression of the divine Logos, but he does so in order to actualize the divine element (reason) within himself. Again the Pharisee fulfills the divine law, but he is concerned with fulfilling this law not because it comes from God, but rather because what he does enables him to earn heavenly reward, and thus the ultimate concern is what he himself desires rather than what God wills. Similarly Brunner sees man as shut up within himself in his service to fellow creatures.

The answer to this is found in man's recognition that his very life, his very self is something which is given to him by God and not something which is fulfilled by his own efforts in seeking after God. It is only with this realization that man can recognize that the Good is not what he himself does but rather what God wills. When man ceases to base his life on himself and begins to base it on the gift of God, he is then able to realize the ethical implications of his being created in the image of God. It is this concept of the *imago dei* which is lacking in naturalistic ethics— which sees man as part of a species rather than as an individual creation of God—and in idealist ethics—which sees man as essentially divine rather than as a finite creature, so that individuality, like the body, is valued negatively as a prison house of the soul.

In Christian anthropology man is neither animal nor divine but is a creature in the image of God, created not only by means of the divine word but also for the purpose of responding to the divine word. As creatures in the image of God we are called to community with God and to service of God, and this obligation is fulfilled through community with our fellowmen and service to them. However, we are guarded from a legalistic interpretation of social service, because the primary emphasis is upon the acceptance of life as a gift. We must seek to make the best of our environment, but our first task is simply to accept our environment. Our environment, including our neighbor, is not primarily something which we must mold and shape; rather we must accept our environment and our neighbor as they are already formed, so our first task is one of adaptation to that which we find around us. And yet this is not all that must be said, for God's will includes an aim for the fulfillment of nature, and the present order has fallen short of what God intends. Man, who was created for communion with God, has perverted his relationship to the creator. Consequently, God is not only the sustainer but also the redeemer of the present world order. In obedience to his will we must not only accept the present order and adapt ourselves to it, but must also commit ourselves to the service of God and our fellowmen with a view to bringing the created order within the redemptive power of God. In other words, we are called not primarily to be reformers but rather to be witnesses to the reconciling power of divine love. Hence we must both adapt to and resist the environment around us; we must both accept it and protest against it.

As creator God works even where he is not recognized. As redeemer God works only where there is a recognition of his word. Christian service is devoted to the extension of those spheres in which God can work redemptively. In other words, the aim of service is not simply the accomplishment of a human project, but rather the facilitation of a response of faith by men to the word of God which creates and sustains them.

The preserving power of God is operative through such elements of the natural order as the family and the state. Brunner is emphatic that we do not know the meaning of the order apart from the revelation given to us through Jesus Christ. But he does insist that the God who is known through special revelation is thus recognized as one who has made himself known, albeit in a fragmentary and indirect form, in the generally acknowledged natural orders. The first, although not the most significant, duty of the Christian is to exert his effort to preserve the natural orders as effective regulating forces. He must first accept life and adapt himself to it as it is naturally structured. The Christian must first serve in his capacity as judge, policeman, bank officer, schoolteacher, politician. But in fulfilling his official role, the Christian must further seek to infuse as much of the personal element of love as is possible without disrupting the order itself. The order must be supplemented and not despised, modified, or relaxed, and we must be able to work alongside unbelievers as we work within the natural orders. In addition to seeking to realize the reconciling power of love within the orders as they are, the Christian must also seek ways of improving the orders so that they become more humane. The Christian must protest against culture without transforming his criticism of culture into a fundamental hostility to culture. The point of the Christian's protest is not the system of law as such but the injustice within it, and not the state as such but the hostility between states.

Of the various orders of creation, it is science that is most directly pertinent to our discussion. For Brunner it is not science as such, but the lack of truth within science, that must be the focus of the Christian's protest. There is no work of man which is not influenced by his essential contradiction as sinner. The scientific quest for the truth is an autonomous quest, and yet the desire and ability of man to know the truth is based upon his being created in the image of God. The search for truth involves an objective perspective upon the world, and this sets man apart from the rest of the animal creation, which is concerned only with the practical use of the world. A scientific understanding of the world necessitates man's transcendence of a purely natural form of being. And yet this achievement of man also has its dangers. Because man understands scientifically by viewing the world around him as an object, there is the danger that he will not simply view his fellowman as object, but will insist that this view is *the* truth about man. Science is a gift of God, and the dedication of scientists in response to this gift is often such as to evoke reverence. However, science is also an expression of man's alienation from God. Science shows the consequences of this paradoxical nature. It is able to serve man by furthering and enhancing his life, and it is also able to destroy life, especially in its communal expression.

The Imago and the Fall

In the preface to *Das Gebot und die Ordnungen* Brunner expressed his appreciation for Barth's elaboration of the theological foundation of ethics, and his hope that by having learned from Barth he might be able to give attention to the second basic task of a Protestant theological ethic, the application to concrete problems. Brunner felt that the test of the theological foundation would be met by a demonstration of its ability to illumine practical problems. However, Barth felt that the direction of Brunner's thought did not proceed from the foundations of the dialectical theology but rather departed from it.

Brunner's attempt to resolve the differences between them was expressed in *Natur und Gnade* (1934). Brunner expresses appreciation for Barth's heavy emphasis upon the biblical themes of the word of God and the revelation in Jesus Christ. He says that the church has only one source and norm, not two, such as commandments and orders; and that the *"und"* in the title of his book *Das Gebot und die Ordnungen* is meant to denote a particular relationship which is to be examined as a problem and is not meant to imply coordination.

In opening the discussion with Barth, Brunner attempts to summarize six theses which represent his attempt to articulate Barth's position so that he can develop his own counter-theses. (Barth's response was to repudiate not only the particular formulations but any formulation whatsoever.) The first of these six theses is the affirmation that man as a sinner has completely lost the *imago dei*. Neither man's reason nor his cultural achievements nor his humanity contain a trace or remnant of the image of God. It has been completely lost. The other theses flowing from this insist that there is no general revelation of God; that grace comes solely through the redemptive activity of Christ, not through creation; that the natural orders are alien to Christian theology; that there is no "point of contact"; and that the new creation is not a fulfillment, but a replacement of the old. All these relate to the issue of *christliche theologia naturalis,* which was a crucial area of difference between Brunner and Barth.

In defending his terminology Brunner distinguishes between the "formal" and "material" image of God in man. The image of God, in the formal sense of the term, refers to that which is distinctly human and applies to man even as a sinner. Man's sin has not forfeited his position as the highest of God's creatures, and the Old Testament continues to speak of man even after the fall as a creature in the image of God. However, as sinner man has lost the material image of God. It is this sense of the term *imago dei* that is employed by the New Testament. The New Testament speaks of the image as destroyed and as being renewed solely by Christ. In the Old Testament, the *imago dei* is closely associated with the doctrine of creation, but in the New Testament it is related to the doctrine of redemption. Brunner contends that the Old and the New Testament understandings of the image can be held together only if we make a distinction between the formal (Old Testament) and material (New Testament) *imago dei*. The understanding of the image as responsibility (in the general sense of being able to respond) enables us to combine these two concepts. Man, as sinner, is still responsible in the sense of being "able to respond"; hence the formal image is not lost through sin. However, sin does destroy the material image, and man is in need of having this restored through Jesus Christ.

As sinner man does not recognize the God who makes himself known through his creation. This is why the Bible can say that man is without excuse. The pagan could know God through his natural creation, but he will not. Because of sin the general revelation in creation does not bring us to a saving knowledge of God, though it does leave us without excuse. Saving knowledge comes only through the special revelation of God in Jesus Christ. When we come to this saving knowledge we recognize that we have been living by the grace of God, although we did not recognize it. This general grace which man can recognize when he has known the saving grace of God is referred to by Brunner as "preserving" grace. The preserving grace of God is expressed partially through the order of life. Even sinful man apart from God is preserved by God. He comes to recognize the grace of God by virtue of the point of contact, which Brunner identifies as the formal (Old Testament) *imago dei* which is present in sinful man. Even as sinner man is able to respond to the word of God, although his response is not at the moment an appropriate one. He is still addressed by God and hence is responsible (i.e., able to respond). Because the point of contact is formal rather than material, the doctrine of *sola gratia* is not undermined. The grace of God renews man in such a way that the identity of the human subject is not destroyed, and yet the final outcome must be spoken of as a *new* creation.

In explicating the *christliche theologia naturalis* of Calvin, Brunner distinguishes between the objective (ontological) and subjective (epistemological) sense of the word "natural" or "nature." The objective sense is the more important. In this usage there is a closer affinity to Stoic than to modern usage, though the content has been modified. "Nature" refers to the original creation or the God-given form of things. Things are natural insofar as this is still recognizable in them. In this usage, nature is contrasted not with spirit or culture, but with that which has deviated from its original form. In this way nature has a normative quality, referring to that which is willed by God. Sin disrupts the divinely ordained natural order, but not to the extent that the will of God is no longer discernible; so that Calvin speaks little of the disturbance of nature in the objective sense except when he is speaking specifically about man, especially the center of the person in his relation to God. Here the objective and subjective aspects merge. God can be known through his work, and the Christian is under obligation to attain such a knowledge of God. The glory of God can be seen in all his works, but especially in man himself. This natural knowledge of God must be complemented by the special knowledge of God given through the Scripture. Revelation does not eliminate the necessity of natural knowledge of God, but it does complete that which is lacking in the natural knowledge of God. Scripture also clarifies the natural knowledge of God. Because it both clarifies and completes the natural knowledge, Calvin speaks of the Scripture as the spectacles or eyeglasses through which we have our vision of natural revelation corrected. As such it does not do away with the need for natural knowledge but renders it effective. The orders of nature must be made known through the special revelation, but they are made known as *natural* orders. For Calvin the *imago dei* forms the transition from the objective to the subjective sense of "nature." Man as sinner must still be spoken of as being in the image of God, and at the same time the image must still be described as thoroughly corrupted and in need of redemption through Christ. This expresses the contradiction which is at the very center of man. The disturbance resulting from sin is at its height in man. Elsewhere, the original order can be seen underlying the derangement caused by sin. But in the case of man there is a central contradiction. Brunner feels that the quantitative implication of the reformers' concept of the remnant or relic of the *imago dei* is somewhat misleading, but that their intention is identical to what he means by the formal image. The relic or formal image is the basis for an understanding of the creativity of man, and even as sinner man is the most glorious of the divine creatures. The image of God that remains in man as sinner provides the basis for the false estimate of man given by idealism, but the falsity of this interpretation is its one-sidedness. To put it in other words, idealism fails because it interprets solely in terms of immanence.

The subjective sense of nature or of natural knowledge of God is never dwelt upon by Calvin, because it is always corrupted by sin and is in need of renewal by Christ. It is in this renewal that we are given the true natural theology, but the relic of the image is nonetheless the principle of the Christian natural theology.

In Roman Catholicism the objective and subjective usages are merged. This is because man is thought to have lost not the image, but rather the *dona superaddita*. In this view sin has no influence upon natural theology, and there is no need of eyeglasses or spectacles to correct it. On the contrary, a self-sufficient system of natural theology can be developed by the exercise of reason, quite apart from *theologia revelata*. It is because Catholic theology thinks of the *imago dei* as uninfluenced by sin that it understands natural theology to be a possibility for unaided reason, which has no obstacles in its attempt to understand the divine will in creation. In other words, the objective and subjective concepts of nature coincide. Revelation and faith are needed only when we come to the realm of supernature, and natural theology provides a foundation for this sphere of examination. Nature and grace, reason and revelation, are related by means of a synthesis which assigns them to different realms, rather than by means of a dialectic that explores the antinomy between them. Far from separating them into different realms, the reformers insisted that natural theology is illumined only by the special revelation in Christ.

Further confusion was added by the interpretation of the Enlightenment, which had a concept of nature that was different from that of both Catholicism and the Reformation. In Reformation theology, autonomous natural knowledge of God is rejected because of the necessity of revelation for its proper understanding, but in the Enlightenment it is independence of revelation that becomes threatened by autonomous reason. The Enlightenment agreed with the Reformation that reason and revelation cannot be assigned to different spheres as in Catholic theologies; but the order of primacy is reversed.

In relating his own thoughts to those of Barth, Brunner says that in Barth's thought natural theology is not only threatened and restricted by revelation (as Brunner would feel it rightly should be), but is actually eliminated by revelation. This is the point at which Brunner sees himself developing a position similar to that of the reformers, in contrast with that of Barth. Nonetheless, Brunner shares with Barth a concern about the misuse of natural theology. However, Brunner's response is that we must find the proper use of natural theology, for the church will suffer as much from the rejection of it as it will from its misuse.

The Imago and Modern Man

The year 1937 brought forth Brunner's most specific statements on anthropology. In this year he published both *Das Wort Gottes und der moderne Mensch* and *Der Mensch im Widerspruch*. The former is a brief work that defends the thesis that modern man can be understood adequately only from the standpoint of the word of God, and that conversely the word of

God can be understood only when we have come to an understanding of modern man. Since modern man is still man, Brunner reiterates his understanding of the basic contradiction of man as a creature in the image of God, who realizes his true nature only by responding to God's word of love with his own answering love. In contrast with other creatures, whose being is formed in their very creation, man becomes himself only through his act of responding to God. And yet we do not answer the divine word of love with our own response of love to God and neighbor. Modern man, like all man, is in contradiction with his origin. When I talk about modern man, I do not make any change in the basic structure which Brunner has established in previous works.

However, there is a distinctive feature about modern man. Modern man has more self-consciously and more forcefully insisted upon his autonomy and self-dependence than has any other generation of man. This characteristic attitude first appeared in the Renaissance, and it has taken various forms. Modern man, whether he be idealist, naturalist, or romanticist, has characteristically asserted the autonomy of human reason; has been reluctant to recognize God as his creator or Lord because he insists that he is his own master; and, insisting upon his own self-dependence, is reluctant to understand himself as one who responds to God. Brunner insists that it is not science but this attitude of autonomy (which is no more scientific than the faith that man is essentially responsible to God) that has made modern man skeptical of religion. It is not the science of modern man but his faith in his autonomous reason that is the opponent of the Christian faith.

But, though the dilemma of Christian faith versus science is a false one, it is nonetheless a real one. Brunner feels that it is incumbent upon the theologian to demonstrate how faith in God, as creator of the world and of man in his own image, and recognition of man's disruption of the divine image are consistent with the understanding of the world in the light of modern science.

There are two basic difficulties that are posed for the Christian understanding of man by the modern orientation of science. The first is a result of a recognition of the vastness of the universe. Any view which takes man and his fate seriously tends to be looked upon as a carry-over from the anthropocentrism of prescientific times. Brunner responds to this by granting that as an *object* in the universe, man has dwindled into insignificance. However, while this has been happening man has become greater as a *subject,* for the enlargement of the universe has been discovered by the mind of man. It is not the cosmos that has enlarged, but man's understanding.

The second difficulty is not so easily dealt with. This difficulty concerns the appropriateness of speaking of man as one who is created in the image of God and who has fallen from his original nature. In the light of the Darwinian understanding of the development of man, Brunner will grant that modern evolutionary theory has invalidated the historicity of Adam and the Garden of Eden, but he will not concede that it is inconsistent with the belief in the uniqueness of man. To show that man developed from prehuman forms of life does not demonstrate that man is nothing more than a highly developed form of animal life, because the unique can develop gradually. However much he may share with animals, man is distinguished from them as the one who is created in the image of God. The act of creation is not the first point of history; it refers rather to the dependence of all things upon God, and for man this dependence upon God involves being created in and for the image of God. And just as every man is created in the image of God, so every man must make his own response to God. But if this is a decision of each man, why do we anticipate individual decisions by saying that man has fallen? Brunner says that we use the past tense because if man is honest with himself he recognizes that he has already made a decision to love himself more than he loves God and his neighbor. He makes this decision anew, though it always springs from a decision that has already been made. Why man has fallen is a question that cannot be answered; and indeed if an explanation could be given there would be a denial of man's responsibility, and he would be turned from a subject into an object determined by prior causes. But although we cannot explain sin as a responsible act of man, we do find ourselves and our fellowmen caught in it in such a way that all men have decided to respond negatively rather than positively to God. We experience this as being not the fault of others but our own free decision, so that man is accountable for each repetition of the negative response to God.

The Imago and Theological Anthropology

Brunner's most exhaustive study of man is found in *Der Mensch im Widerspruch* (1937; translated into English as *Man in Revolt,* 1947). Both the title and the subtitle of the German edition highlight the element of contradiction between man in his true nature and man as he actually is. In the preface Brunner states that although man has theoretically surpassed anthropocentrism, practically he acts as if he were the center of the universe. Indeed, the chaos and disintegration of the world is due to the fact that each man thinks of himself as the center. The only way to overcome the chaos and disintegration is for man to recognize God as the true center of the universe, but the basic obstacle to this is man's misunderstanding of his own nature.

Fundamental to Brunner's understanding of man is his conviction that even the unbeliever is related to God and that neither his own ignorance of this relation nor the gracious activity of God eliminates man's responsibility to God. Brunner avows that the nature of responsibility is the key to the understanding of human existence, for responsibility is not merely an attribute but is the very essence of human existence; if a person were to lose all vestige of responsibility he would thereby cease to be human. Yet Brunner insists that although every human being is aware of responsibility, the true understanding of the nature of responsibility is revealed only through the Christian faith; and a full awareness of responsibility involves living responsibly, which means turning from a life of sin or rebellion against God.

Brunner emphasizes that the moral consciousness, far from being an understanding of responsibility, is a substitute for responsibility, both in the sense of being responsible and of knowing the nature of responsibility. The moral consciousness attempts to preserve humanity by controlling the subhuman forces. But Brunner feels that this attempt is basically inhuman because it operates apart from the knowledge of man's origin and meaning. Emphasis upon moral obligation actually heightens the distance between man and his origin in the word of God, and it turns the unity of responsibility and love into a relationship of tension or opposition.

For Brunner responsibility is a formal term, the meaning of which is love; so we can say also that a true understanding of man involves a recognition of him as one who is created by and made for love. This is both an epistemological and an ontological principle. Man is created by the word of God and thus must be understood in terms of this origin in the divine word of love. But man also continues to subsist in the divine love, so that love is the essential nature of human existence. To be responsible is to be loving; and man is human to the extent to which he loves, and he is inhuman to the extent to which he is alienated. Thus, to know the nature of responsibility, or love, is to know the essence of man.

Things such as the power of the intellect, freedom, and creativity are not the essence of true human existence, but are rather conditions of its realization. Moreover, it is of utmost importance for Brunner that responsibility and love be understood in the light of their origin in God. It is the word of God which calls man to respond, and human love is the fulfillment of responsibility only when it is an answer to the divine love.

Even sinful man in his godlessness was created by the word of God and is upheld by the word of God, and in this sense he is still a responsible being even in his irresponsibility. Hence man does not cease to be man by setting himself in opposition to his origin and his essential nature. He does pervert his human nature; but even this perversion, which results from acting irresponsibly, necessitates an understanding of man as still in relation to the word of God. Just as distorted knowledge is still knowledge rather than ignorance, so distorted responsibility is still responsibility. Even in his sin man does not cease to be the work of God's creation and sustenance. As the apostle Paul said to the pagans in Athens, "In him we live and move and have our being" (Acts 17:28).

Der Mensch im Widerspruch has two major divisions. The first lays the theological foundations for an understanding of man as one who was created in the image of God, who through sin has fallen from this origin and thus has become man in contradiction. The second major portion is an amplification of themes developed on this basis.

Brunner is critical both of attempts to understand man which start from the empirical level and move to the higher, and of those attempts which start higher but run counter to, or ignore, the empirical. Man is misunderstood if he is interpreted as basically a biological phenomenon to which various things must be added, such as consciousness, mind, and religion. Rather the essence of man is his responsibility to God, and man must be understood first and foremost in terms of his relation to the creator. This, however, must include all the empirical data about man, because God created man as a part of this earth. Indeed man's superiority over the rest of creation is not a matter of biology. In many ways he is at a great biological disadvantage in relation to other animals. When man is spoken of as the high point of creation, this is certainly not meant to express the belief that he has greater muscle power or keener sense organs than other animals. Man is the high point of creation in the sense that, unlike the rest of creation, he was made not only by God but also for God. Man must be understood first of all in terms of his relation to God. This relation is known on the basis of revelation which transcends experience, and yet theology must not be oblivious to the value of the empirical study of man. Theological knowledge of man may spring from another source, but it must not conflict with empirical knowledge. Furthermore, that which we know about man on the basis of empirical investigation must be incorporated within our theological perspective. There is a danger that the theological view will try to dictate to or dismiss the results of empirical investigation. On the other hand, there is the danger that empirical investigation will go beyond its rightful province and seek to express views which transcend "objective investigation." And yet despite these extremes, it is most important that the two be brought together. The order of understanding is vital, however. Man is to be understood *first* as one who is responsible to God. *Then* he is to be seen as material, biological, psychical, and rational, in light of this responsibility. As a responsible creature, man's involvement in a material body not only limits him but also gives him a creative potential. Through the body man is able to control and shape matter, and by doing this he is able to imitate the work of the creator and to express his responsible relation to him. Similarly, it is not because man is a rational being that he is responsible; but rather God has created man as a rational being in order that man can respond to him.

Some of Brunner's specific applications of his theological anthropology are of special significance for this study. In discussing freedom, Brunner likens his problem to that of Augustine, who combated, on the one hand, the fatalistic determinism of the Manichaeans and, on the other hand, the concept of unlimited freedom in Pelagian humanism. For Brunner, the parallel opponents are the determinism of naturalism and the humanistic theory of freedom. However, Brunner considers naturalistic determinism to be the more serious threat because it denies responsibility and thereby renders all understanding of the nature of man impossible. Brunner suggests that if Luther had been confronted by a strong naturalistic determinism he never would have written *De servo arbitrio*. The idealist view, on the other hand, starts with man as subject rather than as object and is thus able to understand man as free. However, it goes too far by describing man's corporeality as an obstacle to man in that it limits his freedom. The body is thus despised as that which is not human; it is the lower part which must be ignored when we talk of the true reality of man. It is because the corporeal is thought of as inconsequential that idealists criticize the Christian emphasis on man's sin. In the Christian view human freedom must be understood in terms of man's relation to the word of God. The freedom of man is freedom-in-responsibility (or in love). Thus it is not a freedom of independence but a freedom of dependence. Consequently, the conditional nature of human freedom is most central and crucial. To speak of man as unconditionally free is to ascribe to man the kind of freedom that is proper only to God. Because man is created by and dependent upon God, human freedom is dependent upon man's response to God. Dependent freedom is freedom of decision, forcing a "yes" or "no" so that even the refusal to decide is itself a decision; and it is a freedom which calls man to love, because it defines man as a servant who is the property of God by his very nature and not simply by his decision to become God's property. It is in this way that Brunner describes the limitation of human freedom by the overarching concept of responsibility. He insists that to speak of the will as free to choose whatever it wishes is as erroneous an understanding of freedom as determinism is of human dependence. Human freedom is not man's ability to choose whatever he wishes, but is rather his willing obedience to the divine word of love which calls man to respond in love. Brunner does not consider this limitation of human freedom to be oppressive; far from being a loss for man, it is this limitation which gives life its human meaning and which enables man to achieve the relative independence which is possible for him. The personal meaning of life is found only in freedom-in-responsibility, and man becomes more personal as his life is limited by the claims of other persons.

Brunner says that we commonly think of the problem of individualism versus collectivism as an ethical problem or a practical problem of politics. But underlying this issue there is a definite concept of man from which the ethical or practical implications are inferred. From the Christian conviction that man is created in and for the word of God, we see first that which determines man as an individual. It is responsibility that sets the individual apart from others and renders him independent. Responsibility applies only to the individual person and not to masses, collectives, or species. Insofar as there is a group responsibility, it is to be understood as the expression of the responsibility of individuals who comprise the group. Living together in true community is possible only through the free decision of the individuals involved. God created man to be an individual, but not a solitary self. Not only does community depend upon individuality, but also individuality depends upon community, for if man is to realize his individual nature as responsible he must be related in community and fulfill himself in love. Being-in-community is distorted when the individual is subordinated to the group. This is the mistake which occurs in the various forms of collectivism, both political and ecclesiastical.[5]

In the first third of the twentieth century, new discoveries were being made by microscopic investigation of chromosomes.

---

[5] Martin Buber insists that both individualism and collectivism are abstractions. Individualism understands only a part of man by its neglect of man's relationships. Collectivism understands man only as a part because of its inability to see him apart from the group. For a further discussion of this and Buber's notion of the relation between man and man as the fundamental fact of existence see *Encountering Truth*, pp. 30-31.

Brunner's response is that scientific investigation of heredity as a determining factor on the human being confirms the biblical point of view. He even speaks of it as a scientific "paraphrase" of the biblical statement that God visits the iniquity of the fathers upon the children to the third and the fourth generation (Exod. 20:5). But Brunner disavows any deterministic implications in this. He points out that the statement about "the third and the fourth generation" is qualified by the phrase "of those who hate me." Inheritance gives only a predisposition and is not an absolutely determining factor. We may inherit a disposition toward a certain type of character, but the character itself is not inherited. Brunner also cautions against the interpretation of "nature" to mean our present nature. This confusion of nature, as created by God, with the present state of man's physical existence is detrimental because it neglects the disruption caused by sin, which has rendered our present nature unnatural. Physical existence, such as the bodily organism of man, must be related to the divine purpose in creation; but we must be cautious in delineating this relation, in order to avoid two extremes. It is erroneous to emphasize the disruption of sin to the extent that we obscure the glory of God which is seen in his creation. But it is also erroneous to say that the present situation of physical existence corresponds exactly with the intention of God for his creation.

Brunner says that the modern scientific explanation of things from the viewpoint of their growth raises difficulties for the Christian doctrine of man. The geologist explains a particular feature by the processes, such as folding and faulting, that have produced it. The medical doctor explains an illness in terms of the infection which has brought it about. This orientation, with its implications for the understanding of man, is clearly expressed in the theories of evolution. Brunner distinguishes three basic theories of evolution. The naturalist starts with the elementary and shows how the causal processes, both physical and chemical, have produced the variety of inorganic and organic bodies that are in the world today. The idealist explains all that we have in the world today in terms of the gradual realization of spirit, by which that which was previously latent becomes actual. The romanticist combines elements of the natural and spiritual principles into a concept of creative evolution. Each of these three forms has been especially successful in a particular sphere. The naturalist theory has been particularly successful in astrophysics, geology, and in some aspects of biology. The idealist theory has been especially fruitful in explaining the development of thought. The more recent romantic theory is beginning to replace the naturalist theory in many of the investigations dealing with living phenomena.

There are two major affirmations of Christian anthropology that must be related to these theories of development. The first is the assertion that man is God's good creation. How does this relate to the scientific understanding of human development? The biblical affirmation that man is God's good creation is in quite general terms. It does not speak of the creation of a particular man, such as the Neanderthal or Heidelberg or Peking man, or even homo sapiens. The biblical statement does not make a contribution to our scientific understanding of the development of man. Even so, the biblical writers knew something of the development of the embryo, and this understanding of human development was interpreted within the conviction of faith that man is God's good creation. The Christian understanding of the origin of man deals with the meaning of human existence and with the relation of man to the will and activity of God. This perspective can incorporate varying scientific explanations of the phases through which the process of human development moves.

The second major biblical affirmation concerning man is that he has fallen through sin. Man's fall, like his being created good, is not a stage in the development of humanity and makes no contribution to the empirical study of man. The transition from being created good to having fallen is not some-

thing in the empirical or historical discussion of the development of man.

In short, Brunner's view is that the idea of development is
neither in support of nor in opposition to the Christian concepts
employed in the understanding of man. For Brunner there is an
analogy here to the relation between a beautiful work of art and
the material elements that enter into its composition. There can
be no beautiful picture without paints and a canvas, and yet the
beauty (or ugliness) of a painting cannot be opposed to (or
supported by) the chemical analysis of the paint and the canvas.
The painting is beautiful (or ugly) through the underlying
chemical elements but not because of them. Moreover, Brunner
suggests that suspicion of the process of development as something contrary to the divine purpose is one which has come to us
from Greek idealism rather than from the biblical faith. It comes
from the belief that the divine is eternal and unchanging, combined with man's desire to be divine. But in the biblical view
growth and development are intended by God for all his creatures. Growth is a characteristic, not of sinful existence but
of creaturely existence. This is why the biblical narrative of
the creation connects the procreation of children with God's
good creation rather than with the fall of man. And just as
God has created the human individual so that he develops
out of a fertilized ovum, so also man's gradual development out
of the animal series in no way compromises the biblical statement that man is uniquely created in the image of God.

Brunner says that he has tried to say the same things in *Der
Mensch im Widerspruch* that he said in *Natur und Gnade,* but
that he has tried to do so in different words.[6] Most significantly,
he declares his intention to renounce the use of the phrase
"formal image." He had been criticized for describing that which
has a great deal of content as "formal." He argues that "formal"
and "material" are relative ideas and that it is good usage to

---

[6] *Der Mensch im Widerspruch,* Appendix I.

speak of the image as "formal" even though it has a great deal of content. But in order to avoid occasion for misunderstanding, he declares that he will no longer use the phrase "formal image." In practice, this means that he never relies on this phrase alone, without explaining that "formal image" is equivalent to the Old Testament understanding and "material image" to the New Testament usage.

Brunner specifically rebuts the misunderstanding of his view as an equivalent of the Catholic doctrine of a double image based on Irenaeus' distinction between *imago* and *similitudo*. Brunner says that his intention is quite the opposite of this. Instead of maintaining that there are two elements, an *imago* which can never be lost and a *similitudo* which has been lost, Brunner insists that man must be understood as a unity and that man's one nature has been perverted by sin, although it still retains traces of the image of God. Catholicism teaches that what we have now is the truly original human nature but without the *dona superaddita;* but Brunner insists that we have not original human nature but fallen human nature and yet that even in the fall there is a trace of man's original relation to God.[7]

The Imago and "Personal Correspondence"

Wahrheit als Begegnung (1st ed. 1938) repudiates the object-subject antithesis as a disastrous method for understanding the truth of faith. In this book Brunner attempts to develop an alternative methodology to objectivism and subjectivism. Objectivism seeks to manipulate its objects, but it falsifies the faith which by its very nature is not subject to human control. By way of contrast, subjectivism emphasizes freedom and spontaneity and tends toward iconoclasm. Brunner insists that both methods

---

[7] In Appendix III Brunner deals with two other phrases in *Natur und Gnade* which have given rise to misunderstanding: *"Christliche theologia naturalis"* and *"Anknüpfungspunkt."*

lead to falsification and that there is no middle ground that combines elements from both. In formulating an alternative methodology, Brunner appeals to the doctrine of creation. This doctrine discerns a fundamental relation between God and man which Brunner calls "personal correspondence." He insists that all theological effort must operate within this basic structure.[8] Brunner then sketches out an application of this method to the major doctrines of the Christian faith. Included in this discussion is a treatment of the *imago dei*. In the Old Testament the primacy of God in the personal correspondence with man is of great importance, but the freedom of man in face-to-face relation with God is also a matter of great urgency. The creation of man in the image of God is an expression of God's desire to have a person with the capacity for free choice as his counterpart, and God wills that man use this power to respond to God's love. By way of contrast, the New Testament does not emphasize the likeness of man to God but presupposes that man has lost the image of God and that restoration of it comes through Jesus Christ. The Old Testament speaks of the *imago dei* as a static characteristic; the New Testament speaks in more dynamic terms of the *imago dei* as a relation. In the former, man's sin does not end his personal quality which makes him a counterpart to God; but in the latter, the reflection has been dulled until it is renewed by the light which comes from Jesus Christ and transforms the image of God in man. The relation of lordship and fellowship is realized in Jesus Christ; and now man, who had rebelled against the relation of personal correspondence, is able to affirm it freely and spontaneously. The sovereign God comes face to face with man, bringing the gift of life and God's "yes" to man, who, in his sinful alienation from God and resultant self-contradiction, is not able to say "yes" to God solely by his own free personal decision. Thus Brunner suggests that the New Testament concept of the

---

[8] For a further discussion of this concept see *Encountering Truth*, pp. 40-48.

imago dei is one of the most appropriate expressions of the relation of personal correspondence.

The Imago and Reason

In *Offenbarung und Vernunft* (1941) , Brunner's examination of revelation (*Offenbarung*) defends the concept of a general revelation, or a revelation in creation. He looks to both the biblical and the theological tradition for support. He suggests that opposition to the concept of revelation in creation results from an unwarranted extension of the repudiation of natural theology. Brunner agrees with those who see natural theology as a threat to the principle of *sola fide, sola gratia, solus Christus.* Yet he argues that the revelation in creation is not in opposition to the revelation in Christ, but rather is in dialectical relation with it and presupposed by it. Man is rendered guilty and without excuse by the revelation of God in creation, so that the men to whom the revelation in Jesus Christ comes are not merely ignorant of divine truth but are in willful rebellion against it and thus in need of grace.[9] Thus, revelation in creation serves as the basis for the assertion of man's responsibility to God, as well as the point of contact for the one who proclaims the gospel. But while the revelation can render man guilty, it cannot deal with sin. It is only on the basis of revelation in creation that man can be described as a sinner, and in this sense it is the indispensable presupposition for the revelation in Christ. In the biblical view every man is created by God and every man is the recipient of the word of God, but man distorts the divine revelation and

---

[9] From the Catholic perspective, the criticism of Brunner is that he refuses to acknowledge the valid natural knowledge of God that is implicit in his recognition of revelation in creation. If the knowledge renders man guilty and without excuse, then must it not be true knowledge? "Man cannot be responsible for refusing to glorify God, unless his knowledge of God is true and valid. Otherwise he has committed an error, not a sin."—Joseph J. Smith, *Emil Brunner's Theology of Revelation,* Logos 2 (Manila, Philippines: Loyola House of Studies, 1967) , p. 155.

thus he is in need of saving grace to free himself from the perversion of his nature that results.

Brunner's examination of reason (*Vernunft*) rests on the premise that the understanding of man must begin with responsibility and not with rationality. It may not be false to define man as a rational animal, but it is certainly inadequate; and Brunner feels that theology has the means of overcoming the individualistic concept of reason derived from Aristotle, even though it may not have used this means. To explain responsibility in the light of human nature or of human fellowship is to confuse the basis of responsibility with its object. From Brunner's perspective, reason is not an entity but a relation. Man's reason is in a state of unrest because it is not independent but is made for God. Man is always responsible toward God, even when his responsibility is directed toward his fellowmen or toward himself. Even the use of reason to deny God is, in fact, an expression of the origin of reason in the word of God. Consequently, the Christian must be careful that his attack is directed solely to the arrogance of reason and not to reason itself, for reason affirms the relation of man to God. It is only the arrogance of reason that denies this relation. It is not the nature of reason as such, but the false use which man makes of reason that establishes him in hostility to God. Faith does not repudiate nor even ignore reason, but claims it for God.

The Imago and Justice

In *Gerechtigkeit* (1943) Brunner discusses the concept of the *imago dei* as the basis of the concept of justice. This book was written in response to the disintegration of the Western concept of justice in the totalitarian state, which Brunner understands as simply the political actuality of the positivistic theory of justice which denied an eternal standard transcending man and made justice relative. In his attempt to recapture or reconstruct the concept of justice, Brunner examines law and equality as bases for justice. Law implies egalitarianism, because in order to deal with situations it must ignore the differences between men. However, this is merely a *form* of equality, and justice also involves *substance*. Yet there are inequalities as well as equalities among men, and in some cases justice seems to demand that the inequalities be taken into account. Brunner argues that only in the Christian view can both equality and inequality be adequately appraised, because it sees them springing from the same ground. All men are equal because they are all created in the image of God. When they fell in sin, redemption was given through Jesus Christ in whom all differences are obliterated; and so both the Old and the New Testament concepts of the *imago dei* imply the equality of man. However, the creation of man in the image of God is also the basis for the dignity of the individual. The word of God calls each man to responsibility and establishes him a "thou"; and his dignity as an individual is based on this specific personal relation to God, not on his sharing in any abstract quality which is common to all men. Hence equality and inequality come from the same source, and both are due the same recognition.

Since the inequalities or differences between men are not the result of capricious divine whim, quite inscrutable to man, but are rather the result of God's deliberate and wise choice, it follows that fellowship is an essential goal of man's creation. Brunner rejects social contract theories which attribute the state to man's decision to join together. Brunner insists that the state and other expressions of community are not the result of man's decision but are essential to his nature as one who is created for love and community, by virtue of being given a diversity of natural gifts. By way of contrast, those understandings of man which see him as a rational animal are inclined to understand him in terms of that which each man has in himself and yet which in no way differentiates him from other men. The result is that these understandings have an ethic of universality rather than one of personal communion. Those views which stress the common reason which is in all men tend also toward self-sufficiency; but if we recognize the significance and value of those things which differentiate men, then the goal is not self-sufficiency but a relation of mutual dependence in a community that is understood not as a concession to weakness but as the very goal of creation. Those systems which suppress the differences between men have as their goal unity, rather than community as expressed in the biblical concept of the kingdom of God as the perfection of community.

In a later consideration of the phenomenon of mass man, Brunner denies that depersonalization is attributable to technology. Rather, he argues, it stems from the failure to recognize and appreciate the differences in kind and function which are established by man's creation in the divine image.

The Imago and Christian Humanism

Brunner again returns to social ethics in his Gifford Lectures for 1947-1948, *Christianity and Civilization*. In these lectures Brunner defends the thesis that Christianity alone is able to accomplish the rebuilding of a human civilization on the ruins of the old civilization. Brunner expresses a great sense of urgency and anxiety, and although he feels that Christianity alone could meet this responsibility he is far from certain that it will rise to the occasion. In the hope that the dire predictions of Spengler concerning the decline of the Western civilization might be averted, Brunner sets himself to an examination of the Christian resources for responding to the fundamental questions of human existence which support civilization.

The discussion which is of particular interest to this study begins with the sixth lecture. At this point Brunner begins his investigation of the problems of humanism by examining the issues posed by the universe in which man finds himself. Preliterate man sees no distinction between man and the surrounding world. Nature and spirit are continuous. For preliterate man this affirmation is made, not by a depersonification of man but by a personification of nature. Gradually, especially in the classical Greek tradition, man emancipates himself from nature; and, as he discovers himself unique, he begins to negate the distinction between the divine and the human, on the basis of their common sharing of a nous or logos. This principle of reason premeates all nature and is the basis of its order, so that it is a cosmos rather than a chaos. But only in God and man does it become conscious knowledge, and so man's essential humanity is divinity.

The biblical view is critical of the failure to distinguish man and nature in preliterate thought; yet neither does it agree with the classical Greek position. Instead, it insists upon a distinction between God and the world, between God and man, and between man and nature. The divine is not the immanent principle of reason ordering the world but is the transcendent lord who is creator of the world. And God is distinguished not only from the world but also from man. But, although it is insisted that man is a creature, he is not put on the same level with the rest of creation. Although man is distinct from God, he is created in the image of God; and man alone of all creation is in the image of God. The Concept of the *imago dei* is the principle which distinguishes Christian humanism from Greek humanism. In contrast with the Greek view that man participates in the divine nous or logos, the Christian understanding of the *imago dei* places the emphasis not on man's rational nature but on his relation to the creator. Man does not *participate in* God but is *responsible to* God. The emphasis is not on a static nature automatically possessed by all man, but rather upon man's own free decision—which may be a decision not to realize the nature of man. Indeed, the Christian view says more than this, for it says that man has made the decision to turn against God and thereby to forefeit his true humanity, so that it can be reconstituted only through an act of divine grace. But even when man forfeits his true humanity, he does not completely obliterate his human character. He is still a responsible creature, and therefore even as sinner he is still distinct from the rest of the creation.

However important the differences between Greek and Christian humanism, they both agreed that man is unique, and this common agreement made possible a synthesis of the Greek and Christian humanistic traditions. They remained merged until the Renaissance and the Reformation became separate expressions of these two traditions.

In the modern world, however, the belief in the uniqueness of man is being challenged. Unlike the preliterate man, who personifies nature, the modern man has depersonified man. The continuity of man and nature has been established by understanding man as an object within nature.

Two names are especially significant in this development. Copernicus discovered the vastness of the universe and thus produced in man a sense of his insignificance in the cosmos. Darwin established man's biological continuity with the animal order. The destruction of the geocentric view and the development of the evolutionary hypothesis both produced a tremendous psychological shock when they were first promulgated. But Brunner points to the assimilation of these things by later generations as evidence that the shock was purely psychological and not spiritual. The uniqueness of man is not really disturbed by the quantitative extension of the cosmos in which man lives. Darwin, however, posed a more serious threat to belief in the uniqueness of man. Nonetheless, both idealistic and Christian humanism were able to respond to Darwin's challenge. The response of idealistic humanism is that even if man is to be understood as a species of mammal, he is nonetheless unique by the very fact that he alone produces a culture; and the culture of man expresses his spiritual rather than his animal nature. The response of Christian humanism is that even if man is to be understood biologically as an animal, he is unique in that he alone can hear and respond to the word of God. There is nothing in the work of Darwin or those scientists who have followed him which is

able to produce evidence that man's ability to hear and respond
to the word of God is no longer tenable. Indeed, science itself
bespeaks the uniqueness of man, for it is man alone who has
produced science.

But although there is no theoretical connection between
the discoveries of Copernicus and Darwin, it is nonetheless true
that in the course of history the practical effects of these discoveries have contributed to the breakdown of humanism,
whether idealistic or Christian. But Brunner feels that the impact of these theories upon theology was due largely to the unwarranted extension of theology into realms which were not
appropriate for it. In this sense the critique of science has had a
healthy purging effect, because it has forced theology to gain a
more genuine understanding of its own truth and essence. However, the fault is not attributed solely to theology. Brunner feels
that it was a mistake to oppose science, and that this opposition
was a misguided effort to oppose the drawing of unwarranted
philosophical implications from scientific data. By making such
implications, science has stepped into realms in which it is not
equipped to speak. For example, Darwinism could rightly assert
that man is a highly differentiated animal, but it tended to make
the stronger assertion, unwarranted by its discoveries, that man
is *nothing more* than this.

Brunner's major concern is not to accomplish a right and
just assessment of past guilt, but rather to find resources for a
viable Christian humanism. The key to it is found by Brunner
in the Christian understanding of man as created in the image
of God, which provides a foundation for understanding, at one
and the same time, man's place within nature and his uniqueness in creation. The Christian view recognizes that man must
be understood in natural terms, but the very fact of understanding man in this way is also to be recognized as an expression of
man's uniqueness; and such activity is to be consistent with man's
sense of responsibility to the divine word.

The Imago and Technology

In the second part of his Gifford Lectures, dealing with specific problems, Brunner first directs himself to the youngest of the problems, namely, technics or technology. Although technology was not a problem for earlier centuries, it is of primary concern for modern man. At the turn of the century, technology was the foundation for optimism. However, Brunner is writing in the context of the world wars and the use of atomic weapons, and it is because of this fear of the tremendous power of destruction that has been unleashed that he considers this to be the most urgent of the problems that face man today. In the Introduction we noted the dated character of Brunner's attitude toward technology and raised the question of the possibility of relating to a more optimistic, or perhaps we should say less pessimistic, view of technology; but at this point our concern is restricted to an investigation of how Brunner applies the concept of the *imago dei* to this problem.

In the biblical account of creation, the affirmation that God created man in his own image is followed by the expression of the divine command that man subdue the earth. For Brunner the order is significant. First we must understand man in relation to God, who as the creator of man is the source of the nature and destiny of man. Then, following from this, man is called to subdue the earth, or to transcend nature. Man is first distinguished from God and then distinguished from nature.

Technology is one of the means by which man is able to transcend nature, and thus it presupposes the spiritual life of man. Without the aid of technology, man remains on a level which is close to that of nature and is certainly dependent upon what nature provides him. But man's divine call is not to be dependent upon nature but to subdue nature, not to live as nature allows him but to forge out his own way of living. The construction of shelter and the development of architecture were the earliest steps which man took to protect himself against

the wiles of nature. Gradually, man developed various crafts
and artifices, and each generation was able to pass on its accum-
lated technical knowledge to subsequent generations. From the
beginning, the motivation of warfare was a forceful one in
technological development; this is not a sinister innovation of the
present day. Technology resulted also in the formation of new
class distinctions. However, in the premodern period these distinctions were not as serious as they are today, because the skills
necessary for man to improve his social situations could be easily
acquired. Consequently, Brunner feels that the early development of technology was much more beneficial than detrimental.
But with the coming of the machine age, the dangerous possibilities of technology were greatly heightened. There are still both
beneficial and detrimental aspects, but now both are heightened
tremendously. Brunner feels that were it not for the possibility of
war, technology would produce a veritable paradise. But he
insists that it is a dangerous abstraction to speak of technology
apart from the context of human social and cultural life. And
so technology not only implies the extension of man's power
over nature, but it also speaks of the actual depersonalization
of those men who have had to serve the machine, and the possible
universal suicide by the waging of thermonuclear warfare. Even
with this ominous possibility Brunner is still careful to point out
that it is not technology itself that is the problem, for if technology remains subordinate to the will of man and if the will of man
is obedient to the will of God, it can be a means of realizing the
divine purpose in creation. So the crucial issue concerning the
use of technology resolves itself into the issue of how man will
respond to the word of God.

The Imago as Creaturely Responsibility

In Brunner's *Dogmatik*, the discussions that are most relevant
to this study are found in the second volume, *Die christliche
Lehre von Schöpfung und Erlösung* (1950). In this book

Brunner gives a systematic presentation of the categories and themes that he has earlier developed in various contexts. Though his major concern here is systematic presentation, there are a few developments that merit our attention. In speaking of God's desire to create man with the ability to respond freely to God's love, Brunner distinguishes man from both an automaton, which does not respond in any way, and an animal, which can react but cannot respond since it cannot transcend itself and is not capable of speech nor of free self-determination. Man alone is able to respond as an "I" to a "Thou."

Brunner also emphasizes in this book that the *imago dei,* or responsibility, is to be understood as a relation and not as a substance. Brunner feels that the Catholic understanding of the *imago dei* as man's capacity for reason and for creative freedom has no way of preventing a pantheistic or an idealistic under-standing of man as divine, for in this view the image of God is a substance which man possesses in himself, even though it be but a spark from the divine spirit. A danger of this position is that everything in man that is not a participation in the divine reason is relegated to a status of unimportance or of condemna-tion.

Brunner also says that the important distinction between the formal and material aspects of the *imago dei* does not exist from the point of view of the divine creation. He means by this that God's purpose in creating man is not that man respond with a "yes" or "no." Rather God's will is that man should respond aright. God's will is not simply that man should choose to obey or disobey, but that man should obey as his own free response. And yet the freedom of choice can be known and experienced only when it elects to make the wrong response. Apart from this response, freedom is still there but it is not recognizable. Conse-quently, the very fact that man is aware of this freedom of choice is itself an effect of sin. It is because man has been separated from God that responsibility can be understood only in legal terms. This is identified by Brunner as the origin of the contrast between Law and Gospel. When man in his autonomy separates responsibility from God's grace, the result is legal responsibility. From the side of God, the distinction between the "formal image" that cannot be lost and the "material image," which is man's lost destiny as one who is being-in-love, is nonexistent. And the distinction exists for man only wrongly, when the Law makes him responsible for sin but not able to overcome it.

Because of its concept of the image of God, Christianity is not forced to choose between spirit or body, but affirms both as equally God's gracious gift to man. In contrast with idealism, Christianity can affirm the body not as separate from and inferior to the spirit, but as the spirit's God-given means for expression and realization. In contrast with materialism, Christianity can affirm the spiritual dimension of man through which he transcends the material realm and encounters the word of God.

Brunner considers it too extreme to identify the *imago dei* as the polarity of sex, but he does see these ideas as closely related. To be created in the image of God is to be created for community as well as to be established as an individual confronting another, and the differentiation of man into male and female is a basic element and presupposition of this. Sexual polarity is not, however, the "I" and the "Thou," but only a natural basis for it. Consequently, sexual polarity is not the *imago dei,* but rather a sort of "secondary" *imago.*

Brunner also rejects the identification of the *imago dei* with man's dominion over nature. This is more accurately considered the *consequence,* not the essence, of being created in the *imago dei.* Interestingly, Brunner insists that man's dominance over nature is dependent upon his refusal to regard nature as divine, and he warns that contemporary pleas to regard it so will deprive man of his true humanity as much as will the sole and single-minded determination to exert mastery over nature by civilization and technology. To deify either nature or civilization is not to guarantee man's true humanity, but rather to cause depersonalization. Man does not *become* human through surrendering to nature nor through building a civilized order; rather, man expresses his humanity through either of these activities, or else he forfeits it to them.

Brunner says that the interpretation of the *imago dei* as relation, rather than substance, enables us to deal with the controversy concerning the immortality of the soul. If we interpret immortality as a substantial part of man's nature, the origin must be placed in the Platonist rather than the biblical tradition. If we start from a relational perspective, we speak rather of man being destined for eternal communion with his creator. However, Brunner adds that this relation is an essential part of the substantial structure of man, in that man cannot be understood apart from his divinely intended destiny. Man, in other words, may refuse communion with God, but this does not alter man's nature as a being who is created for communion with God. Man's eternal destiny is founded not on his own substantial nature, but on God's will.

Man is both object and subject. An object is what it is, independently of its being known; a subject cannot have its being considered in isolation from its self-knowledge and will. Idealism tends to consider man exclusively as subject; naturalism, exclusively as object. The understanding of man in terms of his encounter with God permits an adequate recognition of both facets without compromising either element. Man is a unity of body and mind in responsible relation to his Creator. This Christian self-understanding of man as a mind-body unit offers anthropology a most fruitful opportunity for dialogue between the understanding of man in Christian and in non-Christian thought.

In this first part I have sketched the development of the scientific understanding of man in the image of the machine, and I have given an exposition of Brunner's theological understanding of man as created in the image of God. It is now my aim to develop the dialogue between the scientific and theological perspectives on man by focusing upon the implications of developments in cybernetics for our understanding of the nature of freedom and responsibility in man and machine.

Part Two

Freedom and Responsibility in Man and Machine

3 | The Nature of Causal Determination and Freedom

Science has made ethical decision-making more significant and also more difficult. Guides for the conduct of life in the horse-and-buggy age are not adequate in the age of high-horsepower cars and space vehicles. Young adults and their parents alike are often confused, and so they waver between a view that is precise and definite but superficial, and one that is realistic but which undermines confidence and replaces it with anxiety and confusion. It is difficult to come up with a guide for conduct that is sufficiently flexible for our fast moving society and yet adequately firm as a guide for our conduct.

Moreover, the vastness of social and economic life engulfs man; and at the same time that he is moved into greater interdependence, he has lost a sense of personal involvement with those around him. The world is vast, impersonal, and confusing. According to Viktor Frankl, man lives in an "existential vacuum" which makes him fear responsibility and freedom.[1]

It is tempting, therefore, to say that man is not responsible, and thereby skate around the complexities. And many feel that science supports such a course of action. Have we not learned that every event, including every aspect of man's behavior, is

---

[1] Cf. my article, "Existential Analysis and Logotherapy," *Encounter*, XXVI (Summer, 1965), esp. pp. 335-37.

caused? Granted, man is a highly complex machine, but if we get enough knowledge about him will it not be possible to predict his every action? This is a rapidly growing attitude toward life.

Eugene O'Neill speaks for modern man, not just for himself, in the highly autobiographical drama staged after his death. As Eugene O'Neill portrays it, life is a "long day's journey into night" in which events string out as inevitable results of their antecedents, without any intervening power to alter their course. This is true of each member of the Tyrone family. James Tyrone is unable to spend his money for the medical attention his family needs, and spends it instead on worthless real estate. He is unable to break with the past customs of his prime as a matinee idol. Mary Tyrone, with all the tragic events of her life—such as her loss of a child and her illness, drug addiction, and confinement—is still bound by the innocent and naïve view of life that she developed as a convent girl. The eldest son Jamie is bound to repeat his father's success, though he has become cynical and dissipated rather than successful. Edmund is his mother's pride and joy, but his consumption has so upset her that she resumes the use of narcotics which a quack doctor gave her at his birth, starting her addiction. The play ends with Edmund being forced to enter a sanitarium; with Jamie and Tyrone drinking heavily, but recalling rather than drowning their sorrows; and Mary, carrying her wedding gown, still hoping to recover the past. Being bound by the past, each of these people is living a life which is a long day's journey into night.

As man's awareness of the vastness of the universe has increased, God has seemed less and less significant. The psalmist contrasted the smallness of man with the greatness of God.

> When I look at thy heavens, the work of thy fingers,
>   the moon and the stars which thou hast established;
> what is man that thou art mindful of him,
>   and the son of man that thou dost care for him? (Psalm 8:3-4.)

But modern man has translated this passage so that it reads:

> When I look at the (no longer "thy") heavens, the work of cosmic
>   evolution,
>   the moon and the stars;
> What is God that we should be mindful of him,
>   and the deity that we should worship him?

The psalmist thought of the stars as lights suspended from heaven which arched above the earth, and he had no awareness of their vast size and distance. For many men today the heavens declare the glory of mathematics and physics, and the firmament showeth an unbroken cause-effect sequence.

Misconceptions of the Determinism-
Freedom Controversy

The first issue to be confronted in our attempt to merge the scientific and theological views of man is the perennial question of freedom and determinism. Although the issue that we are dealing with in this chapter is one of the perpetual problems of man, our focus is on not the hoary, but the contemporary, aspects of this question. And yet we cannot ignore the influence of traditional discussions, both as they clarify and as they obscure this problem. If man is responsible, i.e., able to respond, then he must be free. And yet the scientific view of man sees him as a machine, involving highly complex, but nonetheless mechanical, systems of communication and control. We cannot proceed further until we show that these two facets are compatible. But before we can deal with this issue, we must clarify the basic terms "cause" and "freedom."

Before we examine the basic terms, it is important to say a word of clarification about the problem itself. There are at least two common misconceptions which should be pointed out.

One misconception considers the problem of determinism and freedom to originate in the attempt to relate science and some other discipline, especially moral philosophy or theology. In this study, we are concerned to combine these two perspectives on man, but we must note that the problem of determinism and freedom is intrinsic to science. As Langdon Gilkey has pointed out,[2] the role of science in our society involves it in the paradox of freedom and determinism. As a body of hypotheses and conclusions, science asserts that man is determined; as a technique for controlling the world, science champions freedom. Even the knowledge about determining mechanisms, such as heredity, if used freely and responsibly can serve both rational and moral purposes. If we cannot move from scientific language to personal language, most would want to reject the former.[3] But, in any case, if we are to understand science itself scientifically—that is, the activities of science and the enhancement that comes through the insights of science—then this "science of science" leads us into the problem of freedom.[4] So this problem is one that has to be faced by science and one that can be raised without any mention of moral philosophy or theology.

Another common misconception is that in the determinist-indeterminist controversy all the passion is exerted in defense of free will, whereas the determinists are scientifically detached. But this is not always the case. There are passionate defenders of determinism. For example, Albert Einstein has refused to accept the idea that things happen which are impossible for man to predict and describe. And he has done so in quite passionate terms; for example, his exclamation: *"Der Herr Gott würfelt nicht"*—"The Lord God does not throw dice" (or "gamble.")[5]

It is interesting to note in passing that there is a certain cir-

---

[2] "Evolutionary Science and the Dilemma of Freedom and Determinism," *Christian Century* (Mar. 15, 1967), pp. 339-42.

[3] Cf. E. M. Adams, "Mental Causality," *Mind*, LXXV (Oct., 1966), 552-53.

[4] Cf. Warner Wick, "Truth's Debt to Freedom," *Mind*, LXXIII (Oct., 1964), 527-37.

[5] Quoted by Percy W. Bridgman, "Determinism in Modern Science," *Determinism and Freedom*, ed. Sidney Hook (New York: New York University Press, 1958), p. 51.

cularity in the hard-nosed attack upon the sentimental believers in free will as underminers of the scientific world view. In this context science depends upon the law of causal determination and is vitally threatened if this foundation is loosened in any way. In other contexts, the law of causal determination is made to rest upon the scientific world view.[6] It may be that this circularity can be straightened out, and I am not claiming that the entire case for determinism is vitiated by this logical lapse. But I am suggesting that it is rather misleading to speak of the defender of determinism as completely unmotivated by subjective and emotional considerations.

Brand Blanshard is a defender of determinism who stands among the ranks of idealist philosophers.[7] Blanshard argues that even in the case of psychic events there are levels of causation, that the higher supervene on the lower, and that an act is most free when it is impelled by an inner necessity of the highest order. Rational determinism, insists Blanshard, is the best kind of freedom for the logical thinker, for the creative artist, and for the religious saint. He reaches the climax of his case for determinism with this passionate affirmation.

The logician is most fully himself when the wind gets into his sails and carries him effortlessly along the line of his calculations. Many an artist and musician have left it on record that their best work was done when the whole they were creating took the brush or pen away from them and completed the work itself. It determined them, but they were free, because to be determined by this whole was at once the secret of their craft and the end of their desire. This is the condition of the moral man also. He has caught a vision, dimmer perhaps than that of the logician or the artist, but equally objective and compelling. It is a vision of the good. This good necessitates certain things, not as means to ends merely, for that is not usually a necessary link, but as integral parts of itself. It requires that he should put love above hate, that he should regard his

---

[6] Cf. John Wisdom, *Problems of Mind and Matter* (Cambridge: Cambridge University Press, 1963) , p. 112.

[7] "The Case for Determinism," *Determinism and Freedom*, pp. 3-15.

neighbor's good as of like value with his own, that he should repair in-
juries, and express gratitude, and respect promises, and revere truth. Of
course it does not guide him infallibly. On the values of a particular case
he may easily be mistaken. But that no more shows that there are no
values present to be estimated, and no ideal demanding a specific mode
of action, than the fact that we make a mistake in adding figures shows
that there are no figures to be added, or a right way of adding them. In
both instances what we want is control by the objective requirements of
the case. The saint, like the thinker and the artist, has often said this in
so many words. I feel most free, said St. Paul, precisely when I am most
a slave.[8]

William Barrett, in his role as critical commentator on Blanshard's paper, notes the difference between Blanshard's case and
the typical defense of determinism. "The psychological examples
usually cited by determinists reflect the more monotonous and
routine aspects of our behavior, as if to reinforce their general
picture of the world as a vast and dreamy machine. Professor
Blanshard is not of this kidney." [9]

In broaching the problem of the relation of determinism
and freedom, we are not, then, forcing science to face a problem
that it could otherwise serenely ignore; nor are we introducing
strident cries of passion and emotion that would not otherwise
grate upon the scientist's ear. Rather, we are simply facing one
of the basic problems of man, in its peculiarly contemporary
form, and we are drawing upon science and theology as two
major resources for coming to grips with it.

The key concept of determinist theories is "cause," because
these theories maintain that every event is explicable in terms of
antecedent causes. In principle we could predict any event, although in theory the cause-effect nexus is so vast that complete
knowledge of the pertinent factors is unattainable, for the present at least. Spinoza asserts that an omniscient knower could
deduce my behavior from his knowledge of who I am, in the
same way that we are able to know the properties of a triangle

---

[8] *Ibid.,* p. 14.   [9] "Determinism and Novelty," *ibid.,* p. 37.

that follow from its nature.[10] So a basic issue involves the nature of cause, and especially the possibility of predicting consequences from a knowledge of causes.

The key concept of indeterminist theories is "freedom," because these theories maintain that the action of the will is not determined by causes. Indeterminists deny not the causal sequence, but merely its all-embracing character. They contend, rather, that some things happen because of purposes, rather than because of causes. Hence, some things are unpredictable in theory, and not simply because of human limitation. So, a basic issue involves the nature of freedom, and especially whether freedom necessitates a supervention of the cause-effect sequence.

Our first task, then, is the clarification of these two terms. There are many others that are relevant, and the literature of analytic philosophy abounds in discussion of them. In view of the focus of our study, however, I think we can advance our discussion with an examination of these two basic terms and then proceed to inquire into the relation between freedom and determinism. Our concern will be to describe the terms "cause" and "freedom" and to examine their complexity. However, we are not concerned to arrive at strict or working definitions because we are not trying to find *a sense* of free will which is compatible with *a sense* of causal determinism. Our concern is with clarification, rather than definition.

The Concept of "Cause"

The assignation of causes involves a context of inquiry.[11] For example, consider the illustration of a man who is suffering from

[10] Spinoza, *Ethics,* First Part, Prop. xvii, Scholion; cf. Schopenhauer, *Essay on the Freedom of the Will,* trans. Konstantin Kalenda (New York: Liberal Arts Press, 1960), pp. 23-24.

[11] Cf. H. L. A. Hart and A. M. Honoré, *Causation in the Law* (New York: Oxford University Press, 1959), p. 34; and Samuel Gorovitz, "Causal Judgments and Causal Explanations," *The Journal of Philosophy,* LXII (Dec. 2, 1965), 699-705.

indigestion. If he asks the doctor what caused the indigestion, he may be told that the cause is an ulcerated stomach. If, however, his wife is asked, she may reply that it was caused by parsnips. The context of inquiry for the wife is: "What gave my husband indigestion when he usually does not suffer from it?" The doctor's context of inquiry is a wider one, namely: "Why does this particular person have indigestion since most people do not suffer from it?" If the doctor were to be an intern, and carried the question back to the classroom, his professor might answer that the indigestion was caused by the production of a gas that resulted from the digestive acids upon parsnips and that this gas irritated the intestinal tract. If we ask the man himself, he might reply that he suffered from indigestion because he chose to eat the parsnips which his hostess had provided for him at a dinner, rather than to risk offending her.

One form of humor proceeds by preparing a person for an explanation at one level of causation, and then upsetting his expectation by providing him with an explanation at another level. The old chestnut, "Why does a chicken cross the road?" may now have gone into deserved retirement, but it has many active progeny; for example, "What is a home without children?" "Quiet."

Even if we restrict ourselves to scientific usage, the term "cause" does not mean the same thing to a physicist that it does to a biologist, nor even to the fields of inorganic and organic chemistry. Scientific determinism is quite different, depending on whether one takes physics or biology as the model. If we consider the economist, the historian, and the sociologist as social scientists, their uses of "cause" are different again.

In dealing with nonorganic matter, such as bouncing billiard balls, one can achieve a high degree of predictability. Yet, even in physics, there is now the custom of talking in terms of probability applicable to large numbers of units. There is little loss in predictability even when one moves to plant life, but it is an obstinate fact in the study of animal life. For example, the biologist Warner Clyde Allee mentions the influence of light on photographic film, on oat seedlings, and on the horseshoe crab (*Limulus*). Let us consider his comments on the latter only.

When exposed to light from two sources that differ in intensity, it will turn and move away in a direction determined by the angles at which the two beams reach the eyes together with the product of intensity and duration of exposure to the lights.

In one of the first experimental series with the horseshoe crab, out of 48 individuals tested, all but ten reacted in fairly diagrammatic fashion; these ten gave unpredictable results. This introduces another principle. It is remarkable and significant that although 38 of these highly complex animals behaved in their reaction to light as though they were slowmoving guided missiles, the other ten reacted in an unpredictable manner. As we used to say at the University of Chicago, the reaction of those ten illustrated what we called the Harvard law of animal behavior, which holds that under controlled conditions animals do as they damn please.[12]

Jennings has commented: "If Amoeba were the size of a dog, instead of being microscopic, no one would deny to its actions the name of intelligence." [13] Although the element of unpredictability is more noticeable in the case of living organisms, it is not confined to this area of scientific endeavor. For example, engineers have developed what is called "Murphy's Law," which states that "if something can go wrong, it will." Paradoxically, the notion of "cause" has, itself, a certain element of unpredictability. But is this inherent, or simply due to complexity?

The word "cause" is misleading when it prompts us to think that we are looking for a single causative factor.

It is a commonplace nowadays that theoretical science has ceased to look for *the* cause of any event. If we define a cause as "that event, upon which a given event follows, in accordance with an invariable rule," then it must

---

[12] "Biology," *What Is Science?* ed. by James R. Newman (New York: Washington Square Press, 1962), p. 251.

[13] Quoted by W. Macneile Dixon, *The Human Situation* (New York: St. Martin's Press, 1954), p. 139.

be confessed that there are no causes in nature; for no single antecedent ever suffices to determine a consequent. When, in a practical science such as medicine, we ask for *the* cause (say of the disease) , we are taking for granted an enormous complex of operative factors, both constitutive of health, and hostile to it. We look simply for the event which upset the balance, and let the enemy into the camp. It would be plainly ludicrous to treat the one event as by itself capable of producing a diseased human functioning. It would have to begin by producing a man, and that is beyond the powers of (let us say) a sudden sharp fall in the temperature.14

The example of the complexity of causality that is perhaps most common is the weather report. We are used to listening to the meteorologist explain all the factors that will cause rain or prevent snow, and it is not too unusual for us to hear him explaining the next day how one or two of the factors did not behave as anticipated so that the promised rain did not come, or the cautiously predicted snow flurries accumulated up to five inches. Use of the term "cause" may deceive us into simplifying the situation, thinking that there is always one cause for each event, or at most a group of causes which for all practical purposes form a unit, so that events are produced in relatively uniform fashion. To the contrary, however, "cause" refers to a highly complex series of interrelations with subtle nuances. Causal determination can result in surprise as well as predictability.

Although many people today assume implicitly that there is but one cause for one event, the realization that an effect is the outcome of several antecedents is hardly a recent discovery. The idea is discussed, for example, in John Stuart Mill's *A System of Logic,* published in 1887 (Book III, chap. v, sec. 3) .

However, even if we can reduce a situation to one causative factor in certain situations, can we establish the assertion that this cause determines the outcome mechanically? Let us consider the celebrated case of Pavlov's dog.15 It is all very simple: cause,

---

14 Austin Farrer, *The Freedom of the Will* (London: Adam & Charles Black, 1958) , p. 195.
15 For a study of learning in machines from the perspective of Pavlov's concept

the ringing of a bell; effect, salivation. But what is the precise connection between cause and effect? Is it a mechanical connection, or is there a consciousness which interprets the bell ringing and anticipates food on the basis of this interpretation? The evidence is not sufficient to establish the theory that behavior is automatically determined by mechanical causes. Or, more accurately, scientific investigation cannot settle this question, because the data can be adequately categorized in terms of either mechanical or interpretive relation. In speaking of the issue of the nature of psychophysical relations, E. M. Adams says: "Whether there are correlations between brain states and experiences and thoughts is something to be found out empirically. It is the task of the neurologist. Whether brain states are to be described as causes of experiences and thoughts correlated with them is not entirely an empirical matter." [16] Adams examines the problem further and rejects naturalistic explanations as an inappropriate mixture of categories. "A brain event can no more 'cause' a personal act than an electron can collide with a baseball or a person can marry a nation." [17] We will return to this concept of mixed categories later, when we seek to examine the relation between causal determinism of behavior and freedom. But our concern at this point is simply to clarify the term "cause," and so we must delay our pursuit of the implications opened up by this discussion.

The term "cause" may hide a significant assumption. No one would deny that some things are best explained in terms of a cause and effect sequence, but are all things best explained in these categories? The term "cause" may smuggle in the affirmation that the causal principle is universally applicable, without

---

of "conditioned reflex," see Helmer Frank, "Pawlows bedingte Reflexe und Steinbuchs Lernmatrizen," *Kybernetik—Brücke Zwischen den Wissenschaften*, ed. Helmar Frank, 4th ed. (Frankfurt am Main: Umschau, 1964), pp. 107 ff.

[16] "Mental Causality," p. 554.

[17] *Ibid.*, p. 558.

an investigation of the evidence for and against this assumption.[18]

Cherbonnier points out that the attack on freedom has often been spearheaded by science and philosophy, and he makes this comment:

> This is all the more astonishing in view of the fact that science and philosophy represent supreme expressions of human freedom. The explanation, however, is fairly simple. It lies in one single assumption which these disciplines inherit from a common source: the assumption of ancient Greek scientists and philosophers that to every question "Why?" it must be possible to give an answer in *causal* terms. To the question, "Why did Socrates refuse to escape from prison?" this position is obliged to reply by resolving Socrates's actions into various causal factors. Human freedom is thereby ruled out in advance. By a subtle transition, as fateful in effect as it is harmless in appearance, the search for causes, in itself so constructive, has thus been converted into a dogma: the assumption that the specialized methods of science and philosophy, instead of being useful tools for the solution of certain kinds of problems, can actually solve them all. The man who subscribes to this article of faith is a determinist. With him the quest for knowledge, which ought properly to be a liberating enterprise, has become authoritarian. When he encounters questions that cannot be answered by the methods of logic or laboratory, he either dismisses them as meaningless or else subtly transposes them into other terms. But these are precisely the questions raised by the fact of freedom. If man really is free, then his behavior cannot be exhaustively explained in causal terms.[19]

Some contemporary scientists are even ready to relegate the concept of "cause" to the language of common sense, and to replace it, for scientific study, with the formulation in terms of a functional relationship which allows for a mathematical expres-

---

[18] Cf.: "People today stop at the laws of nature, treating them as something inviolable, just as God and Fate were treated in past ages. And in fact both are right and both are wrong: though the view of the ancients is clearer in so far as they have a clear and acknowledged terminus, while the modern system tries to make it look as if *everything* were explained."—Ludwig Wittgenstein, *Tractatus Logico-Philosophicus,* trans. D. F. Pears and B. F. McGuinness (New York: Humanities Press, 1961), 6.372, p. 143.

[19] E. La B. Cherbonnier, *Hardness of Heart* (Garden City, N.Y.: Doubleday, 1955), pp. 29-30.

sion of the relationship.[20] We have to be cautious in moving from statistical probability as operative in the subatomic realm to that operative in the human realm. This is especially true in light of the tempting opportunity to argue for freedom on the basis of the indeterminacy of individual events. My own contention will be that freedom and determinism are not simply supplementary, but concomitant. Nonetheless, it may be permissible simply to point out here that statistical probability is used in both realms. We cannot tell whether a particular atom will collide with others, or whether a particular individual will be in an automobile wreck, but we can develop accurate statements of probability in both cases.

The Concept of "Freedom"

"Freedom" seems to be an even more slippery term than "cause." Because we have just been talking about statistical probability, it may be well to begin our clarification by pointing out that freedom needs to be seen in a context of collective action. Yet, most discussions tend to treat freedom as a characteristic of individual action, and this may lead to an oversimplification of the issue. When the collective element is included in the discussion

---

[20] For example, see Herbert Feigl, "Notes on Causality," *Readings in the Philosophy of Science*, ed. Herbert Feigl and May Brodbeck (New York: Appleton-Century-Crofts, 1953), pp. 408-18. For a discussion of adequate explanation as requiring a coherent "nomological net" which encompasses all the involved events, see Herbert Feigl, "The 'Mental' and the 'Physical,'" *Concepts, Theories, and the Mind-Body Problem*, ed. H. Feigl, G. Maxwell, and M. Scriven (Minneapolis: University of Minnesota Press, 1958), pp. 370-483. Feigl's approach is to bring the "dangling" mental events into the "nomological net" by identifying them with neural activities (a view which he subsequently abandoned). Feigl disagrees with those who contend that the mind-body problem arises because of the way that we use language, and consequently he opposes their contention that confusion can be eliminated by assigning concepts to their appropriate spheres. See "Mind-Body, Not a Pseudoproblem," *Dimensions of Mind*, ed. Sidney Hook (New York: New York University Press, 1960), chap. 2. An example of those whom Feigl opposes is Gilbert Ryle, whose contribution to our study will be examined at a later point.

of freedom (often the term "liberty" [21] is employed in such cases) it is usually restricted to the political context. Peter A. Bertocci has a helpful analysis of the phenomenon of freedom. "I experience my freedom most clearly at those moments in my life when something is happening to me which (a) I do not wish or want to happen, (b) which I could terminate, but (c) will not terminate for the sake of some other approved objective." [22] A similar perspective seems to be employed by Leslie H. Farber in this statement: "Will power is the name we give to fiats that run counter to our appetites and inclinations." [23] Bertocci illustrates by citing a case in which a person is handling a hot plate which he wants to drop, but which he wills to continue holding because he desires to avoid splattering the food or breaking one of his wife's favorite dishes. In other words, if self alone is involved, there is no basis for the exercise of free choice because there is no reason to override one's wants. If one insists on reducing "willing" to "wanting" (and Bertocci[24] is convinced that his "phenomenological" analysis of freedom refutes this prima facie at least), then we could say that there is no need to choose between competing "wants." But when we speak in terms of the complexity of social relationships, then we introduce a hierarchy of values in terms of which freedom of choice makes sense. Sometimes the individual may confront competing wants, but often it is only in a wider context that there is any issue concerning freedom.

Freedom can be applied to action or to choice. A person's action is free if he could have behaved differently from the way

---

[21] For a survey and evaluation of a wide diversity of interpretation of the term "liberty," see H. J. McCloskey, "A Critique of the Ideals of Liberty," *Mind*, LXXIV (Oct. 1965), 483-508.

[22] *Free Will, Responsibility, and Grace* (Nashville: Abingdon Press, 1957). p. 16. Bertocci replaces "*Cogito, ergo sum*" with "*Volo, ergo sum*," rather than "*Conor, ergo sum*," because he feels that willing, rather than wanting, most effectively "expresses what I am sure is myself." *Ibid.*, pp. 18-19.

[23] *The Ways of the Will* (New York: Basic Books, 1966), p. 2.

[24] *Free Will, Responsibility, and Grace*, pp. 16-19, 37.

he actually did, provided that he had chosen to act differently.[25] Others would say that freedom applies to the choice, so that a person can be said to be free not merely if he could have acted differently, but only if he could also have chosen differently. In other words, a person's action is determined if he could not have chosen an alternate mode of behavior, even if he could have behaved differently provided he had chosen to do so.

Different senses of the term freedom are sometimes expressed by the addition of the prepositions "from," "to," and "for." [26] "Freedom from" refers to the absence, elimination, or overcoming of unusual restraints or obstacles. For example, the manumitted slave is described as a "free man." "Freedom to" refers to the power to carry out one's intentions or purposes. For example, a man with financial resources may be described as "free to travel." "Freedom for" refers to commitment to a cause. Thus a professor who is considering a position may inquire if it allows "freedom for research." Although the element of personal interrelations is present in all these, the phrase "freedom with" may also be employed to emphasize the social nature of our situation and the need for the harmonious exercise of varying, and sometimes opposed, concerns.

In *Escape from Freedom*, Erich Fromm distinguishes be-

---

[25] Jonathan Edwards adopts this approach to reconcile the freedom of man and the determining power of divine providence; *Freedom of the Will*, ed. Paul Ramsey (New Haven: Yale University Press, 1957). More recently, and minus the theological dimension, G. E. Moore adopts this interpretation of human freedom as the basis of a reconciliation of freedom and determinism; *Ethics* (London: Oxford University Press, 1963), chap. 6. A refutation of this attempt is found in John Austin, "Ifs and Cans," chap. 7 of his *Philosophical Papers* (London: Oxford University Press, 1961). For a disclaimer that Austin has succeeded in his refutation of Moore, see Jane M. Osborn, "Austin's Non-conditional Ifs," *The Journal of Philosophy*, LXII (Dec. 2, 1965), 711-15.

[26] Cf. Paul Weiss, "Common Sense and Beyond," *Determinism and Freedom*, p. 233; and Edgar Sheffield Brightman, *The Spiritual Life* (New York: Abingdon-Cokesbury, 1942), p. 180. Brightman calls freedom *from* "negative freedom" and freedom *to* "positive freedom," and he considers both of these to be in the psychological realm, as contrasted with the physical realm, which includes political freedom as an important aspect.

tween overt and anonymous authority. Overt authority is direct
and explicit. The threat of force is open and naked. We tend to
think of ourselves as "free" as long as we are not subject to overt
authority. But we may be escaping from freedom by replacing
overt with anonymous authority. We have simply replaced the
open threat of physical force with the more subtle means of
psychic manipulation. Our economy actually depends on psychic
manipulation. Our factories and corporations need workmen
and executives who will act as expected, so that the complex
machinery can keep grinding out consumer goods. We have no
place for individuality, which would only disrupt our orderly
procedures. We also need consumers to buy the goods we have
manufactured on a mass scale. Individual need and desire would
hardly be adequate, and so we have what Vance Packard has
aptly described as "hidden persuaders." Motivational research
is designed to make us susceptible to the purchase of goods that
we do not want, and that in most cases will be obsolete before
we have finished paying for them. The obsolescence is due partly
to advances, but is largely planned. Vance Packard discusses this
in *The Waste Makers*. So, in our so-called free society we are
manipulated to become well oiled cogs in a massive machine;
our wants and desires are manipulated to make even our consumption fit the needs of the machine. All this is done in such a
way that everyone feels free, and anyone who suggests otherwise
or in any other way urges deviant values or individual preferences or judgments that do not accord with the accepted ideol-
ogy, is ipso facto uncooperative, if not downright un-American.
Indeed, the whole aspect of the investigation of un-American
activities, supposedly to preserve our freedom, is in fact one of
the most blatant denials of freedom in this country. The threat
of social ostracism is every bit as much a threat as the threat of
incarceration.

Austin Farrer calls attention to what he describes as "the
hybrid character" of the term "freedom." It often, though not
necessarily, includes an evaluative as well as a descriptive ele-

ment. It is often hard to distinguish these, and there is often a choice of value that is implicit in the descriptive element. The use of "freedom" to describe the absence of obstacles can be illustrated with the declaration that the railroad track is free of obstacles. Farrer comments:

And yet no severely physical description would ever call anything an obstruction. Physical process as such is never obstructed; it acts as perfectly, it fulfils its principle as completely, whether the train runs on to Paddington, or crashes at Didcot.[27]

He further illustrates with a slip of the tongue made by a first-aid instructor.

A patient with an open artery, he said, could be saved from bleeding to death by a tourniquet applied at the right point; as soon as you tightened it, it would stop the blood from running out "the way it should." The absurdity lies in the substitution of an invariably evaluative phrase for an ambiguous term like "freely."[28]

Because freedom is often valued for its own sake, we easily consider any denial of freedom to be a denial of value. And yet, not every use of the term "freedom" is intended to express value.

The very form of the word "freedom" is misleading. Because it is a noun, we may assume that we are talking about some entity, albeit a highly intangible one. But the term "freedom" is a substantivized adjective. The basic form is the adjective "free." When we are talking about freedom, we are talking not about an entity, but about a quality. The adjective "voluntary" can be used as a synonym, and there is value in this because in this word the adjectival form is predominant, although we do have the noun "voluntarism." However, the term "freedom" is much more common and points much more clearly to the issue that concerns us. Even if we were to use the term "voluntary," we should be forced to clarify the term "freedom" in any case.

---

[27] *The Freedom of the Will*, p. 107.   [28] *Ibid*.

The term "freedom" is perhaps less exact, but it is more useful (relevant) to our discussion.

Following a clarification of the terms "cause" and "freedom," we must now turn to the question of how they are interrelated. We will first examine the thesis that they are not related, that man is pure freedom and his activity unconditioned. Then we shall seek to defend the view that determinism and freedom are not merely compatible, but are actually concomitants. Then we shall examine our knowledge of computing machines to see if it will bear out this thesis.

The Relation of Causal Determination and Freedom

We have briefly considered some of the complexities of the terms "cause" and "freedom." Our concern now is to examine the relation of these terms. There are complexities enough when the terms are used in isolation, but the pressing problem is not how these terms are to be used, but how they are to be related. Some hold that they are mutually exclusive, and others contend that they are compatible. Those who say that they are mutually exclusive must decide whether all actions are determined, or whether all actions are free, or whether some actions are determined and others free (though no action is both). Those who say that causal determinism and freedom are compatible must deal with the nature of their interrelation. Are they parallel series, both necessary but not affecting one another? Or are they mutually influential; and if so, are they held together in polar tension or are they concomitantly increased and decreased?

In exploring this issue, I want to examine one form of asserting the mutual exclusiveness of causal determinism and freedom, and one form of asserting that they are compatible. For the former, I will examine Jean-Paul Sartre's concept of freedom. Sartre represents "first generation" existentialism, with its antithesis toward science. Then I will attempt to develop a "second generation" existentialism that is seeking to avoid the Romanticism that is expressed in this earlier anti-scientific attitude. In doing this, I will try to defend the view that causal determinism and freedom are concomitants. Through this discussion, my concern will be with human thought and behavior, but the scope will be limited by my intention to treat this consideration as preliminary to a consideration of the relation of machine thought and behavior to that of humans.

The term "freedom" is usually qualified as "finite" or "limited" or some such term. However, the French existentialist Jean-Paul Sartre has developed an extreme libertarian position. Indeed, his system has been referred to as "a freedom intoxicated doctrine." [29] Other existentialists may not have been as blatant in theory, but they often tended in practice to have an equal disregard for the mechanisms of determinism. Because it is our intention to modify this aspect of existentialism, Sartre's concept of freedom merits our attention.

Moreover, it has also been remarked that "Sartre has a philosophy where liberty has never played so large a role, and a politics where it has never played such a small one." [30] This remark perhaps has added significance in light of our intention to argue in the next chapter that freedom and determinism are concomitants. It may be the very refusal to recognize determining factors that has belittled in practice the element of liberty that looms so large for Sartre in theory.

According to Sartre, all men are by nature free, and they can escape their freedom only by a deliberate act of bad faith. Sartre believes not only that man is absolutely free when he makes choices, but also that man cannot avoid making choices. Even when a person refuses to decide on an issue or to make a choice

---

[29] Eric Unger, "Existentialism—II," *The Nineteenth Century*, CXLIII (Jan., 1948), 37.

[30] Quoted in Joseph Frank, "Existentialist Ethics," *New Republic* (Sept. 7, 1953), p. 19; cf. J. C. Gregory, "Sartre's Existentialism," *The Contemporary Review*, CLXXVI (Sept., 1949), 168. For a discusssion of the relation between freedom and moral values in Sartre's thought, see F. H. Heinemann, "Theologia Diaboli," *The Hibbert Journal*, LIII (Oct., 1953), 70.

concerning it, that very decision is itself his free choice; man is, according to Sartre, "condemned to be free." [31] In a sense, the only thing from which man is not free is freedom itself. Freedom "is not a super-added quality or a *property* of my nature; it is very exactly, the stuff [*l'étoffe*] of my being." [32] In this sense alone can freedom be said to be "the free choice to struggle in order to become free." [33] Otherwise, for Sartre, freedom is inherent, innate, and natural, springing from at least two main sources.

The first source of freedom, according to Sartre, is the basic thesis of existentialism that existence precedes essence. Because there is no essence which predetermines what he will be or will not be, each individual is absolutely free and entirely self-responsible for what he becomes.[34] Man cannot, according to Sartre, justify anything by referring to some concept of a fixed nature which in any way necessitates what he will or will not be. Man is free, then, for Sartre, because he is completely undetermined.

The second main source of Sartre's concept of freedom, which is complementary to the first, is man's attempt to overcome his nothingness and become something. He says that Descartes was the first philosopher to stress "the connection between free will and negativity." [35] The self, as *pour-soi*, is lack (*manque*) of being, and because of this it chooses. "Freedom makes only one with lack, it is the mode of concrete being of the lack of being." [36] That which is expressed in terms of lack can be expressed also in terms of freedom. For Sartre, freedom is free-

---

[31] *L'être et le néant* (Paris: Librairie Gallimard, 1943), p. 515. Translations are my own.

[32] *Ibid.*, p. 514. Italics his.

[33] A quotation of Sartre's answer to Camus, in Nicola Chiaromonte, "Sartre versus Camus: A Political Quarrel," *Partisan Review*, XIX (Nov., 1952), 684.

[34] *L'être et le néant*, p. 657.

[35] Sartre, *Literary and Philosophical Essays*, trans. Annette Michelson (London: Rider and Co., 1955), p. 179; cf. pp. 177-80.

[36] *L'être et le néant*, p. 652; cf. pp. 558, 689; *The Psychology of Imagination* (New York: Philosophical Library, 1948), pp. 67, 269-71.

dom of choice of being. As the self chooses to become something, this choice of being is translated into actions. Strictly speaking, in order to avoid inconsistency, Sartre would have to say that each self is solely responsible only for what it does to overcome its lack of being, not for what it becomes, for he has said that what we are is determined by the interpretation others put on our actions. Allowing Sartre this slight inconsistency, however, we may summarize his views on the source of freedom in this way: man is free, first, because he is nothing to start with; and, second, because he makes his own attempt to become something and is solely responsible for what he becomes.

There is certainly a close relationship between Sartre's atheism and his concept of freedom. Whether Sartre assumes atheism and deduces freedom, as Frechtman claims,[37] or whether he deduces atheism from his concept of absolute freedom and the fact that the concept of God is contradictory (because God would have to be both a *pour-soi* [becoming] and an *en-soi* [that which does not become, but is]), as Spier claims,[38] is difficult to determine. Perhaps atheism should be listed as a third main source of Sartre's concept of freedom. In any case, there is certainly a close relation between these two concepts in Sartre's thinking.[39] Because God does not exist, he cannot enforce his laws on men, and thus they are completely free from outside and a priori norms of conduct. Sartre claimed that "Dostoievsky's famous 'If God does not exist, all is permissible,' is the terrible revelation which the bourgeoisie has forced itself to conceal during the one hundred fifty years of its reign." [40] Nor can other selves impose their rules and standards on the self. For Sartre,

---

[37] Frechtman, "Introduction," in Sartre, *Existentialism*, trans. B. Frechtman (New York: Philosophical Library, 1947), p. 3.

[38] J. M. Spier, *Christianity and Existentialism*, trans. D. H. Freeman (Philadelphia: Presbyterian and Reformed Publishing Co., 1953), p. 62.

[39] See my discussion of Sartre's atheism in relation to the thought of Martin Buber in *Encountering Truth*, p. 33.

[40] Sartre, *What Is Literature?* trans. B. Frechtman (New York: Philosophical Library, 1949), p. 113 n.; cf. *Existentialism*, pp. 25 ff.

the concepts of good and bad disappear with the rules and standards.

In order to understand better Sartre's concept of freedom, it is necessary to consider, however briefly, his concept of time. Sartre has defined freedom as "the human being putting his past out of play while secreting his own being." [41] For Sartre, past time is *en-soi* and is thus similar to inanimate things. One does not really have a past; he is his past when he dies. So freedom, which is a characteristic of *pour-soi*, is brought about, or is being brought about, by naughting one's past, or, as the definition quoted above phrased it, "putting it out of play." The present is, for Sartre, the period of time during which this naughting of the past is taking place.[42] For Sartre, the future is that which one has to be only insofar as it is entirely possible that he may not be it.[43] Man projects himself into the future to judge the present.[44] For Sartre, then, freedom is closely related to past, present, and future; to the past as that which it naughts, to the present as the time during which it is operative, and to the future as that which it alone will determine.

For Sartre, freedom is never abstracted from all reality. One always chooses in a situation. What Sartre means by being in a situation is that the self and his environment form a synthetic whole. On one hand, the environment forms the self and determines the possibilities that are open to him; however, on the other hand, the situation has meaning only as the self interprets it and makes his choice within it.[45] As one commentator puts it, "What men have in common is not a 'nature' but a condition, that is, an ensemble of limits and restrictions." [46] Man must resolve the situation in which he finds himself by making a

---

[41] *L'être et le néant,* p. 65.   [42] *Ibid.,* pp. 162-63.

[43] *Literary and Philosophical Essays,* p. 143.

[44] *What Is Literature?* pp. 292-93.

[45] *Existentialism,* p. 52; *Anti-Semite and Jew,* trans. George J. Becker (New York: Schocken Books, 1946), pp. 59-60; *L'être et le néant,* p. 660.

[46] John J. Weisert, "Two Recent Variations on the Orestes Theme," *The Modern Language Journal,* XXIV (May, 1951), 360.

choice. Man is, in a sense, limited by the situation; however, in the last analysis, the situation is itself limited by man, so man is, for Sartre, absolutely free.

Sartre believed that man was free from anything external to himself that would limit his freedom. Man is "pure freedom" and "unconditioned activity." [47] Freedom is not a matter of degree; rather, each individual is infinitely free. Man is not limited by desires, feelings, and passions, for he brings them into being himself and he can put them out of play himself.[48] Sartre even denies that inherited inclinations and character have any influence on the individual's choice.[49] All meaning and all activity arise through the agency of the self and only through the agency of the self. Man is completely and absolutely free within himself.

Sartre believed that responsibility flowed inevitably from freedom and could not, therefore, be avoided. Personal responsibility is at the very heart of Sartre's system of thought. Although the individual was not free to choose concerning his own creation, he is responsible, once he has entered the world, for everything he does.[50] To make a decision is to be responsible for the decision. According to Sartre, man can never choose evil; therefore, when he chooses he affirms at the same time the value of what he chooses.[51] This responsibility was made even greater for Sartre by the fact that he believed that when one chooses for himself, he chooses for all men what they ought to be or do. Sartre's concept, although related to Kant's Categorical Imperative, is different in that it still leaves ethical judgments subjective, while Kant constructed an objective standard.

Sartre maintained that it is through anxiety or anguish that

---

[47] *What Is Literature?* pp. 47-51, 270-71; *L'être et le néant*, p. 648; *Existentialism*, pp. 27-28; *Literary and Philosophical Essays*, p. 185.

[48] *L'être et le néant*, p. 657.

[49] *What Is Literature?* pp. 41-42, 292-93; cf. *The Age of Reason*, trans. Eric Sutton (London: Hamish Hamilton, 1947), pp. 289-90, 359.

[50] *Existentialism*, p. 27.

[51] *Ibid.*, p. 20; cf. *Literary and Philosophical Essays*, p. 172.

man becomes aware of his freedom. He spoke of "this terrible necessity to be free which is my lot." [52] In his novels, especially in *Nausea,* he combines the individual's discovery of freedom with a sense of anguish and discomfort. There are three main sources of this anguish which accompanies freedom.[53] First, man realizes that in making choices he is not only deciding for himself but is choosing what all men should do. The consequent feeling of "total and deep responsibility" results in anguish. Second, because God does not exist there can be no a priori standards of right and wrong in which the self can take refuge and avoid anguish. Third, because man cannot have certainty, but only probability, the necessity to decide fills him with a sense of anguish. Sartre considered freedom to be something which ought not to be shunned, but which is always dreaded.

Sartre believed that it was quite within the self's ability to use his freedom to try to avoid the responsibility ensuing from freedom. Indeed, Sartre felt that the vast majority of people do attempt, by an act of bad faith, to avoid responsibility by subjecting themselves to various laws and norms.[54] The person who acts in bad faith tries to bury thoroughly from himself his consciousness of freedom. In bad faith a permanent, unchanging meaning is imposed on that which is *pour-soi.* Sartre calls for men to be courageous and to live in the freedom which is their calling; he decries the man of bad faith who seeks to actualize himself in order to preserve himself from his rightful freedom and the anxiety which it entails.

Sartre's view of freedom is that of an extremely doctrinaire, but nonetheless carefully reasoned, insistence on the absolute nature and basic role of freedom in the life of men. His view that all men are free by nature is questionable as an assertion that men are free because there is nothing which predetermines

---

[52] *L'être et le néant,* p. 450.   [53] *Existentialism,* pp. 21 ff.

[54] *L'être et le néant,* pp. 86, 88, 94, 105-7, 669. In his novels and plays this is done primarily by joining the Communist party or the church.

them, but is forceful and timely in its assertion that the self alone
is originator of and responsible for what he becomes. In evaluating his view, it is important to recognize his belief that each man
chooses in situation, i.e., as an organic whole with his environment, but that, nonetheless, there are no external factors which
in any way determine the individual's choice. This leads Sartre
to conclude that man can avoid neither choice, nor responsibility
to himself and others for his choice. This results in a feeling of
anxiety, which is perhaps an increasingly pervasive phenomenon.
But even those who recognize the imperious demand of freedom
need not concur in the theoretical structure that Sartre has associated with this kind of sensitivity.

Edgar Sheffield Brightman serves as a helpful example of
one who is in close agreement with Sartre that decisions or
choices are unavoidable, but whose philosophy of personalism
presents some sharp contrasts with Sartre's understanding of freedom. According to Brightman, the two opposite extremes of
philosophy, pragmatism and existentialism, would agree with
personalists that "life demands decision." [55] Although Brightman
contends as strongly as does Sartre that choice is inevitable, he is
prompted by different considerations. There is a more rationalis-
tic tone to Brightman's argument that without free, intelligent
choice rational ideals could not be appropriated, or realized, and
that if the will were determined all opinions would be equally
necessary.[56]

Brightman differed from Sartre, however, in his view of
freedom, for he felt that certain limitations were operative. "Of
course, neither naturalists, personalists, nor Thomists would care
to go to the extremes of Sartre's theory of freedom, which may be
regarded as personalism gone slightly daffy." [57] Brightman be-

---

[55] *Nature and Values* (New York: Abingdon-Cokesbury, 1954), pp. 103-4.

[56] *A Philosophy of Ideals* (New York: Henry Holt and Co., 1928), p. 84;
Moral Laws (New York: The Abingdon Press, 1933), p. 282.

[57] "A Meeting of Extremes: Operationalism and Personalism," *The Journal of
Religion*, XXXI (Oct., 1951), 235-36. Brightman has referred to Sartre, by name,

lieved that freedom was limited to the freedom to choose among various possibilities. The possibilities which confront the individual were referred to by Brightman as that which is given, or "the Given." [58] The Given is determined by both environmental and subjective limitations. The environment limits the individual's choices and determines, to a large degree, the situation in which he will be after making his free choice. For example, freedom cannot enable us to disregard the laws of nature or to escape sensations. Moreover, there are a number of subjective influences on freedom. One of the most important of these is the past experience of the individual: and the purpose of the individual also exercises considerable control over his choices.[59] Brightman felt that it was important, though not necessary, that reason exercise control over the individual's choice. "Without rationality freedom is irresponsible, ruthless, egoistic, and ruinous." Further, freedom becomes license if not controlled by reason, and license in turn becomes bondage.[60] Other influences on the individual's freedom of choice are his approval of certain actions, his own habits and influences, and his present consciousness.[61] In spite of these numerous and powerful limiting factors which Brightman acknowledged, he staunchly maintained that man is free. He is not under the control of fate. Even though in certain cases, such as the use of drugs, it is possible to control a person's personality through his body, Brightman insists nonetheless that the control of the personality ultimately lies in the will.[62] In contrast with Sartre, Brightman says: "True freedom

---

as a personalist in "Personalism," *A History of Philosophical Systems,* ed. V. Ferm (New York: Philosophical Library, 1950), pp. 341, 349. However, note the second reference to Sartre, on p. 349, which refers to him as "peripheral."

[58] *The Spiritual Life,* pp. 62, 189, 194-95; *A Philosophy of Religion* (Englewood Cliffs, N.J.: Prentice-Hall, 1940), p. 382; *Moral Laws,* p. 283.

[59] *The Spiritual Life,* pp. 62, 184, 194-96; *A Philosophy of Religion,* p. 382; *The Problem of God* (New York: The Abingdon Press, 1930), p. 131.

[60] *The Spiritual Life,* pp. 191-92.

[61] *Ibid.,* pp. 62, 177-79, 189; *Moral Laws,* p. 249.

[62] *Is God a Person?* (New York: Association Press, 1932), pp. 10-11.

is the recognition of limits and conditions; it is the self-imposition of law." [63] It is in this qualified sense of the term that Brightman insists that man is truly free. But if we adopt a view that freedom is limited rather than unconditioned, what is the relation of the limits and conditions to freedom? The next chapter will defend the thesis that these limitations are to be recognized not as obstacles to freedom, but as necessary concomitants of freedom.

---

[63] *The Spiritual Life,* p. 33; cf. pp. 30-33, of which this quotation is a summary.

4 | Determinism and Freedom as Concomitants

The extremity of Sartre's position has been rejected, but with appreciation of the concern that prompted it. Could this tension be resolved by some emendation of Sartre's position? Perhaps we could make some concession to Sartre's extreme libertarianism by saying that freedom requires indeterminacy, though not indeterminism. I will argue that determining factors are necessary to freedom, but perhaps we could grant that they are necessary though not sufficient conditions.

However, the basic thrust of this argument takes a different direction. My concern is not to modify Sartre's theory of freedom, but to present an alternative view which conceives of freedom and determinism as concomitant, rather than as opposed.

Does such an extreme statement of the nature of freedom as that of Sartre's really accomplish what is intended? I assume that the aim of an advocate of freedom is to assert some significant difference between man and nature. (Later we will ask how the machine that "thinks" fits into the picture.) One way of making this distinction is to say that human motives are outside the causal order. And yet, if men are not subject to the influence of motives they are not different from inanimate objects. However, if they are, then motives are a type of cause, albeit a highly specialized type. Another way of making the distinction is to insist that man's freedom of choice is not subject to the influence of motives. But neither are inanimate objects subject to the influence of motives, and it is hard to see how this line of argument does anything to support the view that man is unique. It seems more profitable to explore the line of argument that maintains a concomitance of freedom and determinism.[1]

The Compatibility of Freedom and Determinism

But before we can argue that freedom and determinism increase together, we have to show that they are even compatible. A helpful way to open up this issue is to consider the chapter entitled "The Queen's Croquet Ground" in *Alice in Wonderland,* Lewis Carroll's delightful mixture of phantasy and philosophy. At the beginning of the chapter, three gardeners were busily painting roses red. They had mistakenly planted white roses and were trying to conceal their error from the Queen. But they were too late, and the Queen ordered their beheading, though Alice thwarted this execution by hiding them. Then the croquet game began. The balls were live hedgehogs, the mallets live flamingos, and the arches were soldiers standing on their hands and feet. Alice found that it was only with great difficulty that she could handle the flamingo and that it was almost impossible to straighten its neck out. By that time the ball had crawled away, and the arch had moved to a different position. There were

---

[1] Cf. Marvin Zimmerman, "Is Free Will Incompatible with Determinism?" *Philosophy and Phenomenological Research,* XXVI (Mar., 1966), 415-20, esp. p. 416. Charles K. Robinson contends that the analytic wing of philosophy tends toward a thoroughgoing determinism and the existential wing toward a thoroughgoing indeterminism; see "The Polar Context of Freedom," *International Philosophical Quarterly,* VI (Dec., 1966), 538. In his article (pp. 538-56), Robinson rejects both extremes, although he recognizes that they stand on a kind of "faith" and cannot be "refuted" in the strict sense. He advocates a position which mediates between both extremes by discussing freedom in the context of polarity. He is not thinking of freedom as one of the poles, as in Tillich's polarity of freedom and destiny, but is rather thinking of freedom in light of the polarities of individuality and relationality, and power and structure (these two polarties are derived from Plato). In this light, freedom "may be seen as constituting *spontaneity—the self-*determining side of power—at the distinctively personal level of reality" (p. 553).

no such things as turns, but there was an abundance of quarrel-
ing. In the heat of the game, the Queen ordered a beheading
about once every minute.

In light of our discussion of the determinist controversy, the
general import of this chapter is quite clear. Unless things are
determined, there is chaos rather than freedom. Freedom is possible only within a structure of rules that limit the possibilities,
and yet create possibilities by defining the goals. Unless things
behave in accord with some law, there is no dependability on
which responsible action can be based. Lewis Carroll wrote,[2]
"I pictured to myself the Queen of Hearts as a sort of embodiment of ungovernable passion—a blind and aimless Fury." And
Carroll's words "blind and aimless" sum up the situation in
which nothing is determined, and consequently in which free,
purposive action is impossible. This is why the Queen of Hearts
is so heartless as to order executions about once a minute. Alice
had no quarrel with the Queen, yet she was anxious to escape,
because there was no reliability that this situation would have
any meaning in the next moment.

The absurdity of the situation is well brought out in the
order to behead the Cheshire Cat. Its ability to appear and
disappear in varying degrees, which was the cat's own violation
of natural law, made it impossible to carry out the Queen's wish.
It was not "free to be beheaded," and the situation led to the
chaos of the executioner's argument that you cannot behead
something that does not have a body for the head to be cut off
from, and the King's argument that if anything has a head it
can be beheaded.

As we find out in the next chapter, the game ended with all
the players under sentence of execution except the King, the
Queen, and Alice. And there were no more arches, as all the
soldiers had to leave this duty to guard the prisoners.

---

[2] "Alice on the Stage," *The Theatre* (April, 1887).

Without determinism, there is not purpose, but whim; there is not freedom, but frustration; there is not life, but death. This contention can be supported from the wisdom of the Hellenistic era and the insights of contemporary cybernetics.

The man who is under education ought to approach education with this purpose in his mind: "How can I follow the gods in everything, and how can I be content with the divine governance and how can I become free." For he is free, for whom all things happen according to his will and whom no one can hinder.

"What then? Is freedom the same as madness?"

Heaven forbid! frenzy and freedom have nothing in common.

"But," you say, "I want everything to happen as I think good, whatever that may be."

Then you are in a state of madness, you are out of your mind. Do you not know that freedom is a noble thing, and worthy of regard? But merely to want one's chance thoughts to be realized, is not a noble thing; it comes perilously near being the most shameful of all things. How do we act in matters of grammar? Do I want to write Dion's name as I will? No, I am taught to will the right way of writing. How is it in music? Just the same. So it is universally, in every region of art or science. Otherwise it would not be worth while to know anything, if everything conformed itself to each man's will.[3]

And in the contemporary era, Norbert Wiener remarked: "In a world ruled by a succession of miracles performed by an irrational God subject to sudden whims, we should be forced to await each new catastrophe in a state of perplexed passiveness." [4] But the wisdom and insight of the views expressed need to be supported and analyzed. How can freedom and determinism be compatible? If they are in different spheres, how can they be related and mutually interdependent? If they are in the same sphere, must they not stand in opposition to each other?

Some have felt that the principle of indeterminacy has re-

---

[3] Epictetus, "Discourses," I, xii, ed. Whitney J. Oates, *The Stoic and Epicurean Philosophers*, trans. P. E. Matheson (New York: Modern Library, 1940), pp. 247-48.

[4] *Cybernetics*, p. 50; cf. Gilkey, *Maker of Heaven and Earth*, pp. 190-92.

solved this dilemma, but this argument has not been convincing. We need to be careful about moving back and forth from statistical probability in the realm of subatomic particles to statistical probability in the realm of human behavior. Schrödinger concludes his study of the physical aspect of the living cell with the statement that the behavior of living matter cannot be reduced to laws of physics.[5] This is not, according to Schrödinger, because we are dealing with a new force when we move from physics to biology, but because of a difference in construction. Indeed, Schrödinger feels that the orderliness of a living organism surpasses that of anything in the field of inorganic matter, especially in its power of self-maintenance and in its ability to produce orderly events. Whereas the physicist must deal with aggregates in order to discover orderliness, the biologist can discover it when dealing with a single organism. The physicist, in this sense, then, is more tied to probability than is the biologist, and determinism is stricter at the biological than at the inorganic level. Schrödinger explains that this is because there are two different "mechanisms" for producing orderliness. These are described by Max Planck as "the dynamical and the statistical type of law" (*dynamische und statistische Gesetzmässigkeit*), and by Schrödinger as "order from order and order from disorder." Although both ultimately rest on physical principles, one of them is operative in that which is studied by physicists, and one in that which is studied by biologists.

In *Depth Psychology and Modern Man*, Ira M. Progoff distinguishes between two types of images—enacting images or dynatypes, and formative images or cognitypes.[6] The dynatype has the power of directing behavior. For animals, the dynatype is standard; but for human beings a wide variety of styles of behavior are both possible and appropriate. As the existentialists express it, there is no predetermined essence for man; rather he

---

[5] *What Is Life?* chap. 7.
[6] (New York: Julian Press, 1959), pp. 182-88.

decides what he will make of himself. Cognitypes have the capacity for expressing reality in a form in which man can apprehend it. They organize experience into some meaningful pattern or classification. They make possible cognition, provided we do not restrict this to apprehension by the intellect but include feeling, intuition, and so forth.

The scientist is personally involved in his so-called objective observations, as Michael Polanyi and Jacob Bronowski have shown in such thorough detail.[7] They are not saying that scientific work is purely subjective, but are insisting that the personal element is significantly involved, despite the usual disclaimer of the scientist. In Progoff's terms, the scientist examines the evidence and then turns within himself, groping in the depths of his being for cognitypes that will express the meaning of his observations. This personal involvement fulfills his dynatype, i.e., his image of himself as a scientist, seeking truth in the examination of the external world for the discovery of unitary principles. In Teilhard de Chardin's terminology, the "without" and the "within" act concomitantly and are known interdependently. The creative scientist must see the relation between the observations of the "without" and the images that are "within."[8]

There is a progressive development from matter to life to thought. With the heightened ability to use symbols, men have opened up a wide variety of possibilities for themselves. Ants and bees go on filling the same dynatypes, but man's possibilities are always open. Though subject to the same determinisms that operate on matter and animals, man has opened up such a variety of responses that he is able to shape the course of his life to a remarkable degree. Man has both the privilege and the responsibility of shaping his life. This gift and task comes to man from

[7] Polanyi, *Personal Knowledge* (Chicago: University of Chicago Press, 1958) and Bronowski, *Science and Human Values* (New York: Julian Messner, 1956). Both have been reprinted in the Harper Torchbook series.
[8] Cf. Progoff, *Depth Psychology and Modern Man*, pp. 233-41.

his Creator. A Midrash expresses man's God-given capacity for self-transformation in this way:

And Isaac asked the Eternal: "King of the World, when Thou didst make the light, Thou didst say in Thy Torah that the light was good; when Thou didst make the extent of the firmament and the extent of the earth, Thou didst say in Thy Torah that they were good; but when Thou hadst made man in Thine image, Thou didst not say in Thy Torah that man was good. Wherefore Lord?" And God answered him, "Because man I have not yet perfected, and because through the Torah man is to perfect himself, and to perfect the world." [9]

Man, then, has developed out of the inorganic and organic. But he is to move ahead to realize new possibilities. He has sufficient freedom and sufficient creativity to enhance and perfect himself and his world, and he is responsible to develop in this direction.

We need, at the very least, to distinguish basic types of causality. F. S. C. Northrop argues that we must distinguish between two types of causality. Mechanical causality determines inorganic systems. But a cultural system has a different organization and is determined by what Pitirim A. Sorokin calls "logico-meaningful" causality.[10] In the former, behavior within the system is not influenced by conceptualization, and for this reason mechanical causation is inadequate and must be replaced by the more inclusive explanation in terms of "logico-meaningful" causality. The significant role of meaning is seen in the differences that we find between cultures. People have the same type of nervous system, and the differences between people are not differences in the experiencing of the world. Rather, the differences are in the differing concepts employed in different cultures, and this produces a difference in the meaning of experiences.

---

[9] Quoted in *ibid.*, pp. 250-51.

[10] Northrop, *Man, Nature and God* (New York: Simon and Schuster, 1962), pp. 30-38. For Sorokin, see *Society, Culture, and Personality* (New York: Harper & Bros., 1947), pp. 145-49, 333-35; and *Social and Cultural Dynamics* (New York: American Book Co., 1937).

In his final chapter, entitled "The Poetry of God's Playfulness," Northrop employs game theory as a means of coming to a better understanding of the nature of both God and man. In his act of creation God was not mechanically carrying out a job according to blueprint specifications. His act of creation was done for "the sheer fun of it," like a child swinging. But this is not all. We can play without rules, but there is no game without rules; and so creating out of playfulness is to be distinguished from sheer arbitrariness. His creatures also must play within certain rules. It is within the rules that both our creative strategy and our fumbling and errors have meaning.

Northrop analyzes three components of "God's complete nature and creative sportsmanship."

(1) Pure playfulness, without any lawful reason, for the sheer fun of it. . . . (2) God's lawfully regulated sportsmanship (expressing His intellectual love of *Logos*) within the rules of the game. . . . (3) Essential also is His creation of some first-order factual natural creatures who are capable of committing errors and the inclusion of them in His game.[11]

Northrop goes on to point out that God's play includes not only play like that of a child in a swing, or that of a game, such as baseball or cricket; God also plays at dice. He rejects Einstein's deterministic insistence that "God does not play dice." Northrop sides here with those who interpret the principle of indeterminacy to mean not simply that man's powers of observation are limited, but that the universe is by nature beyond precise determination.

What God's playing of games of chance means is that His intellectual love of lawful universalism is not absolute. Instead, it is exactly like that of the rules of the games of cricket and baseball in which the rules restrict the players within certain limits, but not so completely that everything they do is antecedently determined, thereby making error meaningless. This suggests that if God in His playful creation of nature and natural

---

[11] *Man, Nature and God*, p. 250.

man did not play dice, human error and, therefore, moral, legal, and political man or even religious man, would be meaningless and impossible. In short, for God to create human beings who are not mere puppets, He has to play dice when He creates His universe.[12]

A fully determined world would be a boring world, both for us and for God. But a world that is not fully determined always has the possibility of human error, and this means that man is always responsible. He must be responsible not simply for his actions, but also for the relation of his actions to his ever-changing environment. The meaning of life cannot be constant but must involve a perpetual quest.

Gilkey has pointed out that the scientist denies freedom with one voice but asserts it with another.[13] In scientific descriptions of man there is no place for the concept of freedom. But when the discussion turns to the issue of the *use* to which this knowledge is to be put, then the vocabulary of "free choice," "responsibility," "purpose," and related concepts comes into full play. As a body of knowledge science is "the destroyer of freedom," and as an enterprise of the scientific community, science is "its most robust champion." For the scientist man as an object of inquiry is not free, but man as an inquirer is. And yet, as Gilkey points out, this involves an inherent paradox. This is the scientific form of the dilemma of freedom and determinism. The scientific distinction between determined man as the object of inquiry and free man as the inquirer (subject of inquiry) is not an adequate resolution of the dilemma for the simple reason that these are not mutually exclusive classes. This objection can be "summed up in the reminder to the scientific community that the 'man' whom they study as the determined object of knowledge is the same creature whom as knower and

---

[12] *Ibid.*, pp. 253-54.
[13] "Evolutionary Science and the Dilemma of Freedom and Determinism," *Christian Century*, pp. 339-43.

manipulator they recognize as a free and rational being." [14] Gilkey analyzes this into two elements: "Man is *less* determined than science, understood as a body of knowledge, seems to indicate, and *more* determined than the possibility of its own creative use of that knowledge apparently implies to the scientific community." [15] Men are not merely "objects" to be manipulated, and social engineers are more determined by internal and external forces than they have been willing to acknowledge. We will return in chapter seven to the issue of benevolent versus malevolent control of society by means of the power of science, and we will continue here by focusing on the combination of freedom and determinism in man. Man is never absolutely and wholly free, nor absolutely and wholly determined, but is both free and determined.

The Mixed History of Man

It is this mixture of freedom and determinism that is referred to in speaking of the two histories of man. A mixed history is actually quite commonplace. We can say that someone is short of breath because he is both overweight and is rushing to keep an appointment. We can say of a king that he died in battle because of a sword wound, because of his courageous and noble leadership of the army, or because of his pride which was fed by military conquests.

Man is a mixed history, indeed. We have been considering only two dimensions—one characterized by determinism, and one by freedom. But there are actually many histories or dimensions of man. These dimensions are self-contained points of observation and analysis, but no one of them is the complete picture of man. Some are better for understanding certain aspects, but although they all seem to have imperialist ambitions, no one of them has a monopoly.

---

[14] *Ibid.*, p. 342.   [15] *Ibid.*

Let me suggest some of the possibilities, though this is not intended as a complete list, if indeed such is possible. The physicist sees man as a part of the matter-energy system, subject to the same laws as rocks and pulleys. The biologist sees man as an organism assimilating vegetation and reproducing his kind to perpetuate the species. Man is simply a highly developed species of animal life, whose nervous system gives him an exceptionally remarkable ability to adapt to his environment. Psychologists, when they are not engaging in a specialized branch of biology, see man as an organism subject to basic needs and drives which he is able to meet through the exercise of consciousness. Sociologists see man as a leader or follower within the power structure of social organization. Economists see man as a producer and consumer of goods and services.

But how are we to relate the components of freedom and determinism in the mixed history of man? Are they rival or opposed forces? Are they complementaries? Does one set the context or boundary within which the other must operate? [16]

The view that I wish to defend here is that the relation between freedom and determinism is not one of contradiction, nor even of contrariness, but rather one of concomitance. Freedom and determinism increase mutually. We need order and regularity in order to have freedom and responsibility; and further, freedom increases as determinism increases. Although he is using it as an analogy of God's influence on man, Bertocci has an illustration that points out how freedom and determinism can increase concomitantly.

As a teacher I can affect my students in the classroom in a general way: the same words are there for all of them, but it is up to them to listen, and they must decide what to think of what I say. . . . But supposing one of

---

[16] Cf. John Herman Randall, Jr., speaking of "historical causation": "I take 'determination' and 'determinism' very literally as a setting of 'termini' or boundaries and limits."—*Nature and Historical Experience* (New York: Columbia University Press, 1958), p. 167 n.

my students, of his own free will, follows me to my office and asks further questions there? I can, then, without turning his will agency, be allowed the opportunity to make other suggestions relative to his particular need. Again, it is still "up to him" what he will do with my suggestions, but at least I have a stronger opportunity to influence him, and without infringing on his freedom. For I become a larger factor among the forces which will influence what finally takes place in his life. I can help him and be more of a power in his life because I want to be, and because he is willing to commit himself to me. Thus I influence his final will power but not his will agency. That remains free![17]

The Relation of Concomitance

We commonly tend to think of lower forms of life as more determined, and higher forms as more free and responsible. However, I would contend that lower forms are both less determined and less free, and that higher forms of life are both more determined and more free.

An amoeba, a paramecium, and other such microscopic forms of life are motivated, for example, by the desire to secure nourishment, to reproduce, and to avoid painful experiences. Each of these motivations involves highly complicated factors and processes, and it is only in comparison with higher forms of life that we can describe these forms as simple. Yet the range from such forms of life to that of homo sapiens is staggeringly vast.

Man's life is much more easily affected by such physical influences as injection of drugs, or by such psychical forces as ambition. Consider, for example, the matter of death. Man is much more determined than a sponge. There are numerous ways of death for man—suffocation, poisoning, failure of one of the vital organs, brain damage, excessive bleeding, and so on. Man is

---

[17] Bertocci, *Free Will, Responsibility, and Grace*, p. 106. For another illustration of the combination of freedom and determinism in the interpretation of history, see C. A. Coulson, *Christianity in an Age of Science* (London: Oxford University Press, 1953), pp. 22-24.

very much determined in this regard. But "living sponges literally can be torn cell from cell, as by squeezing them through the meshes of a common linen handkerchief. Providing enough cells are present, those falling in the water near each other fuse and grow into new sponges." [18] The sponge is not simply less free and responsible, but is also much less vulnerable to determining influences.

Let us consider an example further up the scale. The same principle holds for rats. This is an especially significant example, because psychologists have gained tremendous understanding of human behavior, especially the learning process, by the study of rats. As one wag has remarked: "A psychologist is a man who gets habits out of rats." Rats have been made to run through mazes so psychologists can test their ingenuity and imagination. They have been forced by a blast of air to jump toward a circle, a triangle, and a square, one of which swings open and leads to food, and two of which give him a bang on the nose and drop him to the floor, without any reward. How long will it take a rat to learn to jump every time toward the right symbol, and what will happen if that door is locked and a new one opened and supplied with food? Surgical procedures also have been employed, so that the experimenter can observe the effect on behavior of the removal of specific regions of the cerebral cortex, or the injection of DNA from another rat who has learned some specific pattern of behavior.

Such experiments have been extremely valuable, but even a behavioristically oriented psychologist is fully aware that one cannot make predictions about human behavior on the basis of experimentation on rats, since, among other differences, lower forms of life are less dependent upon the cerebral cortex than is man. Again, man, whose life is more determined, is more vulnerable to such influences than are lower forms of life. For example, removal of the visual region from the brain of a rat prevents him

---

[18] Warner Clyde Allee, "Biology" in *What Is Science?* p. 258.

from distinguishing spatial patterns, but it does not prevent him from perceiving differences in illumination, as it does in the case of man.[19]

For the philosophical interpretation of such scientific data, Spinoza and Kant provide a counterbalance to the emphasis of Sartre on freedom.

Spinoza and Kant were right: freedom involves a greater determination than human bondage, which is mere partial determination. Freedom is the power to add determination by "reason" or intelligence. Spinoza and Kant went wrong, however, in making freedom "complete" determination by reason. That is not human freedom, but Divine freedom, appropriate to God's will, not man's, which never enjoys "perfect" freedom, but rather, specific and determinate freedoms, and always within narrow limits.[20]

However, there is also a contrast between Spinoza and Kant in their understanding of the relation of freedom and determinism. Spinoza's monism leads him to speak of a freedom of attitude within a determined world order (reminiscent of the exhortation of the Stoics in the Hellenistic era). Kant's distinction between appearance and reality leads him to locate determinism in the phenomenal realm and freedom in the noumenal realm. But both are in agreement on the necessity of allowing a significant place to determinism in their understanding of man. Yet neither succeeds in relating freedom and determinism. Spinoza merges and Kant separates, but neither relates these two dimensions of man.

Viktor Frankl is an ardent defender of freedom and responsibility against psychologism. He will grant that we are conditioned as to the ideas and values that are offered to us, but not that we are determined by them. We are free as to how we will respond.[21] Cherbonnier has a statement which is a valuable

---

[19] Edwin G. Boring, "Psychology" in *What Is Science?* p. 326.

[20] Randall, *Nature and Historical Experience*, p. 170.

[21] Frankl, *The Doctor and the Soul*, trans. Richard and Clara Winston (New York: Alfred A. Knopf, 1957), p. 18. Despite his emphasis on freedom and

guide as to how the formula "conditioned but not caused" is applied in the area of personal relations. He emphasizes the supreme significance of love as opposed to hardness of heart (which he considers the essence of sin in contrast to the prevailing interpretation of sin as pride).

> The way in which *agape* actually does liberate the free agent instead of cramping his style can be illustrated by an experience common to most people. In any stimulating conversation, especially spirited dialogue between persons in love, each suddenly finds himself exercising unsuspected gifts of wit and insight which neither could generate by himself. The stimulus of creative interchange evokes resources which would otherwise have remained dormant. Although a remark by one party does indeed "condition" the other's reply, the effect of this "conditioning" is not negative but positive. Instead of circumscribing one's freedom, it provides the occasion for his own creative response. Instead of tyrannizing, it liberates.[22]

The Apostle Paul often called attention to the paradox that the man who is a bondservant of Christ is one who has found true freedom therein. George Matheson has given expression to this theme in the hymn which opens with the lines: "Make me a captive, Lord, and then I shall be free."

An element of determinism plus an element of freedom seems to be the most profitable combination for an understanding of human behavior. For example, consider the alcoholic who wishes to stop drinking. If we say that his condition is determined by various personal and social factors, then there is no point in talking about a cure. On the other hand, a sheer act of will is not likely to produce a cure. What is needed is a desire to stop drinking which leads to a recognition of the causes which produced ("determined") the alcoholism. Only with some considerable degree of knowledge of these determining factors is it possible to implement the free choice to stop drinking.

---

responsibility, Frankl is often accused of advocating a stoical acceptance of one's fate. See my refutation of this charge in "Existential Analysis and Logotherapy," pp. 338-39.

[22] *Hardness of Heart*, p. 48.

Freedom and determinism are concomitants, but not equivalents. The *imago machinae* and the *imago dei* language are not interchangeable. Each makes possible a history of man which is descriptive and self-consistent (internally consistent). One talks about synapses, ganglia, dendrites, impulses. One talks about intentions, motives, purposes. One history is describing the level of the nervous system and its operative mechanisms; the other history is describing the level of the person and his activities. I consider it misleading to speak of this difference as due to the adoption of two alternative, and presumably mutually exclusive, standpoints, such as inner and outer.[23] It is not so much a difference of standpoint as a formal difference; that is, the difffer-ence is not due to the choice of a position from which to view the object, but is due to a choice of what objects are to be viewed.

The Fallacy of Cartesian Dualism

Paul Ricoeur criticizes the Cartesian and descended schemes which operate on a mind-body dualism, and which combine "physical causalities" and "mental causalities." He says that one is never sure whether the "physical causalities" are completely free of anthropomorphism, and that the "mental causalities" are "tainted with a 'thingism.' " [24] However, the classic critique of Cartesian dualism comes not from the tradition of existential phenomenology, but from that of linguistic analysis. I am thinking, of course, of Gilbert Ryle's *The Concept of Mind,* and also of the work of his contemporary and colleague at Oxford University, John Austin. Although my major concern is to show how the insights of science can be incorporated within a modified existential perspective, and although the incorporation of science

---

[23] E.g., Teilhard de Chardin, *The Phenomenon of Man,* chap. 2.

[24] *Freedom and Nature: The Voluntary and the Involuntary,* trans. Erazim V. Kohak (Evanston, Ill.: Northwestern University Press, 1966) , pp. 396-97; cf. pp. 8-13, 66-72, 216-22, 343-47, 396-401, 444-47, 451.

within the analytic tradition of philosophy is no problem, we must nonetheless attend briefly at this point to the contribution of Ryle and Austin to the project of this study. We will also consider, but much more briefly, some of the insights of other analytic philosophers.

Gilbert Ryle makes a forceful refutation of the belief in a dualism of mind and body.[25] Although dualism roots in Plato, Ryle considers the formulation of the doctrine in Descartes to be the source of contemporary belief in the doctrine, and he sees fear of mechanism as the major motivation in its continuation. But Ryle rejects this Cartesian "official doctrine" as "the dogma of the Ghost in the Machine," and the fear that freedom is surrendered is referred to as "the bogy of mechanism." Let us consider these phrases in reverse order.

In the final chapter Ryle distinguishes between his own task and that of the psychologist. Ryle expresses the thesis that the repudiation of the Cartesian dichotomy forces us to look at psychology in a new light. We should no longer expect from psychology the discovery of information that is not available to economists, historians, anthropologists, novelists, and other such students of man. The psychologist is not, as he first thought, opening up a new facet of man for exploration and discovery. Let me illustrate.[26] If somebody hates the police, do we have to explain this as rebellion against authority because of an overly strenuous toilet training or a tyrannical father figure, when common sense tells us that he hates the police because they beat the hell out of him? This is a normal and understandable reaction.

Where does psychology fit into the picture then? Ryle's answer is that it fits in when behavior is not readily understandable on the basis of good common sense. In other words, psychology is giving us new insights, not into normal human behavior, but into the treatment of unusual behavior. Psychology is a branch

---

[25] *The Concept of Mind* (London: Hutchinson & Co., 1949).
[26] See *Ibid.*, p. 325, for Ryle's own illustrations.

of medicine. It is needed to help men who are sick, but it is not a means of tapping an otherwise unexplored area for explanations of behavior that are hidden to all men who are not initiated into its rituals and the esoteric gnosis it possesses.

Ryle also points out that the mechanism of Newtonian physics is no longer the dominant scientific image. The rise of biology has challenged the image of man as a machine with the image of man as an organism. Ryle suggests that we might even be more venturesome than this. "Man need not be degraded to a machine by being denied to be a ghost in a machine. He might, after all, be a sort of animal, namely, a higher animal. There has yet to be ventured the hazardous leap to the hypothesis that perhaps he is a man." [27] It is with this daring hypothesis that man is a man—explicated by Tillich's concept of man as a "multidimensional unity" of inorganic matter, of vital energies, of psychic drives, and of spiritual meanings—that we will venture to ask the question of how determinism and freedom are related in man.

Ryle uses the phrase "the bogy of mechanism" to refer to the false fear that mechanism is incompatible with freedom.[28] Descartes wanted to incorporate the new understanding of man that the sciences had made possible. But mechanistic necessity, operating according to mathematical laws, seemed to threaten the religious belief in freedom. Descartes wanted to preserve this. His solution was to apply mechanistic determinism to the body and freedom to the mind.

One mistake that Ryle finds in this solution is a misunderstanding of natural laws. They are not fiats or legal commands. They are hypothetical propositions that apply not simply to a particular instance (such as, "If it rains, the picnic will be cancelled"), but to all cases. For example, "If anything is water, it is composed of two parts of hydrogen and one of oxygen." Or, "Whenever a traveling object is hindered in its forward move-

---

[27] *Ibid.,* p. 328.   [28] *Ibid.,* pp. 76-82.

ment, it continues to exert a forward thrust." In other words, natural laws are not affirmations that certain things exist, but rather expressions of our observations about relations that hold generally or universally. Natural laws do not describe things, they predict behavior; and there is no contradiction in describing a process as operating in accord with different principles.

A second mistake is involved in the fear that mechanistic explanation of natural events is a threat to human freedom. Although many questions about human behavior can be answered by the physicist or biologist, there are others that cannot. Often the same thing is explained on different levels, and even though one level may depend on another it cannot be equated with it or reduced to it. For example, if a novice asks why a certain chess piece was moved as it was, the appropriate answer may be in terms of the rules that determine the movement of pieces in the game of chess. If an expert chess player asks the same question, the appropriate answer would be in terms of strategy, tactics, or logistics, or some combination of the three, though all these presuppose and depend upon the rules which determine the progress of the game of chess. Natural laws are always appropriate, but they are often not adequate. They explain why billiard balls bounce as they do, but not why we have billiard balls and tables, nor why we bounce one ball against another or against the side of the table.

In developing this idea of different levels of explanation, Ryle distinguishes between the *causes* of human behavior and the *reasons* for human behavior. Everything we do must be caused, but the explanation of the causal relationships involved is on a different level from the explanation of the reasons for which one so behaved. Causal explanations are always appropriate, but seldom complete.

Why, then, do men consider freedom and determinism opposed? Here we need to turn to Ryle's examination of the official doctrine of Descartes and the notion of category mistakes.

According to Descartes, minds inhabit bodies but operate

according to quite different principles. Bodies are part of the material world and operate according to mechanical laws which determine their behavior. Minds are immaterial and free. Yet they somehow influence bodies and the material world. So here we have a machine—for this is exactly what the body is according to Descartes—inhabited by a mind, which is immaterial. Although immaterial, the mind is able to respond to the material world and act upon it. So here we have an immaterial ghost opening doors and windows as if it were material, and yet it is quite immaterial. This "dogma of the Ghost in the Machine" [29] has become the Cartesian official doctrine. In his Manson Lecture,[30] C. A. Mace contends that even with this derision Ryle let his opponents off too lightly. The ghost theories were at least scientific theories, even if faulty ones; but the Cartesian theory is not merely mistaken but unintelligible. Mace suggests that the road ahead involves a surpassing of behaviorism, which was more or less Ryle's substitute for Cartesianism.[31] Mace urges a widening of the natural sciences to deal with all knowledge (including that about which certainty is less attainable) and to assimilate psychological elements, and correspondingly urges that medicine deal with not only the prolongation but also the quality of life.

Ryle feels that the theory of mind-body dualism is based on what the analytic philosophers refer to as a category mistake. This refers to the use of a term on a different level from that to which it is appropriate. For example, you show a guest around the campus, and he says: "You have shown me the library, the classrooms, the administration building, and the dormitories, but you have not yet shown me the university. When will we see it?" This is a category mistake, because it assumes that the university is in the same category as the component buildings.

---

[29] *Ibid.*, pp. 11-18.

[30] "The 'Body-Mind Problem' in Philosophy, Psychology and Medicine," given at the Royal Institute of Philosophy, Oct. 15, 1965, and printed in *Philosophy*, XLI (Apr., 1966), 153-64.

[31] Cf. G. E. Myers, "Motives and Wants," *Mind*, LXIII (Apr., 1964), 173.

The university is in another category, and is not a thing that we can show or point out. To take another of Ryle's examples, it is a category mistake to say: "She came home in a flood of tears and a sedan chair." And the same category mistake is made by one who responds: "You must choose. She came home either in a flood of tears or in a sedan chair." [32]

Category mistakes are delightful when they are in the form of riddles and jokes, but they are harmful when they occur in philosophical discourse. Yet, in any discussion dealing with abstract terms and complex issues it is very easy to commit a category mistake.

According to Ryle, most of our thinking about mind has been vitiated by commission of the category mistake. The mind is talked about as if it were a thing that had somehow to be related to the body. According to Ryle, the mind is not a thing. What we say the mind does—for example, knowing or choosing—is really an action of a person. There are no such things as mental processes or mental acts in the sense that these are done by the mind, as opposed to physical processes or acts which are done by the body. It is persons who are in process or who act.

In elaborating his view that speaking of the mind as a thing is a category fault, Ryle discusses disposition-words and occurrence-words.[33] A disposition-word is one which asserts a capacity, tendency, propensity, etc. For example, to say that someone knows French is not to assert that his body houses a mind which performs the action of knowing French. What it is, rather, is an assertion of the hypothetical proposition that if he is spoken to in French he responds appropriately, which may mean anything from responding with more French, to bowing, to running for shelter, according to what was said.

Occurrence-words apply to the higher activities that are commonly referred to as "mental activities." A person who heeds

---

[32] For these and other examples, see *The Concept of Mind,* pp. 16-18, 22-23.
[33] *Ibid.,* pp. 116-53.

what he is doing is thought to be engaging in a mental activity. For example, he may be engaging in the physical action of driving and in the mental action of heeding. But Ryle insists that these are not two parallel activities, but one. Heeding is not something separate from driving, but is a form of driving in which one is alert to possible dangers to oneself or pedestrians or other drivers.

The Voluntary and the Involuntary

It is my contention that the terms "voluntary" and "involuntary" are not of the same order or category. To ask how we can do something both voluntarily and involuntarily, or to insist that we do something either voluntarily or involuntarily, is to commit what Ryle calls a category mistake. It is not, of course, obvious that the insistence that we do something either voluntarily or involuntarily is a category mistake, but I hope to show that we must incorporate both dimensions in our description of human behavior. These two "histories" are both present, but not as two things of the same type or category that must be added together. Each is a history apart from the other, and yet in talking about man we are talking about a composite of such histories, because we are dealing with a category of a different order. The problem of relating the two histories of man that we have been considering in this section is not one of relating two different realities. We are not talking, for example, of determined bodies and free minds which are somehow linked together. Rather, we are speaking of one reality, and our problem is how to relate two different universes of discourse.

The reader may still be skeptical. After all, are we not dealing with opposites—with determinism versus freedom, or with the involuntary versus the voluntary? How can we say that these pertain to different spheres of discourse? Does not the very language we use show their opposition? To assign them to different types or categories seems to be a way of evading a difficult if not insoluble problem, so that we can have our cake and eat it too. But let us look more closely at the language we use and see whether analysis bears out this initial impression. Let us do so under the guidance of one of the leading Oxford Analysts, whose concern is with ordinary language—John Austin.

In his presidential address to the Aristotelian Society in 1956, "A Plea for Excuses,"[34] John Austin examined the process of excuse-making, and then drew thirteen general lessons to be learned from such a study. At least four of these (nos. 1, 2, 3, 6) are relevant to the problem we are considering. Austin pointed out that in the majority of cases, adverbial modification is inappropriate. The normal or standard case neither requires nor permits a modifying expression. For example, one may say, "Late in the evening, alone, I yawn." But it distorts the meaning to say that one yawned voluntarily or involuntarily. Austin also notes that adverbial expressions have a limited range of application and cannot be applied to any and every verb of action. Here again "voluntarily" and "involuntarily" can serve as examples:

We may join the army or make a gift voluntarily, we may hiccough or make a small gesture involuntarily, and the more we consider further actions which we might naturally be said to do in either of these ways, the more circumscribed and unlike each other do the two classes become, until we even doubt whether there is *any* verb with which both adverbs are equally in place. Perhaps there are some such; but at least sometimes when we may think we have found one it is an illusion, an apparent exception that really does prove the rule. I can perhaps "break a cup" voluntarily, *if* that is done, say, as an act of self-impoverishment: and I can perhaps break another involuntarily, *if,* say, I make an involuntary movement which breaks it. Here, plainly, the two acts described each as "breaking a cup" are really very different, and the one is similar to acts typical of the "voluntary" class, the other to acts typical of the "involuntary" class.[35]

---

[34] *Proceedings of the Aristotelian Society*, 1956-57, reprinted in *Philosophical Papers*, pp. 123-52, and in *Twentieth-Century Philosophy: The Analytic Tradition*, ed. Morris Weitz (New York: The Free Press, 1966), pp. 329-51.
[35] Austin, *Philosophical Papers*, p. 139.

Austin then goes on to deal with negations and opposites, which in common usage are not opposed in the obvious way that is employed in philosophy or jurisprudence. He suggests that in common usage "voluntarily" would be the opposite not of "involuntarily," but of some sort of constraint, as of duress or obligation or influence. Opposites of "involuntarily" would include such expressions as "deliberately" or "on purpose." A little later Austin returns to the treatment of opposites, and makes this comment:

A belief in opposites and dichotomies encourages, among other things, a blindness to the combinations and dissociations of adverbs that are possible, even to such obvious facts as that we can act at once on impulse and intentionally, or that we can do an action intentionally yet for all that not deliberately, still less on purpose. We walk along the cliff, and I feel a sudden impulse to push you over, which I promptly do: I acted on impulse, yet I certainly intended to push you over, and may even have devised a little ruse to achieve it: yet even then I did not act deliberately, for I did not (stop to) ask myself whether to do it or not.[36]

Necessary Causation and Language Strata

Friedrich Waismann[37] attacks Kant's principle of necessary causation as lacking support either from modern science or from common sense. In discussing modern science Waismann deals with quantum mechanics, which, he points out, gives us a theory which is neither causal-deterministic nor indeterministic and which combines features of both. The deterministic element is the law concerning the propagation of de Broglie waves, but the interpretation of them is indeterministic and cannot be rendered deterministic without producing an inconsistency in the theory. Waismann recognizes that this theory may be superseded at

---

[36] *Ibid.*, p. 143.
[37] "Verifiability," *Logic and Language* (1st and 2nd Series), ed. Antony Flew (Garden City, N.Y.: Doubleday Anchor Books, 1965), pp. 136-41.

some future date, but his point is that it is possible to depart from Kant's principle of necessary causation without killing science. Kant had insisted that the principle of causality is indispensable to any scientific knowledge of the world, but modern science has shown that causation is not an a priori principle and that it is not an indispensable condition of knowledge of our world. Waismann deals much more briefly with the issue of common sense. Here his basic point is that we must presuppose some kind of order in order to manage our lives, but that it need not be a strictly causal order. The orderliness of probability is quite satisfactory as a basis for our prediction of behavior and as a ground for our action.

In another article, Waismann contends that there are language strata and that each stratum has a logic of its own. "Whether a melody is a sequence of air-vibrations, or a succession of musical notes, or a message of the composer, depends entirely on the way you describe it." [38] With regard to the two strata that are of particular concern to this study, he states that actions may be viewed as determined by causes and also by motives or reasons.

An action may be viewed as a series of movements caused by some physiological stimuli in the "Only rats, no men" sense; or as something that has a purpose or a meaning irrespective of the way its single links are produced. An action in the first sense is determined by *causes*, an action in the second sense by *motives* or *reasons*. It is generally believed that an action is determined both by causes and by motives. But if the causes determine the action, no room is left for motives, and if the motives determine the action, no room is left for causes. Either the system of causes is complete, then it is not possible to squeeze in a motive; or the system of motives is complete, then it is not possible to squeeze in a cause. "Well, now, do you believe that if you are writing a letter you are engaged in two different activities?" No; I mean that there are two different ways of looking at the thing; just as there are two different ways of looking at a sentence: as a series of noises produced by a human agent; or as a vehicle

---

[38] "Language Strata," *ibid.*, p. 247.

of thought. For a series of noises there may be causes but no reasons; for a series of words expressing thought there may be reasons but no causes. What we must understand is that the word "action" has a systematic ambiguity. And yet we are continually invited to regard motives as a special sort of cause; perhaps because we have only the word "Why?" to ask both for cause and motive. We do not see the ambiguity of the interrogative.[39]

A critique of the Kantian interpretation of causation is also found in G. J. Warnock. His basic contention is that arguments that support the view that the law of causation is synthetic and those that support the view that it is a priori are opposed to one another. He is not denying that both can be defended, but only saying that we cannot defend both of them at once. He specifically mentions the principle of indeterminacy, and says that it provides evidence against the insistence that every event has a cause, but does not establish the falseness of this insistence. He also adopts the notion of language strata, and employs this illustration: "To say that the golf ball finished short of the green because the player wanted to keep out of the bunkers does not make it either incorrect or impossible to explain its flight in terms of the elasticity of ball and club face, the velocity of impact, and the state of atmosphere and ground." [40]

One problem that is posed for any theory which understands the mind-body problem as due to linguistic confusion is that if we are dealing with two different languages here, it ought to be possible to translate from one to the other.[41] But it seems to me that this criticism is weakened if we are talking not only of two different languages, but of two different levels as well. We are not simply using different languages to talk about

---

[39] *Ibid.*

[40] G. J. Warnock, " 'Every Event Has a Cause,' " *ibid.,* p. 314.

[41] Cf. John Beloff, "The Identity Hypothesis: A Critique," *Brain and Mind,* ed. J. R. Smythies (New York: Humanities Press, 1965), p. 41; cf. pp. 44-46. Beloff refers to the breakdown in translation as a "fatal weakness of a two-language theory," and he contends that there is a similar flaw in Ryle's approach. For a response by Lord Brain, see *ibid.,* p. 55.

the same thing, but are speaking about different levels of organization.

If we still feel uneasy, another possibility is to employ Wittgenstein's concept of "language-games." Sometimes this concept is interpreted as an equivalent of Waismann's concept of "language strata," but such an interpretation of Wittgenstein is refuted by Dallas M. High.[42] High argues that Wittgenstein did not simply replace the sharp line separating cognitive and emotive uses of language with many sharp dividing lines so that we have many separate realms of discourse rather than two. High feels that Wittgenstein's emphasis in the concept of language-games is not on the drawing of boundary lines but is rather on the dependence of language on persons as players or users. The person who stands in and behind language moves about freely from one form of language-game to another and he combines the forms in any way that best serves his desires in communication. Such an interpretation of language fits well with my contention that the language of causation and the language of freedom are not hermetically sealed off from each other but rather are related concomitantly.

---

[42] *Language, Persons, and Belief* (New York: Oxford University Press, 1967), pp. 86-92.

5 | Machines, Freedom, and Responsibility

In his essay "What Is Man?" Martin Buber points out that a peculiar feature of the contemporary crisis of man is the way in which he is being superseded by his works. "Man is no longer able to master the world which he himself brought about: it is becoming stronger than he is, it is winning free of him." [1] Even allowing for overstatement, we can readily sense the significance of this situation for the notions of freedom and responsibility. If machines are becoming more and more prominent features of modern life, perhaps becoming even stronger than man and certainly independent of him, what are the implications for the concepts of human freedom and responsibility that we have just described as concomitant with determinism? It is my purpose in this chapter to argue that the developments in machines do not diminish, but increase the responsibility of those who work most directly with them. Following this, we can turn to the tantalizing question of whether machines themselves are characterized to any degree by freedom and responsibility.

Fred Gruenberger distinguishes two extreme opinions: "the overwhelmed view" that computers are taking over; and "the relaxed view" that computers do only what they are told.[2] He thinks the latter view is a decided minority. But I would

---

[1] Martin Buber, *Between Man and Man* (New York: Macmillan, 1947), p. 158.
[2] "The Unpredictable Computer," *Datamation*, XIII (Mar., 1967), 59-62.

venture to say that a person often holds both views, and fears that machines are superhuman in their power but subhuman in their nature. His fear is often that the subhuman nature of machines makes it tempting to harness their superhuman powers for malicious purposes.

It may be that futurists are much too optimistic concerning the possibilities opened up by cybernetics and automation. The situation may parallel the first impact of science, when its startling accomplishments so excited us that we assumed the application of scientific method could eliminate illness, crime, war, poverty, and any other problem. It is too early to tell how much cybernetics and automation can accomplish. For the purpose of this discussion, let us assume a highly optimistic appraisal of the future accomplishments of the new era of scientific activity, for this era has certainly accomplished amazing feats already. The fruitfulness of proceeding upon such an assumption is hinted at by Paul Tillich. He says that a purely objective view of nature is never fully applicable. To illustrate, he says that "the highly complicated machines created by the applied sciences are, in many ways, analogous to the basic organic forms; they can gain a new magical power over the minds of those who serve them." [3] Machines are even more complicated and more fantastic than when Tillich wrote these words, and the analogy between man and machine is even clearer. Further, man is even more a slave of machines than when Tillich made that statement. Machines may have eliminated the need for much tedious work, but they have also provided management with a "collection of mechanical slaves" and, as Wiener observes, "any labor that accepts the conditions of competition with slave labor accepts the conditions of slave labor, and is essentially slave labor." [4]

It seems that machines are taking over. The high-school

---

[3] Tillich, *The Protestant Era,* trans. James Luther Adams (Chicago: University of Chicago Press, 1948), p. 100.
[4] Wiener, *Cybernetics,* p. 27.

dropout could find a role in years past, but our society has nothing for him to do. Whatever he can do can be done less expensively, more accurately, and more dependably by machines that do not become bored or inattentive or ill, that do not go out on strike nor even take time out for a coffee break. Machines handle everything from gasoline credit-card invoices to space flights. It is not simply that man can be replaced by a machine; often it takes only a transistor to replace him. The "takeover" of our world by machines has quite astounded us, and I think that at least some of the humor about it is a nervous humor, as, for example, the remark that one of the most recent electronic computers is so human it blames its mistakes on others.

Are machines becoming "so human" that they are characterized by responsibility, which Brunner has identified as the essential ingredient of man as created in the *imago dei*? This question necessitates two preliminary clarifications. First, what do we mean by "responsibility" in man? Second, what kinds of machines are we talking about when we ask if they might also be responsible?

Definition of "Responsibility"

The term "responsibility" is used with wide variation in scope. Generally speaking, the range is increased as one moves from psychology to jurisprudence. A person may be acquitted of legal responsibility, or may achieve a reduction of the charge, if psychological evidence supports the contention that he was not responsible for his actions. In some cases, however, the psychologist would consider a person "ill," but the law would insist that he is "guilty." An individual can even be held legally responsible for actions that he has not committed himself, but that have been performed by his child or agent. The scope of the term "responsibility" is usually widened further when it is used in ethical discussions. A person may be said to have moral obligations to do that which he is not required to do by the law.

However, the concept of responsibility in law is a "hybrid" of morality and expediency.[5] And as a result a person is sometimes legally responsible for situations in which he bears no moral responsibility. If we recognize that the statement is subject to much exception, we can generalize that responsibility is most narrowly conceived in psychology, its range is extended in jurisprudence, and further extended in ethics.

"Responsibility," as Brunner uses the term, has an even wider scope than it does in psychology, jurisprudence, and ethics. Indeed, each of these latter three uses has a conditional element, but Brunner applies it universally and unconditionally.

Brunner is especially concerned to distinguish his use of "responsibility" from its use in ethics. Most ethical discussions make the concept of responsibility contingent upon certain aspects of the situation; for example, did the person know what he was doing? or were there mitigating circumstances? An alternative to this is a theory which makes responsibility contingent upon some form of prior commitment and acceptance.[6] But for Brunner, the term "responsibility" is not a normative term that is applied in certain cases, but a universal description of the human situation. Brunner specifically dissociates responsibility and moral consciousness and even opposes them.

The moral consciousness is still far from being a knowledge of the meaning of responsibility. On the contrary, there is no clearer proof of the fact that man does not fully know what responsibility is than the moral. The moral is the substitute for the loss of responsibility.[7]

For Brunner, all human existence is responsible existence whether or not responsibility is consciously acknowledged or

---

[5] Cf. Walter Moberly, *Legal Responsibility and Moral Responsibility* (Philadelphia: Fortress Press Facet Books, 1965), p. 24.

[6] For a development of this approach see Herbert Fingarette, "Responsibility," *Mind, LXXV* (Jan., 1966), 58-74.

[7] Brunner, *Man in Revolt*, p. 51.

even understood. Responsibility is, moreover, a uniquely human characteristic.

> Responsibility is not an attribute, it is the "substance" of human existence. . . . It is the absolutely universal human element. . . .
>
> The being of man, in contrast to all other forms of creaturely being, is not something finished, but it is a being-in-self-knowledge and a being-in-self-determination, but in a self-knowledge and in a self-determination which is not primary but secondary; it is self-knowledge and self-determination on the basis of being known and determined.[8]

It is in this sense that Brunner speaks of the *imago* as a reflection, for man is not completely intelligible in and from himself, but only in relation to the ground of his existence and to his fellow creatures. However, we are primarily concerned not with an "image" and a "reflection," but with a "word" and an "answer." [9] In Brunner's sense of the term, I am responsible in the sense that I must respond or answer to each situation of life. I may respond in a destructive manner or in a creative manner. These are equally responses, in Brunner's sense of the term (though not responses of equal value), because I am deciding what to do, rather than following a predetermined course of action. Even the denial of responsibility is a response. God calls us to a creative response, but our responsibility is not primarily a task or a demand, but is rather a gift. Whether we accept or reject his word, we respond to it.

Responsibility in Machines

Do machines only act, or can they genuinely respond in any sense of the term? In order to consider the relation between man and machine, it is important to distinguish different types of machines. The earliest machines could be described as auto-

---

[8] *Ibid.*, pp. 50, 97.
[9] *Ibid.*, pp. 96-99.

matic, but later developments produced machines that are described as stable and ultrastable.

With Newton's work the *imago machinae* became a popular way for thinking of man. However, Newton was thinking of an automatic machine, i.e., one which could be turned on and off and which performed set operations, such as the calculation of future velocities and positions on the basis of present velocities and positions, by means of the manipulation of gears and levers. The principle of the automatic machine is seen in the concept of preestablished harmony in the thought of Newton's contemporary, Leibniz. Further, Leibniz's contention that the monads have no windows may be taken as an expression of the absence of feedback devices.

Although the *imago machinae* became pervasive in Newton's time, man is not mechanical in this automatic sense. A machine marked by stability is more similar to man. The basic difference between an automatic and a stable machine is that the latter incorporates feedback. A stable machine operates on a more or less trial-and-error method of self-correction. It allows for slight errors but compensates for them. The term "cybernetics" comes from the Greek word for "steersman" or "helmsman," and thus pictures the shifting of the rudder when the ship veers too far off course. A common example of stability in the modern situation is provided by the thermostat. If the heat falls too far below the selected level, the furnace is set in operation and continues to supply heat until it reaches a point slightly above the selected temperature.

But even the stable machine is less than manlike. The question of the relation between man and machine was not fully realized prior to the development of machines that are ultrastable. The major characteristic of these machines is a capacity for self-reorganization. It is the ultrastable machine that confronts us with the possibility of performing operations beyond those which it was designed to perform and even beyond the knowledge of its maker. We have here a refutation of the principle that a cause must be equal to or greater than its effect. This principle is basic to one of Descartes' theistic proofs. W. Ross Ashby, who along with Norbert Wiener is one of the pioneers of cybernetics, examines this Cartesian principle, because if it is true there is no possibility of developing a brain that will "produce cleverness of its own and not just give us back the ingenuity we have put into it." He concludes that Descartes' principle holds for the designer of a machine if we mean by that term the person who plans "every detail that contributes to the machine's performance," but not if we mean the specific individual who guides its construction.[10]

Ashby has examined adaptive behavior in the nervous system of living organisms by constructing a machine called the "homeostat." [11] The homeostat will suffice for our purposes as an illustration of higher-order machines. There are other fascinating machines, however. For example, the perceptron can learn to recognize patterns, such as faces, objects, or letters of the alphabet. Another example is the cybertron, which substitutes for the usual programming a period of learning quite similar to that of a developing child.

What is striking about the homeostat is its "ultrastability." Perhaps the best way to describe this for our purposes is to refer to Ashby's example, rather than to formal definitions.[12] In an airplane the automatic pilot is connected to the ailerons, so that if the plane rolls to the right the situation is stabilized by a corresponding roll to the left. Thus, whatever the turbulence the variations from the programmed flight are insignificant.

---

[10] W. Ross Ashby, "Can a Mechanical Chess-Player Outplay Its Designer?" *British Journal for the Philosophy of Science,* III (May, 1952) , 44-52.

[11] See Ashby, *Design for a Brain,* 2nd ed. rev. (New York: John Wiley & Sons, 1960) for a description of the principles, procedure, construction, use, and interpretation of the homeostat. Further discussion of the concepts and notation involved can be found in Ashby, *An Introduction to Cybernetics* (John Wiley & Sons, 1956) .

[12] The following example is taken from chap. 8 (p. 108) ; on stability see chap. 4, and on ultrastability see chap. 7.

Such a system is described as "stable." In the words of Fred S. Grodins, "A stable system is one whose output will always return to zero in the absence of input." [13] But imagine that the wires are reversed. In such a case a roll to the right will produce a further roll to the right. In an ultrastable system, however, the machine would at first roll to the right but would soon correct itself. The ultrastable system is not blindly automatic, but is sensitive to the environment so that it is self-correcting. The machine does not simply do what the living organism directs it to do, but actually shares the capacity for adaptive behavior. It can be trained by means of "punishment and reward" so that it can later adapt to unusual and unforeseen conditions.[14] Ashby discusses the limitations of the homeostat, i.e., circumstances to which it is unable to adapt, but he points out in each case that the living organism is also likely to fail to adapt to such environments. "Since this book was first published, I have often had put to me some objection of the form 'Surely an ultrastable system could not . . .' When one goes into the matter, it is surprising how often the reply proves to be 'No, and a human being couldn't do it either!' " [15]

At the New York University Institute of Philosophy, May 15-16, 1959,[16] considerable attention was given to the relation between machines and human brains. Norbert Wiener[17] discussed the prospects arising from the development of machines that can do their own programming. In the past we used to say that a machine could do only what man feeds into it, but this is no longer true. "We now have an application of mechanism not merely to the slavish following out of a program

---

[13] *Control Theory and Biological Systems*, p. 37. For a mathematical statement of stability, see pp. 38-41, 71-76; for a discussion of stability in various types of systems, see pp. 77-97.

[14] Ashby, *Design for a Brain*, pp. 110-18.

[15] *Ibid.*, p. 121; see pp. 118-21.

[16] Proceedings published as *Dimensions of Mind*.

[17] "The Brain and the Machine," *ibid.*, pp. 113-17; see also *Cybernetics*, pp. 109-12.

into which all the essential elements of human thought have been put in advance." [18]

The most significant and practical use of machines that do their own programming is the development of automatic factories, but perhaps a more interesting illustration is found in game-playing machines. The older type of chess-playing machine, for example, was a rigid legalist about the game. It took into account such factors as the significance of the squares controlled—with center squares having high priority—the number of squares controlled by a chessman in a particular location, the relative value of the pieces, and so forth. But the higher-order computer takes into account the personality of the opponent. It does not operate on a set program, but adapts the program in terms of its memory of the success or failure of earlier games and moves, both by itself and by its opponent. If the opponent is a weak player, the machine will beat him, but it will not develop into a strong player. If the opponent has some favorite tricks up his sleeve, the machine will catch on to them and counter them so that they are no longer effective.

In the case of the first-order machine, we tell it how to play to win; in the case of the second-order machine, we tell it to play to win, but we leave it to the machine to develop its own strategies, priorities, and so forth, and to revaluate these as it gains experience.

Wiener points out the ethical issue raised by the development of such higher-order machines. We employ such machines as servants of man. A servant is chosen for his intelligence and subservience. But Wiener points out that the more intelligent a servant is, the more he will insist on doing things his own way, so that he is no longer subservient. We have now developed machines that will not conform to the patterns of action that

---

[18] "The Brain and the Machine," pp. 113-14.

man might desire of them. The problems posed by this new development are expressed by Wiener.

There is nothing which will automatically make the automatic factory work for human good, unless we have determined this human good in advance and have so constructed the factory as to contribute to it. If our sole orders to the factory are for an increase in production, without regard to the possible aspects of this new and vast productivity and without regard to the problems of unemployment and of the redistribution of human labor, there is no self-working principle of *laissez-faire* which will make those orders redound to our benefit and even prevent them from contributing to our own destruction. The responsibilities of automation are new, profound, and difficult.[19]

In the past mankind had to wait for decades and even centuries for men of creative genius, but we are now able to develop machines that can create as well as simply compute. But even if we are able to create artificial geniuses, man will not be superseded. Machines have heightened, rather than diminished, the responsibility of those who work with them. In Part Three we will consider the wider social implications of the cybernetic revolution, but at this point we want to focus on the responsibilities faced by the scientist in particular.

The Social Responsibility of the Scientist

The role of science in the social order is raising increasingly complex problems about the responsibilities of the scientist to the values of science and to those of his society. For example, should a vaccine be made available to all people in order to save as many lives as possible, or should it be made available to only one group, with the other group serving as a control group, in order to hasten refinement and improvement of the vaccine? And however one may evaluate the relative responsibility to the present practical problem and to the theoretical

---

[19] *Ibid.*, p. 117; cf. *Cybernetics*, pp. 27-29, 175-77.

problem and its value for the future, one is still confronted
with the problem that while science can save man from plagues
it cannot save him from his own folly.

A problem of paramount significance today is that of the
relation between science and politics. This is certainly a rival
to the old problem of the relation between religion and science.
The scientist is now confronted with the problem of objective
detachment and political expediency. For example, if politicians
thrive on the fiction that nuclear war will disintegrate the
enemy in flame but leave us relatively unscathed, thanks to Civil
Defense shelters, then the scientist becomes involved in this
fiction by virtue of the fact that he depends on the appropria-
tions of politicians for research grants, and he is further vulnerable to loyalty purges conducted by politicians. If the scientist
discovers evidence contrary to the popular view, should he be
frank in publicizing his evidence, as if he were dealing with a
fellow scientist, or should he maintain a discreet silence? Some,
such as Linus Pauling, J. Robert Oppenheimer, and Edward U.
Condon[20] have chosen to speak out and have paid a heavy price.

In the 1960 Harvard University Godkin Lectures on the
Essentials of Free Government and the Duties of the Citizen,[21]
C. P. Snow dealt with the strengths and weaknesses of scientists
in the conduct of government. Snow pointed out the dangers of
such involvement, but also showed why he considers it a necessary involvement and made some practical suggestions as to how
to minimize the risks and appropriate the strengths. He based
his analysis on a case study of the opposition between Sir Henry
Tizard and F. A. Lindemann, later Lord Cherwell.

In this analysis Snow made a distinction between "open"
and "closed" politics. Snow's opening statement did not employ
these terms, but it did state the problem involved: "One of the

---

[20] See biographical sketch in *What Is Science?* and his own statement, p. 153.
[21] C. P. Snow, *Science and Government* (Cambridge: Harvard University Press, 1961).

most bizarre features of any advanced industrial society in our time is that the cardinal choices have to be made by a handful of men: in secret: and, at least in legal form, by men who cannot have a firsthand knowledge of what those choices depend upon or what their results may be." [22] The Tizard Committee was in such a position. Radar was not yet known to be workable, but they were convinced that it was Britain's only hope against the *Luftwaffe*. The decision to go ahead with the development of radar was probably not known to more than a hundred people, of whom less than twenty were effectively involved, and the final decision was made by no more than five or six people.[23] Such a situation is inevitable in projects of this sort, all our slogans about "the free world" and "the freedom of science" notwithstanding.[24] What further highlights the disjunction between open and closed politics in the radar decision is that it was opposed by Lindemann, who was Sir Winston Churchill's scientific advisor. At this time Churchill was not in power, but was waging a vigorous campaign on the basis of the apathy toward Nazism on the part of those presently in power. In open politics Churchill was the symbol of those who wished to resist Nazism. Yet had he gained power earlier, the result in closed politics would likely have been devastating to Britain's ability to withstand the Nazi attack, in which radar played such an essential role.[25] When Churchill did come into power, Lindemann was in and Tizard was out. Lindemann was now able to put across pet projects, even though his scientific justifications were not sound.[26] Snow makes the startling claim that

---

[22] *Ibid.*, p. 1; see definition of "closed politics," p. 56. He expressed apprehension that in the future the use of computers in decision making will further reduce the number of those who are knowledgeable.—"Scientists and Decision Making," *Computers and the World of the Future,* ed. Martin Greenberger (Cambridge, Mass.: The M.I.T. Press, 1962), pp. 10-11.

[23] *Ibid.*, p. 36.   [24] *Ibid.*, pp. 1-4, 55, 76.

[25] *Ibid.*, pp. 36-38.   [26] *Ibid.*; see the example given pp. 47-51.

personality factors are considerably more significant in closed than in open politics, even in such technical areas as military science. Here, where the life and death of millions of people are involved, "all countries are not unlikely to be at the mercy of scientific salesman." [27] Snow gave a sobering account of the way in which scientific judgments can be distorted by the "euphoria of gadgets" (from egg beaters to hydrogen bombs— "the kind of mind which is fascinated by the one is likely to be fascinated by the other") [28] and the "euphoria of secrecy" (even though other countries are probably hoarding the same "secret") .[29] But Snow pointed out that while there are scientists who are only "technically bold and advanced," there are others who are also "socially imaginative." [30] Such men have qualities and insights which ought to be involved in government in more than an advisory capacity, for they, along with political administrators, have a responsible and vital contribution to make to the creation of a new society.

The development of cybernetic machines provides no *cause* for denial of responsibility. These machines may be *occasions* for the denial of responsibility, but if a man decides to evade responsibility it is impossible to remove all occasions for such denial. This is illustrated in the case of the alcoholic who was urged to give up drinking. He replied, "Oh, it's too late. I've gone too far." He was told that it was never too late. He then responded, "Fine, I'll do it sometime later."

Sometimes there are more subtle ways of evading responsibility by reinterpreting the term. One method is to restrict it to refer to responsibility to myself. As we noted in our discussion of Brunner in chapter two, this tends to happen when responsibility is understood as a quality of man, rather than as a relation

---

[27] *Ibid.*, p. 57.   [28] *Ibid.*, p. 88, n. 43.   [29] *Ibid.*, pp. 68-73.

[30] *Ibid.*, p. 80. Another interesting case study of the interrelations between science and government is found in Robert C. Batchelder, *The Irreversible Decision* (Boston: Houghton Mifflin, 1962), which deals with the factors leading up to the decision to drop the atomic bomb.

between men and between God and man. "Responsibility" then comes to mean: "I owe it to myself." Others feel uneasy about the self-centeredness that is near the surface of this approach, and they affirm that we are responsible to God; but what they mean by this is that God depends upon us and we ought not to let him down. Being responsible does not mean being responsible *to* myself, nor responsible for God, but rather it means being responsible *for* myself *to* others *under* God. And there is nothing in the latest developments of cybernetics that has rendered this passé. Indeed, the tremendous capacities and creative potential that have been released have heightened this meaning of responsibility.

Machines as Determined and as Free

I have spoken of man both as determined and also as free and responsible, and have seen no reason to eliminate the latter element of this compound affirmation. But what about the machine? Does the compound affirmation make any sense when we are speaking of machines rather than of men?

In the case of a machine, the analogue of causal determinism is input and the analogue of free behavior is output. If we were dealing with only these two phases we might well question the appropriateness of describing the final phase as free. It is true that input and output are the more obvious activities to an outside observer, but the intermediate process between input and output is of vital importance for a full analysis.

We can recognize determinism because a variation of input results in a variation in output. But is the variation itself variable or invariable? What goes on inside the "black box"? The output is unquestionably causally determined in the sense that it is influenced by the input. And so there is no question at this point. The question concerning the machine, as well as man, is whether the causal determinism is such as to be incompatible with the notion of free response. Those machines that are purely mechanical would certainly seem to be causally determined, but I am not sure that this idea can be extended to apply to stable machines, and I seriously doubt that it can be applied to ultrastable machines. Here it seems more accurate to talk of a concomitance of causal determinism (input) and free behavior (output), analogous to that which we discussed earlier when speaking of man. Since the freedom and responsibility increase as the determinism increases, we do not see much of it in machines now. But I think we need to prepare ourselves for recognizing more of it as increasingly complex machines are developed.

As long as computers do *only* what they are programmed to do, which is still true of most of them, it is inappropriate to speak of them as having free will. But when they go beyond the understanding and intention of the programmer, however much he may determine the initial phase of the process, we have to consider seriously the possibility of free will in computers. When they manifest a capacity to reject or modify the suggestions of the programmer (and I do not mean just the response, "that does not compute"), then I believe that we will be unable to deny free will to such machines.

Most concern with machines emphasizes the element of determinism because the aim is control and because the focus is upon a portion of the total phenomenon. The scientist, engineer, and physician are all concerned with systems, but usually their focus is on different aspects. The scientist is seeking to use the inductive method to discover laws which describe the operation of the system. The engineer is concerned primarily with designing a system to do a specific task. The physician is dealing with given systems and is concerned to enhance their functioning and to correct their malfunctioning. Nevertheless, all these concerns interrelate, and the major consideration in one approach is a subordinate but contributory consideration in other approaches.[31] Yet, the limited focus does give an overemphasis on determinism. This is true whether the system being examined is man or machine. Determinism of component elements is concomitant with the free response of the man or machine as a whole.

Furthermore, the concepts of mathematics and physics as applied to control systems are not applicable to biological systems without difficulty, especially because the problems of physics are much simpler than those of biology and much more amenable to treatment in quantitative terms. Even the simplest biological systems are nonlinear, so the whole corpus of material on linear systems is not applicable ipso facto to biological systems. Nonetheless, after a slow beginning, there is a growing trend toward the application of the methods and concepts of control-system engineering to an increasing range of biological control systems.[32]

Walter B. Studdiford describes our present computers as, at most, "zomboid"—zombie-like, soulless, will-less creatures that resemble humans only in externals. But he feels that there is a definite possibility that man can design and construct a true android—a manlike computer with free will and perhaps consciousness. Such an android, with free will and awareness, can be given values and goals. Moreover, it can be considered responsible, both in the sense of "being held accountable" for its decisions and in the sense of being able to "give an accounting" of its decisions. Studdiford suggests five basic elements in the "prescription" for making a computer responsible; namely, ability to account for its decisions, freedom to make decisions within a hierarchical structure involving both humans and machines, ability to distinguish between right and wrong and conscientiousness in pursuing the former, ability to change its

---

[31] Grodins, *Control Theory and Biological Systems*, pp. 2-4.

[32] *Ibid.*, pp. 197-99. See also J. H. Whitlock, "Bionics and Experimental Epidemiology," *Biological Prototypes and Synthetic Systems*, I, 39.

environment, and capacity to feel guilt when it does something wrong. Studdiford sketches a set of minimum specifications for an android and includes responsibility, along with such other things as needs, feelings, emotions, a self-concept, and capacity for learning.[33]

There may be such significant differences between machines and humans that no matter how highly we develop our machines they will never cross the threshold into humanity. For example, do machines worry that their parts are wearing out or do they feel pain or experience consciousness? Do similarities in external behavior provide any evidence for internal states? We will turn to this larger issue in a moment, but for the present our concern is with the specific question of freedom and responsibility. Could we develop a machine, program it not to tell lies, and then ask it whether it felt that it had free will or consciousness or felt pain? And whatever it said, could we rely on it to be expressing itself in its own terms, or would it simply be accommodating itself to our way of expressing things? In other words, if it said that it was free, could we know that it meant by that what we would mean by it?

It may be that man's "no trespassing" signs for machines, keeping them out of the reserve of thought, consciousness, and feeling, is purely arbitrary and prejudiced. Man may prejudge the case, so that even if a machine does what a man does, we will have decided in advance that nonetheless men and machines differ. For example, I may try to prove that I have free will by having someone predict whether I will hold up one finger or two. By constantly frustrating his prediction I may demonstrate my freedom of choice. But suppose we have a machine so rigged that when the tape reads, "I predict that the light will be on in one minute"—or five seconds, or whatever time is preferred—this is read by the machine with the result that it turns

---

[33] "Willing in Androids," *The Concept of Willing*, ed. James N. Lapsley (Nashville: Abingdon Press, 1967), chap. 5.

the light off. Likewise, if the prediction reads "off," the machine will respond by turning the light on. If this is not sufficient evidence that the machine has free will, then should we accept man's ability to disobey orders as evidence of human free will? A similar problem with regard to the debate concerning human freedom is raised when Antonio and Lorenzo Valla go through some pedal and dialectical gymnastics in the latter's "Dialogue on Free Will." [34] Antonio poses for Lorenzo the dilemma of predicting which foot he will move first—a seemingly insuperable dilemma because whichever foot Lorenzo mentions, Antonio will move the opposite. Lorenzo claims that the situation is nonetheless not free, because by *saying* that Antonio will move one foot he is capable of *knowing* that he will move the other. The case for freedom and responsibility in machines may not be conclusive, but the difficulties seem to be of the same order as those that prevent a decisive demonstration that man is free.

But whether this debate is just a matter of words or much more, and whether the issue can be resolved or not, the more significant result of this kind of investigation is that, as Michael Scriven states, "It is now readily proveable that the kind of free will required to make sense of the idea of responsibility and punishment is perfectly compatible with determinism and third-person predictability, and there is no evidence for any other kind." [35]

I would personally be inclined to be a little more modest in the latter half of the assertion, and more bold in the former half. Instead of saying that there is no evidence for any other kind of free will, I might want to qualify this by saying "no significant" or "no decisive" evidence. But the more important assertion, to my way of thinking, is in the first half. Here I

---

[34] *The Renaissance Philosophy of Man*, ed. Ernest Cassirer *et al.* (Chicago: University of Chicago Press, 1948), pp. 155-82, esp. pp. 165-67.

[35] "The Compleat Robot," *Dimensions of Mind*, p. 122; cf. Stephan Korner, "Science and Moral Responsibility," *Mind*, LXIII (Apr., 1964), 161-72.

would not want to say merely that determinism is "perfectly compatible" with free will and responsibility. I would like to insist further that there is no possibility for free will and responsibility apart from determinism. In a world that is chaotic and unpredictable, we are not free to do as we wish, but are subject to the whims and fancies of a fickle fate. We are not free when we are unable to determine the consequences of our actions. Freedom is impossible apart from determinism. The same is true of responsibility. There is no such thing as responsibility if it is impossible to anticipate the consequences of our actions. We are free and responsible because we and the world we live in are not chaotic and uncontrollable, but rather orderly and determined. Freedom and responsibility develop along with determinism. It is as we develop our understanding of the factors that determine the operation of machines that we are able to develop machines that are free and that introduce the problem of responsibility.

6 | Machines as Artificially Created Forms of Life

I have argued that it is appropriate to speak of a concomitance of determinism and freedom-responsibility in machines as well as in man. Can we carry this a step further and say that machines are artificially created forms of life? Man has been a creator of life through sexual procreation. Has man now devised another means by which he can create life?

The Imago Dei and Machines

In chapter two I gave some attention to Brunner's understanding of the doctrine of man in the light of the theory of evolution. In that connection we noted that Brunner speaks of man as created in the *imago dei,* even though man's evolutionary predecessors may not be considered to be created in this image, and even though it may not be possible to indicate the precise point in the development of man at which it became appropriate to speak of him as being in the image of God. The theological principal that Brunner develops is that man is not understandable in himself, nor in his origin from the evolution of species; but is understandable only in terms of his relation to God as the one who calls him to respond. In his newly written introduction to the second edition of *Truth as Encounter,* Brunner captures his essential viewpoint in this formula: "To understand what man is, we must start from his divine *principium,* and not from his temporal *initium,* not with the prehuman becoming man, but

168

with God becoming man in Jesus Christ." [1] But if this principle defends theology from the attack of naturalistic and mechanistic reductionism, it also opens up for theology the possibility that some of the latest creations of cybernetic science may be able to establish a claim to possess those qualities regarded as the essential basis of man's creation in the *imago dei*. If the *initium* does not preclude man from being in the image of God, then why should it preclude the machine? The fact that man can be considered in the *imago dei* in spite of the fact that he has evolved from that which is not in the *imago dei* does not settle the question as to whether there can be a similar evolution in machines, but it certainly does open the question.

In the past, man has been willing to consider partial analogues. For example, the camera has been spoken of as analogous to the eye. But this refers to the function of seeing, which is not unique to man. To say that man can create an artificial eye does not have the same import as to claim that man can create an artificial life. And it is this more staggering claim that cybernetics forces us to face, for it is dealing with systems that are analogous to the uniquely human powers of reasoning and choosing. Some would prefer to phrase the question in this way: If the human mind operates on the basis of a network of electrical currents, then how is it different from an electronic computer? In other words, there are some who would prefer, instead of asking whether machines are alive, to ask if man is anything more than a machine. Whichever way it is stated this is a most profound issue for the contemporary period. We must rethink our understanding of man in the light of cybernetics.

Although Wiener emphasizes that "cybernetics is nothing if it is not mathematical, if not in *esse* then in *posse*," [2] he is still

---

[1] Emil Brunner, *Truth as Encounter*, 2nd rev. ed., trans. Amandus W. Loos and David Cairns (Philadelphia: The Westminster Press, 1964), p. 34.

[2] Wiener, *God and Golem, Inc.*, p. 88. Perhaps it is wisest to follow Wiener's opinion that it is "best to avoid all question-begging epithets such as 'life,'

keenly sensitive to its economic and sociological implications. He also indicates specific areas that are of especial significance for religion. "There are at least three points in cybernetics which appear to me to be relevant to religious issues. One of these concerns machines which learn; one concerns machines which reproduce themselves; and one, the coordination of machine and man." [3] In one sense, cybernetics is simply a new phase of the industrial revolution. But it introduces a significant change of character to that line of development. It is now mental power, rather than muscular power, that is being amplified. It is because of the new features of machines in the modern world that we can no longer be satisfied with a repetition of statements such as that of Pascal: "The calculating machine produces results which come closer to thought than anything animals can do; but it does nothing which can make us say that it possesses will-power like animals." [4] The issue is not so easily settled now. Some indication of the new force of this problem is indicated by the amount of attention it has received. Alan Ross Anderson states that in the thirteen years after 1950, more than one thousand published papers explored the problem of whether machines can "think." [5] Unfortunately, not all the papers and discussions were marked by careful deliberation. But even allowing for emotional reactions and precipitate judgments, it is obvious that the question has received some substantial treatment. Answers range the entire

'soul,' 'vitalism,' and the like, and say merely in connection with machines that there is no reason why they may not resemble human beings in representing pockets of decreasing entropy in a framework in which the large entropy tends to increase."—*The Human Use of Human Beings*, p. 32. But it does not seem as feasible to avoid this question now as it did when Wiener wrote these words. For one thing we have more evidence on which to base a decision, and furthermore the issue is becoming more pressing as machines are further developed.

[3] *God and Golem, Inc.*, p. 11.

[4] *Pascal's Pensées*, trans. Martin Turnell (London: Harvill Press, 1962), p. 164 (#340 in Brunschvicg, ed.).

[5] "Introduction," *Minds and Machines*, ed. Alan Ross Anderson (Englewood Cliffs, N.J.: Prentice-Hall, 1964), p. 1.

spectrum from assertions that machines are in principle incapable of thought to assertions that machines are on the threshold of humanity. Nonetheless, we cannot proceed directly to the establishment of a position without first exposing the inadequacy of many of the forms of argument that are still current.

Inadequate and Obsolete Distinctions

On the one hand, it is too simple to move from observation of similarities between man and machine to the assertion of identity and equality. To show that machines and organisms have certain properties in common, even that they have *many* properties in common, is not to establish that they lack distinguishing characteristics.

This is important to keep in mind because cybernetics is in the family of physiological and neurological disciplines, and it shares the behaviorist orientation common to this approach. This is illustrated when Turing bids us think of a machine that is so capable of matching any form of human behavior that an observer whose field of observation was restricted to the behavior would not be able to determine whether it was being performed by a human or by a machine.[6] But such a reduction to the observation of behavior is an oversimplification of the issues. An illustration of this that is most pertinent to the subject that is occupying our attention is found in this statement:

When a part is removed from any interrelated device, very odd things may happen. Consider removing a spark plug from a car engine; we get vibration, spitting, coughing, and loss of power. Now if a neurologist removes part of the brain he may get loss of motor control, or memory, or some defects in vision or hearing. He may get changes in personality, or in motor control—a host of possible changes may take place. He then

[6] A. M. Turing, "Computing Machinery and Intelligence," *Mind,* LIX (Oct., 1950), 433-60, reprinted in *Minds and Machines,* pp. 4-30.

tends to say that the function of a part of the brain is shown by a corresponding loss in behavior when that part is removed. But how does this
work out for our test case of the spark plug removed from an engine? Is
the function of the plug to suppress or inhibit vibration, spitting, and
coughing? Did the plug contain part of the power of the engine? This may
sound silly, but it is very much the way areas of the brain have from time
to time been described and imagined through ablation studies, and this is
hardly surprising, for in the absense of a working model, what other type
of description is available? [7]

On the other hand, some objections to the recognition of
"personality" in machines are based on unfair comparisons.
For example, it is sometimes argued that the human brain may
have some resemblance to analogue computers but none at all
to digital computers, which are much more common because
of their greater precision and ease of engineering. The point
that is supposed to distinguish the digital computer from the
human mind is its "yes-or-no" or "all-or-none" construction, i.e.,
the circuit is either open or closed. But if we consider the
function of neurons in humans, we find the same basic principle
of operation. A neuron either fires or is in repose, and there is
no in-between.[8] On the basis of a *network* of open or closed
circuits a machine may deal with complex issues, just as man
may operate on the basis of neurons that are activated or not
activated.

It is not an accurate comparison to deal with the machine
in terms of component elements and with man as a total system.
This kind of unfair comparison is often operating when the
rhetorical question is posed: "Can machines fall in love?" If we
are asking about the capacities of a machine conceived of as a
box of wires, transistors, and so forth, then the parallel question
is: "Can a bundle of protoplasm, nerves, cells, blood cells, etc.
fall in love?" In other words, if we are thinking of man as a

[7] Richard L. Gregory, "The Logic of the Localization of Function in the
Central Nervous System," *Biological Prototypes and Synthetic Systems*, I, 51.
    [8] Wiener, *Cybernetics*, pp. 120-21.

personal entity, it is only fair, when we are asking whether there is any basis for comparing the two, to think of the machine as a total entity.

Moreover, we should not be unfair in setting up conditions that must be met by a machine if it is to be recognized as "conscious." As the tradition of philosophical literature indicates, it is a prodigious task to "prove" that human beings, let alone machines, are conscious beings. We must not demand that machines meet criteria that have been adjudged impossible or irrelevant where human beings are concerned. The demonstration of consciousness on the basis of observation of behavior does not provide a certain result, whether we are speaking of human or machine consciousness.[9]

Many of the things that are said about machines in order to discredit their claim to be an artificial form of life are also true of humans. For example, it is often said that a machine cannot solve a problem unless it is programmed to do so. But this is only to say that it must learn; and neither can man do what he has not learned to do. In order for man to be able to solve mathematical problems, he must learn to add, subtract, multiply, and divide; and this learning of mathematics is the way in which man is "programmed" for certain tasks. If we say that we cannot learn what memory is simply by contemplating a cybernetic machine, it is also true that we cannot do so simply by contemplating a human being. If a machine learns or remembers only because man already knows what it is to do these things and guides the machine accordingly, how different is this from the guidance of a child?[10]

Many of the differentiations that have been drawn between man and machine no longer hold, or are at least losing their

[9] Cf. Donald M. MacKay, "From Mechanism to Mind," *Brain and Mind,* pp. 184-86; "The Use of Behavioral Language to Refer to Mechanical Processes," *British Journal of the Philosophy of Science,* XIII (1962), 89-103.

[10] Cf. Geoffrey Madell, "Action and Causal Explanation," *Mind,* LXXVI (Jan., 1967), 34-48.

force as new developments blur these lines of distinction. These are what we might classify as "obsolescent" arguments, and there are several examples that can be considered.

It was once held that machines, unlike man, were unable to benefit from experience. This is true of mechanical machines, but not of stable and ultrastable machines. With the development of feedback systems, this distinction had to be abandoned. Not only is learning from experience possible, it is actually essential to many of the tasks now assigned to machines.

However, even if we grant that a machine can be susceptible to feedback, we might still deny that it is influenced by purpose. For example, the thermostat maintains a constant temperature because man desires a constant temperature. The element of purposiveness in its behavior is attributable to its maker, rather than to the thermostat itself. Indeed, because the purpose sought by the machine is not self-chosen, the machine is usually more tenacious in its pursuit than is man. Neither snow nor rain nor hail nor sleet nor boredom nor distraction, nor any such things, deter the machine from pursuing its purpose. There is a story of the lawyer who presented to the court twelve reasons why his client could not appear, and in the course of his pleading it turned out that one of his twelve reasons was the death of his client. This lawyer was like the computer that patiently explores all possibilities and exhausts a problem before it ceases. By way of contrast, if man finds one compelling reason he normally wastes no further time searching for or presenting additional supports for his position or case. Perhaps the most sobering example of tenacity of purpose in machines is seen in the guided missile, which tracks down its target, no matter what moves it might make to escape. The missile does this not because it is a sinister destroyer, but because man has designed it solely to carry out this one purpose. With this understanding, if we are to distinguish between man and machine with regard to purpose it would be more accurate to say that the machine is more purposive than man, rather than lacking in purpose. Sometimes we could describe the machine as "too purposive," because its single-mindedness not only results in greater efficiency, but also leads to a wasting of time with that which a human would dismiss as trivial and unimportant.

However, because of the economic advantages in the improved use of the computer's time, there is research into the development of a capacity for machines to make some judgments about what is significant. Machines that search out every conceivable solution are sometimes too complicated and expensive, and a machine that tries to find a solution by random trial-and-error method may be too slow. Therefore, there are efforts to combine these two principles in machines that operate heuristically. Such a machine would need to be capable of (1) organizing a limited method of search, (2) recognizing similar situations for the contribution they may make to the present task, (3) concentrating its energy upon selected activities, and (4) improving its existing methods and introducing new methods.[11] In short, the view that machines are incapable of self-direction and purposive action is increasingly less tenable.

Spontaneity, novelty, and creativity were once thought to be exclusively human phenomena. But these qualities can no longer be denied to machines. Machines have made unexpected moves in games, have discovered original proofs of theorems, have composed works of art,[12] and so forth. In assessing the

---

[11] M. A. Wright, "Can Machines Be Intelligent?" *Process Control and Automation,* VI (Jan., 1959), 3. Cf. M. Minsky, "Steps Toward Artificial Intelligence," *Proceedings of the IRE,* XLIX (Jan., 1961), 8-30.

[12] The first substantial computer composition (its counterpoint has been evaluated as of fair quality, reminiscent of passages from Palestrina, although more monotonous) is the *Illiac Suite for String Quartet* (1951), which is available on Heliodor records H/HS 25053. For a brief discussion of the procedure of the Illiac computer and a comparison of computer-composed music to the work of such men as Arnold Schönberg and John Cage, see Lejaren A. Hiller, Jr., "Computer Music," *Scientific American,* CCI (Dec., 1959), 109-20. For a fuller discussion see Lejaren Hiller and Leonard Isaacson, *Experimental Music* (New York: McGraw-Hill, 1959). A more advanced work is the *Computer Cantata* (1963), which is on the reverse side of the above-mentioned record.

impact of computers on science, technology, and business organization, the main focus is not on their instrumental use as
aids to research, but rather on their creative role as developers
of scientific theories or engineering designs, or as managerial
decision and policy makers.[13]

When most people think of the use of computers in business, they think of their application to such clerical chores as
billing. John Diebold laments that too many businessmen think
in the same terms. He urges management to make use of the
speed and accuracy of these machines and their ability to make
decisions on the basis of the information which they make so
much more readily available. Diebold encourages an imaginative
approach which is alert to take advantage of the more creative
contribution which computers can make, and questions whether
any lesser use is economically justified.[14] Although he concurs
in recognizing the capacity of computers for more creative uses
than clerical chores, Melvin Anshen does add a cautionary note.
In cases in which special and elaborate programming is needed
to prepare a machine for a decision, he feels that it may often
be more efficient financially to spend the time and money on
deliberation and decision by executives.[15] But the debate, let
it be noted, is grounded on present economic feasibility, and
not on any dispute concerning the creative capacity of computers for reaching managerial decisions.

Man has extended his sensory capacities, as in the use of
telescopes or microscopes to extend the sense of sight. Now the

---

For a discussion of this composition, see Lejaren Hiller and Robert Baker
"Computer Cantata: A study in Compositional Method," *Perspectives of New
Music*, III (1964) , 62-90.

[13] Anthony G. Oettinger, "The Uses of Computers in Science," *Scientific
American*, CCXV (Sept., 1966) , 161-72; Steven Anson Coons, "The Uses of
Computers in Technology," *ibid.*, pp. 177-88; Martin Greenberger, "The Uses of
Computers in Organization," *ibid.*, pp. 193-202.

[14] Diebold, *Beyond Automation*, chap. 4.

[15] Melvin Anshen, "Managerial Decisions," *Automation and Technological
Change* (The American Assembly; Englewood Cliffs, N.J.: Prentice-Hall, 1962) ,
pp. 66-83.

computer is making possible an extension of human thought that is tending toward an independent exercise of the ability to think. The problems that lie ahead can be seen in the issues that are being raised about copyright laws in the light of development in cybernetics. One of the problems posed by computers is whether the input of published material into the memory bank violates or endangers the rights of author and publisher. One book fed into the memory bank of a computer may be consulted by thousands of people who heretofore would have required many copies of the book. Where does this leave the author and publisher who have depended on volume sales? As baffling as this problem is, the computers face us with an even more startling problem in this area. The "creative" works of computers (i.e., those in which the expression is a matter of the computer's rather than of man's choice or arrangement) have already posed a claim to authorship for machines. The 1965 Annual Report of the Register of Copyrights states: "In past years the Copyright Office has received an application for registration of a musical composition created by computer. This year copyright was claimed for an abstract drawing, and for compilations of various kinds, which were at least partly the 'work' of computers." [16] Computers not only share in the creativity of the normal imaginative powers of man, but also have analogues of illusion ("a real input evokes a false percept") and hallucination ("a synthetic percept appears to have qualities of reality") .[17] So machines seem to be evolving toward not only the potentials but also the drawbacks of human creativity.

The components of a system no longer provide a sound basis on which to classify it. The components may be physical, chemical, biological, or any combination of these. "Physical" would include such things as mechanical, electrical, and thermal

---

[16] Quoted by Curtis G. Benjamin, "Computers and Copyrights," *Science*, Apr. 8, 1966, p. 181.

[17] Donald M. MacKay, "From Mechanism to Mind," p. 179.

components. Man and machine cannot be distinguished simply on the basis of difference of components. The original differences are becoming even less significant because of inventions such as the pacemaker, by which human hearts are kept beating. Also, the old answer that machines are not like humans because in machines you can exchange parts is not quite as definitive as it used to be. Surgeons have faced problems of tissue rejection that are not confronted by those dealing with mechanical systems. For example, plastic surgeons can graft skin taken from the leg or the back to the face of the same person from which it was taken, but cannot graft skin taken from exactly the same part of the face of another donor. Nonetheless, surgeons are developing techniques of replacing parts and organs with others either taken from other living organisms or even built from foreign substances, such as plastic. On the other hand, machines are developing the capacity of self-repair and are theoretically capable even of self-reproduction, although, like man, they cannot extend their life-span indefinitely.[18]

Can we say that machines are nonetheless different because they do not have a thalamus and cortex? Unquestionably, the thalamo-cortical system has developed in man in such a way that he is capable of reacting to a vast complex of messages in a unified manner. However, this is not the only means by which living organisms receive, interpret, and act upon information. Other animals than man are also able to react to complex patterns of information, even though their capacity may fall short of that of man. Some of these other organisms have developed in ways that are similar to human development. However, a

[18] J. von Neumann, "The General and Logical Theory of Automata," *The World of Mathematics,* ed. J. R. Newman (New York: Simon & Schuster, 1950), IV, 2070-98; Lars Lofgren, "Kinematic and Tessellation Models of Self-Repair," *Biological Prototypes and Synthetic Systems,* I, 342-69; Gordon Pask, *An Approach to Cybernetics* (New York: Harper & Row, 1961), chap. 7. For a discussion of the self-reproduction of machines in relation to the doctrine of the *imago dei,* see Wiener, *God and Golem, Inc.,* chaps. 3-4; *Cybernetics,* pp. 177-80.

biologist who has had considerable experience with the octopus makes the interesting observation that "the octopus has a nervous system that has evolved independently of ours for more than 500 million years and has no thalamus or cortex or other such parts." [19] But he goes on to point out that the brain of the octopus does provide in other ways for the interaction of information from various sources. The essential feature of living organisms is not a specific system, such as the thalamo-cortical system. The machine may not duplicate this system, yet we cannot immediately assume that it consequently lacks any equivalent of it.

The development of machines is indeed having a strong impact. A recent sociological survey pointed to a need for an improvement of the image of computing machines, which tend to be misunderstood and feared by the general public. According to this survey, the uneasiness concerning computers is primarily due not to the threat of job displacement, but rather to a fear concerning the encroachments on what has formerly been considered unique to man.[20]

Equal Rights for Machines

As we have seen, many of the differences between man and machine have become obsolete. But does this mean that all the differences are bound to fall sooner or later? Hilary Putnam raises this question in the context of his article "Robots: Machines or Artifically Created Life?" [21] He avows at the outset that his concern is to bring a new perspective into the philosophy of mind, and that his interest in machines derives from his concern for greater clarity in talking about humans. I would

---

[19] J. Z. Young, *Doubt and Certainty in Science: A Biologist's Reflections on the Brain* (New York: Oxford University Press; Galaxy Books, 1960), p. 81.

[20] Robert S. Lee, "The Computer's Public Image," *Datamation*, XII (Dec., 1966), 34.

[21] *The Journal of Philosophy*, LXI (Nov. 12, 1964), 668-91.

predict, however, that the problem of machines will increasingly demand attention in its own right, and that the analysis of machine minds will be an intrinsic rather than an instrumental study, even though the close relationship with the problems of the nature of the human mind may never be severed.

Putnam's first task is to argue and defend against objections the view that a man and a robot are "psychologically isomorphic," i.e., that they obey the same psychological laws. By this he does not mean that their behavior is identical, but that "the behavior of the two *species* is most simply and revealingly analyzed, at the psychological level (in abstraction from the details of the internal physical structure), in terms of the *same* 'psychological states' and the same hypothetical parameters." [22] In other words, he is asserting that a man and a robot obey the same psychological laws, whether or not the robot is conscious and even though the man's system may be based on neurons and the robot's on flip-flops. When the robot has the "sensation" of red, can we drop the quotation marks? In other words, is the robot, who is psychologically isomorphic, sensing in such a way that we would recognize him as living or as conscious? In the terms of the title of his article, do we confront a machine or do we confront a form of artificially created life? Putnam calls this the problem of "the civil rights of robots" and suggests that, with the rapid acceleration of technological and social change, this may be a crucial problem much sooner than most of us expect.[23] But thus far it is still a hypothetical question, though not a farfetched one, to pose the problem of a robot saying for his people, "We are alive and conscious, and we demand equal rights!" Putnam examines the pros and cons of granting civil liberties to robots. There are three basic arguments for those opposed to granting them. The "phonograph-record argument" contends that the robot is not itself creative, but only "plays" behavior that has been created

---

[22] *Ibid.*, p. 677.   [23] *Ibid.*, p. 678.

by others and grafted into it. For example, if a robot tells a joke, we are laughing at the wit of its maker, not the wit of the robot itself. Putnam rejects this argument as inadequate, because it neglects the possibility of learning and spontaneity on the part of robots. When such a robot learns enough to tell jokes, we are laughing at its wit. We may marvel at the skill of the programmer who created a system which could produce new jokes; but the sense of humor is not his, it is the robot's.

A second argument is the "reprogramming argument." This argues that a computer can be reprogrammed to do just the reverse of its previous mode of behavior. If we "reversed" a human being, it would be monstrous. This is because a human being has character, and we would be violating it by such reprogramming. But there is no such consideration on the part of a robot. Putnam points out that this argument, like the previous one, neglects the possibility of learning and spontaneity. Suppose a lobotomy enables a person to reverse psychotic or criminal behavior, but without destroying his capacity to learn. We would not consider this monstrous. A robot can be reprogrammed to the same extent without any denial of character.

The third argument is the "question-begging argument." This asserts that the alleged "psychological" states of the robot are nothing more than physical states, whereas in humans there is a distinction. This assumes the very question that is at issue.

Putnam thus rejects the "anti-civil-libertarian" arguments as having failed to show that robots are not conscious. He notes that "pro-civil-libertarian" arguments are rare and also fail to establish their case. They do not show that robots are conscious. Even if we define sensations (such as seeing red) or states (such as being in pain) or emotions (such as feeling angry) as nothing more than, or as identical with, brain processes, it does not follow that men and robots are identical. Indeed, psychological isomorphism does not imply similarity in construction, and the robot may not even have brain processes. While the identity theory may allow for consciousness in robots, it does not necessitate it.

Putnam then turns to an anti-civil-libertarian argument that does not, like the previous arguments, rest on observation of behavior, but rather focuses on structure. No matter how manlike a robot (or android) may be, it is an artifact. The gist of this argument is that if something is mechanically constructed we cannot speak of it as living and conscious. The argument is analytic, rather than synthetic. It says that the notion of a "living robot" is logically contradictory, like the notion of a "married bachelor." The argument is based on the incompatibility of the terms "machine" and "living." But Putnam replies that this argument is refuted if it is possible for us to conceive of robots as living (e.g., as loving, hating, thinking, becoming power-mad, and so forth), whether they really are so or not. And the very fact of the debate over the issue establishes that this conception is possible; and therefore, though it may be false, it is not contradictory.

Putnam next examines what is probably the most widely held position, namely, that we cannot know whether robots are living or not. It is quite possible that the robot is a living mind or soul; it is quite possible that it is a lifeless machine. The basic trouble with this view is that the evidence that human beings are living souls, rather than lifeless machines, has little if any greater probability than that for robots. We believe other humans are living because they act analogously to ourselves; but if the robot acts this way, especially if it is an android which resembles us even in appearance and touch, then the argument seems equally strong that it is living.

Then, as if he did not have us in as deep a quandary as possible, Putnam raises the possibility of robots who create ROBOTS, and who consider themselves, the creators, as conscious, but who consider their creations as lifeless. And so Putnam carries us through the whole problem again, with the suggestion that "our position with respect to robots is exactly that of robots with respect to ROBOTS." [24]

According to Putnam, the failure to establish that robots are or are not conscious, or that we cannot know one way or the other, leads us to conclude that the question of whether robots are machines or artificially created life

calls for a decision and not for a discovery. If we are to make a decision, it seems preferable to me to extend our concept so that robots *are* conscious—for "discrimination" based on the "softness" or "hardness" of the body parts of a synthetic "organism" seems as silly as discriminatory treatment of humans on the basis of skin color.[25]

Differences Between Man and Machine

In view of the heartbreak and tragic intractability of our present civil rights problem, I certainly would not want to spawn another one. Nonetheless, I think that it is possible to inquire in a fair-minded way into the possibility of there being some insuperable differences between man and machine. With full recognition of man's temptation to defend his unique position and the consequent danger of rationalization, we can nonetheless explore some differences suggesting that the appropriate attitude toward machines is not acceptance of them as equivalents of man.

T. B. Steel, Jr. suggests that a plateau has been reached in the development of artificial intelligence. Consequently, the extreme claims and countercharges that were common earlier are seldom heard today. He sees the contemporary controversy resolving into two poles of thought. One holds that the creation of artificial intelligence is still the ultimate goal, but recognizes that it will be a long, slow process of development. The other group holds that the ultimate goal is more practical, namely, to

---

[24] *Ibid.*, p. 689.   [25] *Ibid.*, p. 691.

CYBERNETICS AND THE IMAGE OF MAN

perform certain operations more accurately or more cheaply than is possible for human operators. In other words, the goal here is a division of labor between men and machines.[26]

It is now our task to examine the evidence supporting the view that the promise of cybernetics is not so much a duplication of human processes as a partnership between man and machine.[27] In other words, are there differences between man and machine that make it likely and/or desirable for machines to remain different from man even as they reach higher levels of development? Or, to put the question in terms of the civil rights issue: Is the view that man and machine retain certain fundamental differences a product of man's prejudice, or is it founded on the recognition of different principles of operation?

Norbert Wiener recognizes the machine as having the advantages of greater speed and uniformity. One of the chief advantages of the human brain that is recognized by Wiener is its ability to handle "vague" and "formless" concepts, such as those that are prominent in literary and artistic endeavors as contrasted with the more sharply defined concepts of science and mathematics. Consequently, he suggests a policy of division of labor for the most efficient cooperation of man and machine. Rejecting the extremes which consider machines as holy objects of worship or as blasphemous and depersonalizing forces, Wiener suggests the motto: "Render unto man the things which are man's and unto the computer the things which are the computer's." [28] A failure to appreciate the import of this motto is illustrated in the interrogation of Alice by the Red and White Queen.

---

[26] "Artificial Intelligence Research," *Computers and Automation*, XVI (Jan., 1967), 24.

[27] For a discussion of the requirements, problems, and guidelines for such a partnership, see Aiko M. Hormann, "Designing a Machine Partner," *Datamation*, XIII (Feb., 1967), 29-33. Cf. J. C. R. Licklider, "Man-Computer Symbiosis," *IRE Transactions on Human Factors in Electronics*, HFE-1 (Mar., 1960), 4-11.

[28] *God and Golem, Inc.*, p. 73

"Can you do Addition?" the White Queen asked. "What's one and one and one and one and one and one and one and one and one and one?"

"I don't know," said Alice. "I lost count." "She can't do Addition," the Red Queen interrupted. "Can you do Subtraction?"

What is established by this examination is not that Alice is unable to add, but that she is unable to add *like a machine*.

The fact that human beings are complex does not mean that it is impossible, let alone improper, to understand them in relation to machines, even those of the most simple construction. For example, it is possible to see some analogy between even a doorbell and a living organism. The process of pushing the button, sending an electrical impulse along the wires, and ringing the bell is analogous to the process of stimulus, neural impulse, and resultant behavior. But analogy is not identity, and this particular analogy is a weak one for at least two major reasons.[29] First, the doorbell system depends upon a single impulse, whereas organisms involve much more complex systems of communication. Further, the doorbell system is one-way, whereas organisms are able to receive feedback. Young uses the illustration of a father working at a table, under which his baby son is tickling his leg.[30] If the relationship were as simple as the wiring of a doorbell, the stimulus would bring about the same response each time, just as pushing the button results in the ringing of the bell. But in the case of the man at the table, the situation is more complex. The original response to the tickling of the leg may be withdrawal of the leg, and this may be repeated two or three times. After that the father will put his hand down to his leg or look down in order to see what is happening. The human organism does more than react to a stimulus, it responds to its environment. It is because of the

---

[29] For a discussion of analogy as a mode of communication which necessitates both a basis of similarity and a principle of modification, see *Encountering Truth*, pp. 48-49.

[30] *Doubt and Certainty in Science*, p. 26.

element of feedback as a means of achieving stability that biologists, and even zoologists, have an interest in cybernetics. With the development of feedback loops, machines developed characteristics that were formerly unique to living organisms.

In *The Computer and the Brain,* John von Neumann undertakes a comparison and contrast of computing machines and the human nervous system. He discusses many analogies between the two systems, and is convinced that the human nervous system may be viewed as an automaton and that it must have not only a logical, but also a mathematical part that is equally important to it. But although he concludes that it is valid to discuss the nervous system in terms of concepts that have been devised for dealing with computers, he also points out dissimilarities between the systems. There are both superficial and fundamental dissimilarities. Superficial dissimilarities include size and speed. The natural componentry can perform more operations within less space, and the artificial componentry can operate more rapidly.[31] Natural componentry tends toward automata with more, but slower, organs that operate in parallel (i.e., several items are received and processed simultaneously). Artificial componentry tends toward automata with fewer, but faster, organs that operate serially (i.e., the process handles things in successive operations).[32] Fundamental differences are found in operation and organization. In computers, precision is of crucial significance. Because the calculations are carried out in long sequences, errors become both accumulated and amplified. The

[31] As James L. O'Leary has put it, "electrically the brain is a very busy organ, and so much occurs simultaneously that it is not surprising we have been unable to extract more concrete information this early in the elaboration of electronic techniques."—"Matter and Mind," *Brain: A Journal of Neurology,* LXXXVIII, Part 4 (1965), 779. Cf. Karl Steinbuch, *Automat und Mensch,* 3rd rev. ed, (Berlin: Springer-Verlag, 1965), p. 194.

[32] For a discussion of the distinction between sequential and multiple processes in computers and the implications for the understanding of human thinking, see Ulrich Neisser, "The Multiplicity of Thought," *The British Journal of Psychology,* LIV, Part 1 (Feb., 1963), 1-14.

human nervous system, however, can achieve a higher level of reliability with a lower degree of precision than that required by a computer. The loss or the insertion of one, or even several, nerve impulses in the nervous system does not have the devastating effect that would result in a computer system. This points to a radical difference between computers and human nervous systems in organization and in type of language or message-system employed. The nervous system is not dependent upon the arithmetical formalisms that are essential to the operation of computers. Not only does it use a different (less formal and precise) form of language, but also it employs a different operation. Von Neumann illustrates with the reorganization of the visual image by the retina. Although there is considerable reorganization, it is accomplished by means of only three successive synapses (or three successive logical steps). The nervous system not only receives messages in a less precise language system, but it operates with a system that requires far fewer steps and that more than compensates for its lack of precision by the reliability that it attains.

It is commonly stated that one of the advantages to be gained by the cybernetic revolution is the demand it places upon us for stating problems fully and accurately. I do not for a minute question the contention that we have often been extremely muddled and vague in our approach to problems. However, I would also insist that questions are to be asked on the basis of their significance rather than on the basis of the clarity with which they can be stated.[33] If machines are constitutionally unable to deal with questions that are necessarily stated in a way that does not conform to rigorous criteria of completeness and precision, then I would conclude that they are different from men. Let us recognize them as partners and learn from them the lesson of stating our problems as precisely as possible, but let

---

[33] Cf. my article, "A New Trinity: One God in Three Deaths," *Religion in Life*, XXXVI (Spring, 1967), p. 69; see also pp. 65-66.

us not identify with them to the extent of concluding that something is insignificant simply because it does not compute.

Machines share some of the principles of physical and mental health that apply to man. For example, machines as well as men deteriorate through lack of use. This is true not only of complex industrial computers, but also of home appliances, much to the consternation of householders who have left their washing machine or some other appliance idle for a lengthy period of time. There are also some startling similarities between the treatment of a "sick" machine and methods of healing the human mind.[34] If a machine malfunctions, the simplest way of restoring it to order is to erase the data which seem to include the "troubling" material, and then to start the machine in operation again. This is similar to tranquilization. When this is not effective, a more severe method is tried. If it is a mechanical machine, it may be thoroughly shaken. If it is an electrical machine, a surge of power is sent through it. This attempt to clear out the disorder is similar to shock therapy. If this does not succeed, an even more drastic method is employed. The part of the system that includes the trouble spot may be cut out of the unit, and the machine, it is hoped, will function on a reduced but undisturbed basis. This is analogous to a lobotomy. But despite the startling similarity of methods of treatment for man and machine, there is, as far as I know, not a single instance of curing a machine by means of counseling, either in individual or group therapy. The machine can respond to the more "chemical" and "surgical" types of therapy, but not to the dialogical approach of counseling.

This does not mean, however, that machines are incapable of handling verbal concepts. Machines have languages of their

---

[34] For different perspectives on the application of cybernetics to psychotherapy, see Wiener, *Cybernetics*, chap. 7, and E. Lakin Phillips and Daniel N. Wiener, *Short-term Psychotherapy and Structured Behavior Change* (New York: McGraw-Hill, 1966), chap. 5.

own, such as FORTRAN and ALGOL, and they also deal with the natural languages of man. The verbal capacity of machines is a major factor in examining them from the viewpoint of the theological concept of the *imago dei*. As we observed in chapter two, Brunner distinguishes in the second volume of his *Dogmatik* between an automaton, an animal, and a man. The automaton is incapable of any kind of response, and many of the creations of the cybernetic revolution have far exceeded this stage. Should we then classify automatons as animals, or as "living" in the terminology I have been using, or do they belong in the category of human life? Brunner's principle of distinction is that the animal can react but not respond because it is incapable of self-transcendence, whereas man, possessing a capacity for speech, is able to exercise his self-determination to respond as an "I" to a "Thou." Linguistic capability is the crucial factor. Are machines characterized by a language capability which would render them able to respond in an I-Thou relation? To examine this, we must come to some understanding of how computers function when they deal with language. The two most prominent applications have been in the areas of abstracting and translating.[35]

Before we look directly at automatic abstracting and translating, a few words of a more general nature are in order. People often think it strange that machines should be able to handle language, since they associate computers with numbers rather than with words, which seem to be a purely human phenomenon. And yet language, like mathematics, is highly symbolic. People who consider the machine less than human simply because it employs arbitrary symbols need to reconsider the

---

[35] For a collection of articles dealing with machine abstracting and translating, see Harold S. Sharp, ed., *Readings in Information Retrieval* (New York: The Scarecrow Press, 1964), pp. 373-440. A helpful introduction to the process of translating, but not abstracting, can be found in Fink, *Computers and the Human Mind*, pp. 227-38. See also E. Delavenay, *An Introduction to Machine Translation* (New York: Frederick A. Praeger, 1960), and A. G. Oettinger, *Automatic Language Translation* (Cambridge: Harvard University Press, 1960).

process of language learning in man. This is a process of learning to use and respond to arbitrary symbols in an appropriate way.

So the use of language is important for understanding the relation of man and machine. Furthermore, there is an analogy between language and the physical and mental dimensions of man. Language, like man, has a physical (e.g., marks or sounds) and mental (semantic) dimension. This is an interesting analogy, not only because computers have been influential in dealing with language but also in light of our earlier claim that determinism and freedom are concomitant in man and machine.

Automatic abstracting requires at least two readings by the machine. The first reading produces a word frequency list on the assumption that in technical writing the most significant words, however rare they may be in general usage, will recur more often than those that are not crucial to the argument. For this purpose, various word forms are considered uses of the same word. For example, the frequency count would lump together the variants "differ," "different," "difference," "differently," "differential," and "differentiate." It is usually adequate if the machine counts word frequency on the basis of the first few letters. In the example cited, all the words begin with "differ." Also, common words such as pronouns, conjunctions, copula and auxiliary verbs, prepositions and articles are disregarded in preparation of the word frequency list. The second reading detects sentences which have the greatest concentration of highly frequent words. The assumption is that sentences which relate the most frequently used words are sentences which represent the crucial steps of the argument. The abstract can be made up solely by gathering together such sentences. However, it is possible that frequency alone will isolate more general terms, that is, those common to all technical writing rather than to this specific case of it. To overcome this it is possible to refine the technique of automatic abstracting. For example, the position of a word or sentence may be taken into account, with a high priority being given to words occurring in the title or headings, and to the opening and closing sentence of each paragraph. A semantic rather than positional criterion is involved when sentences containing such key words as "summary" or "conclusions" are given a higher priority.

Even with the use of the more complicated techniques there will be imperfections. There may be stylistic flaws, such as pronouns without a referent. The sentences that make up the abstract often fail to flow together, because no connectives or transitions are supplied by the auto-abstracter. The relevance of the material, that is, its relation to the general body of knowledge, cannot be supplied by the auto-abstracter. However, it is possible for people, especially those who understand how auto-abstracts are prepared, to read them and to get an idea of what an article is dealing with; and that is what an abstract is for, after all. With the flood of articles, most scientists feel that the time saved by this method of abstracting more than makes up for minor defects.[36] The plea of the scientist seems to be more for abstracting the abstracts than for improving their literary merit. In our more leisurely past we could take time to explore the meaning of meaning, but since the advent of the knowledge explosion we can no longer know what we know.

Machine translation has been greeted with the same attitude as auto-abstracting. It also stems from similar pressures, namely, the amount of material published and the need for its availability without delay. Human assistance, by means of preparing the input and editing the output, helps the final product but loses much of the speed advantage that is gained by machine translation. By feeding a basic lexicon into its memory bank, machine translators can provide a literal translation, listing more than one word for the reader's choice when the word in question does

---

[36] Cf. H. P. Edmundson and R. E. Wyllys, "Automatic Abstracting and Indexing—Survey and Recommendations," *Communications of the ACM*, IV (May, 1961), 226-34; reprinted in *Readings in Information Retrieval*, pp. 390-412.

not have a clear-cut equivalent. Fortunately for the word-by-word translation machines, the primary concern at the moment is for Russian-English translation, and these two languages have a close similarity of word order. More elaborate machines can take the context into account, but the final product is still rather rough.

Some researchers are attempting to develop symbolism for a universal language that would serve as an intermediary in translation. For example, a document would be translated from Russian into the universal language and then from the universal language into English, or vice versa; but there would be no direct movement from one natural language to another.

The product of translating machines, like that of abstracting machines, is able to provide a scientist with the basic ideas but without any of the literary amenities. It is the scientists who have been clamoring for translations, and they seem to find the machine translations adequate to their needs.

The basic problem in translation is not the "big" words, but the "little" words—as a glance at any lexicon will show. The technical words need but a few lines in a lexicon, but the shorter words, such as prepositions, require column after column. It is the multiplicity of meanings of the "small" words that plagues the efforts of translating machines. One of the recent machines was given the sentence: "Time flies like an arrow." This was translated into a Russian phrase meaning "Time flies like to eat arrows." Besides the ambiguity of "like" meaning "as" and "enjoy," there is also an ambiguity in the first two words of the original sentence. The first word could be taken as an imperative, yielding the command: "Clock some winged insects." [37] Such shortcomings on the part of machine translators may be of no consequence to scientists who wish to avail themselves of such services. But these shortcomings are of great significance for the question of the relation between men and machines, for they

---

[37] *Science News,* Mar. 18, 1967, p. 265.

suggest that the machine's handling of linguistic concepts is of a different order than man's, even though man may be able to make use of the machine's products in some areas of discourse.

Further support for this distinction is found in John Austin's examination of the perhaps all too human act of excuse-making. After his elucidation of concepts employed in making excuses he draws several conclusions. One of these concerns "the exact phrase and its place in the sentence." Under this heading Austin points out that it is not enough to pay attention to the key word in a sentence. For example, in considering excuses, the word "mistake" is a key word. But we have to distinguish between "by mistake," "owing to a mistake," "mistakenly," "it was a mistake to," "to make a mistake in or over or about," "to be mistaken about," and so forth. As we have noted, the abstracting machine would lump all these expressions together as one use. Even the precise position of the adverbial expression in a sentence may vary the meaning. It is commonly recognized that the position indicates what is being modified by the adverbial expression, but Austin is arguing more than this. He insists that even the *sense* of the expression is influenced. He illustrates:

a_1 He clumsily trod on the snail.
a_2 Clumsily he trod on the snail.
b_1 He trod clumsily on the snail.
b_2 He trod on the snail clumsily.

Here, in a_1 and a_2 we describe his treading on the creature at all as a piece of clumsiness, incidental, we imply, to his performance of some other action: but with b_1 and b_2 to tread on it is, very likely, his aim or policy, what we criticize is his execution of the feat.[38]

A machine may take the position of a word into account, but its concern is not the same as Austin's. The machine is concerned

---

[38] John Austin, "A Plea for Excuses," *Philosophical Papers*, p. 147; *Twentieth-Century Philosophy: The Analytic Tradition*, p. 347.

with the importance of a word as indicated by its position, rather than with the variation in meaning that is expressed by a variation in position.

Speaking more generally, we see that machines are adequate to handle verbal symbols only as vehicles for the communication of information. But human beings have other interests in communication. It is to be hoped, if not assumed, that scientists have other uses for language than the communication of scientific discoveries and theories. What distinguishes human and computer use of language is not the fact that computers prefer their own languages, such as FORTRAN or ALGOL, for there are various forms of human language, and indeed language is not even restricted to verbal forms. The difference is rather that the use of language by machines is restricted to the manipulation of information in symbolized form; whereas the human use of language includes the further capacity of self-expression. Until this latter facility is achieved, computers do not have a language capacity that enables them to make an I-Thou response.

To say that computers have not achieved this ability yet is not to say that they will be unable to achieve it in the future. As a matter of fact, computers can already simulate counseling.[39] Such a capacity for counseling may conceivably be a major step in the development of machines toward the capacity for establishing I-Thou relations with man. And perhaps simultaneously with this, machines will become susceptible themselves to psychotherapy through counseling.

It might be urged that the computers I referred to earlier which compose music might be considered to engage in self-expression. However, although their creations do have genuine aesthetic value, their compositions are more didactic than expressive. In the notes for the jacket of the phonograph album,

---

[39] J. Weizenbaum, "ELIZA—A Computer Program for the Study of Natural Language Communication Between Man and Machine," *Communications of the ACM,* IX (Jan., 1966) , 36-43.

Computer Music from the University of Illinois, Lejaren Hiller emphasizes the importance of taking into account the primacy of the didactic element in evaluating and responding to computer music. So the situation of machines used in composing music is not appreciably different from that of those used in abstracting, translating, and counseling.

In his critique of abstracting and translating machines, Daniel J. Boorstin observes that literary form may be subordinate to ideas and concepts in scientific books and articles, but that in other areas of human expression the particular literary form in which a book or article is cast is inseparable from the ideas it seeks to convey.[40] Philip H. Phenix argues that learning another language is implicitly an occasion for the worship of God.[41] The divine life is manifest in all things, and hence God can be discovered in the phenomenon of language. Language is not only fundamental to the educational procedure, but is also a basic mode of participating in the life of the spirit. From this theological perspective, Phenix draws some valuable insights for pedagogy. For example, he says:

The aim of learning a language other than one's native tongue is not to be able to think the same thoughts and communicate the same ideas in other words. The goal rather is to enable one to enter into a new world, to categorize existence in novel ways, and to organize experience into fresh modes of understanding. In so doing, the learner is shaken out of his limited and partial conceits. His easy assumption of adequate knowledge of reality is brought into question, and his vision is opened to wider ranges and profounder depths in the interpretation of being. It is the boundlessness of possible interpretations that makes language learning revelatory of the divine. The limitlessness of symbolic formations is

---

[40] *The Image: Or What Happened to the American Dream* (New York: Atheneum, 1962), pp. 138-42, esp. p. 139. For a discussion of the nature of language and the philosophical differences between language families, see Michael Girsdansky, *The Adventure of Language* (Englewood Cliffs, N.J.: Prentice-Hall, 1963).

[41] *Education and the Worship of God* (Philadelphia: The Westminster Press, 1966), chap. 2.

evidence of the infinitude of God, who is the ground of all being, and who cannot be comprehended within any finite categories.[42]

Computers do not, at least yet, learn language with a view to discovering new categories of thought and experience, let alone for the purpose of worshiping God, whose infinitude is a stimulus to the quest for new categories because it renders all categories inadequate.

Freedom in Man and Machine

This discussion of language behavior in man and machine illustrates that similarity of external behavior is not an adequate basis for asserting an identity of nature. Even if a machine wags its tail every time you walk in the door, this does not prove that it is happy to see you. At the beginning of this chapter I warned that identity of external behavior is not adequate to establish the identity of man and machine. At this point we need to explore this idea further, because a critique of the behavioristic approach can itself disclose fundamental differences between man and machine. For example, R. C. Skinner has argued that despite similarities in behavior we cannot assume an identity between machines and minds. He first illustrates with a mechanical tortoise that is constructed to turn at random to the right or to the left (and possibly to turn around and go in the opposite direction, to stop dead, or any other behavior possible under the given circumstances). Skinner will grant that it has as much freedom of action as a person under such circumstances, but not that it has freedom of choice. He explains:

This is partly because of the fact that the tortoise is not aware of the alternatives available to it—it does not have a firm belief that it is able to turn either to the left or right, or to stop dead, and so on. But it is also

---

[42] *Ibid.*, p. 41.

because of the fact that since the tortoise is built to select at random between the alternatives, it cannot help doing so: it cannot turn to the left because someone advises it to, or turn to the right because the last time it came to an obstacle it had turned left, or jump over the obstacle because it had not done so before that day.[43]

In other words, human freedom always contains an element that is missing in machine freedom, no matter how much that freedom may be developed. Skinner then deals with the more complex case in which a machine is built to select behavior for specific reasons. He cites as an example a chess-playing machine which is designed to play the best move (i.e., the move most conducive to winning). But in this case, Skinner argues, "it could not select a move at random, or a move that was more interesting than the 'best' move, or a move designed to let its opponent win the game." [44] Moreover, Skinner contends that this situation cannot be evaded by making the machine choose at random either to select at random or to make the best move, for then it cannot choose which of these it will do, as a human could, but will have to select between them at random. Skinner holds that whatever complication we build in, a man can always go the machine one better, because he can make selections of a different kind at whatever the level may be.[45]

---

[43] R. C. Skinner, "Freedom of Choice," *Mind*, LXXII (Oct., 1963), 477. Cf. "The theory of cognitive systems deals with an old subject, inductive inference, from a new point of view, that of constructibility. The latter has the merit of bringing to light almost immediately a basic paradox: a machine that can be defined cannot be intelligent. Suppose this machine has a basic strategy Q_1; then either this is fixed, in which case it cannot be intelligent, being incapable of self-improvement, or Q_0 must be the subject of another strategy Q_1 to which the same argument applies, and so on."—M. C. Goodall, "Induction and Logical Types," *Biological Prototypes and Synthetic Systems*, I, 381.

[44] "Freedom of Choice," p. 478.

[45] In his efforts toward the development of a machine that can learn, R. M. Friedberg notes that the difference between man and machine is little in principle, but in fact there is a tremendous gulf. For example, an examination of the parts of a thermostat reveals how it does its job, but we cannot gain this kind of clarity when we examine the brain. Hence, he seeks to develop a machine that can learn and develop its own methods rather than a machine in which

Behaviorism has had the value of emphasizing the mechanical foundation of mental activity. The human brain and the computer can be understood in terms of the same mathematical structures. This is why both neurologists and engineers have been attracted to cybernetics. But to say that the two are the same, even to say that they are fundamentally the same, is not to say that they are absolutely the same. In other words, an accurate description of man may still not be an adequate description.

Motivation in Man and Machine

Let us consider the android used for teaching anesthesiology that we mentioned earlier and his probable descendants. They will look like man and they will act like man. Will they become so manlike that it would be permissible to drop the "like"? As far as appearance and behavior are concerned, there is little and perhaps eventually nothing to distinguish between man and such an android. Indeed, the similarity of behavior, at least, if not of appearance, is essential to the purpose of the android. But this brings us to a difference. The heart of a man beats in order to keep him alive; the heart of an android beats not in order to keep it alive, but in order to train physicians to keep the human heart beating. Similarly, the android breathes not because it will die if it is unable to get air, but because it is designed to simulate a process which is vital to man. The similarity of action in man and android expresses a difference of purpose. The android simulates human behavior, but not the intention that is behind the human behavior. It is for this reason that it is inadequate to speak solely in terms of behavior, although there is some point to the criticism that we should apply the terms "intentional" and "unintentional" not to actions, but to re-

---

the mechanism leads obviously to the method of operation.—"A Learning Machine: Part I," *IBM Journal of Research and Development,* II (Jan., 1958), 2-13.

sults.[46] Even when the appearance and behavior of man and machine are indistinguishable, we may nonetheless find basic underlying differences.

Ulrich Neisser[47] contrasts the prevailing view a generation ago, which held that machines could never duplicate human thought, and the current view, which expects this imitation of human thought to be imminent. He brands both as "unsophisticated." "Yesterday's skepticism was based on ignorance of the capacities of machines; today's confidence reflects a misunderstanding of the nature of thought." Neisser has no doubts about the capacity of machines to imitate man in translating, for example, and even to beat their inventors in games of skill such as chess. But Neisser's point is that even when they imitate human behavior, machines are operating according to a different set of underlying principles. The key area that Neisser singles out is motivation. Here, he feels, is where the machine necessarily differs from man. In this connection he makes three assertions. First, human growth and development cannot occur in just any order. Certain skills are prerequisite to others, and as a result certain attitudes are formed before certain skills are possible. This means that while a computer can match human beings in assimilating its environment, it cannot match them in accommodation, i.e., in adapting the very apparatus by means of which it assimilates. For example, in game playing, a child at first will not abide by the rules of the game. Later, he is staunchly legalistic about the rules. Finally, he recognizes that arbitrarily established rules can be arbitrarily changed. This de-

---

[46] For philosophical treatments of "intention," see G. E. M. Anscombe, *Intention*, 2nd ed. (London: Oxford University Press, 1963) ; see esp. pp. 35-36 for the distinction between intention and cause, and pp. 89-90 for the distinction between voluntary and intentional; and A. I. Melden, *Free Action* (New York: Humanities Press, 1961) . For the view that "intention" is improperly applied to actions, see J. W. Meiland, "Are There Unintentional Actions?" *The Philosophical Review*, LXII (July, 1963) , 337-81.

[47] "The Imitation of Man by Machine," *Science*, Jan. 18, 1963, pp. 193-97.

velopment influences the human attitude, but such a development is not present in the machine. Even if it plays a better game of chess, its comprehension of the nature of games and play is not comparable to that of man. A second and more obvious difference is that human learning has an intimate relation with emotions. Even the activity of a newborn baby is prompted by the desire to satisfy needs. Moreover, needs and emotions continue to accompany human learning, and grow and develop with it.[48] The detachment and objectivity of the machine is in contrast with the emotional matrix of all human thought and learning. A third difference is that a machine follows a single motive, while men follow a multiplicity of motives. If a machine plays chess it plays to win, and all other goals, such as capturing men or controlling certain squares, are subordinated to this. For a human, other goals may enter in. A particular move may be prompted by curiosity or by aesthetic sensitivity, and while the player may hope it will lead to a winning game, winning may be a subordinate motive at the time. Also, chess is played for social reasons, and the purpose of winning the game is combined with the purpose of deepening a friendship. Or the game of chess may be used as an outlet for feelings of aggression and hostility. The computer is concerned simply with problem-solving; human life is much more multifaceted. Neisser concludes that concern for the regulation of society by machines is justified. If machines thought as we do, there would be no occasion for fearing their use in social regulation. But machines are "inhuman." In technical application, the prospects are bright; in social application, they are dim.

Neisser's analysis supports the view that there are some very significant differences between man and machine. For example, machines are more docile than man. They can erase all

---

[48] For a discussion of the inseparability of intellectual and emotional expression in language, see *Encountering Truth*, pp. 186-94.

earlier learning with little or no trauma, and the old memories do not linger on to haunt them or to frustrate efforts to program in new values and patterns of behavior. Human beings do not have the same control over their processes of learning and forgetting. The greater control of the machine in this regard does provide certain advantages, but it also has disadvantages. Men cannot avoid learning, and they are almost forced to develop and mature, even when they do not want to. Wiener calls attention to the fact

that the machine is intended for many successive runs, either with no reference to each other, or with a minimal, limited reference, and that it can be cleared between such runs; while the brain, in the course of nature, never even approximately clears out its past records. Thus the brain, under normal circumstances, is not the complete analogue of the computing machine but rather the analogue of a single run on such a machine.[49]

The machine is frighteningly conformist in its outlook, and while it never gets at cross purposes with itself, it never dreams dreams nor sees visions.

These differences are especially important for determining the extent to which machines are responsible and whether they should be granted civil rights. In the light of the evidence examined, my contention would be that we have to grant that machines have a wide range of responsibility, but that for the forseeable future it is not wide enough to entail civil rights. Because there are areas in which men are responsible but machines are not, we cannot say that man and machine are identical, although we may readily admit that they are similar, indeed increasingly similar. We can, then, recognize machines as having the potential for life, but the present evidence does not support the further claim that they have the potential for human life.

---

[49] *Cybernetics*, p. 121.

Concomitance of Imago Dei and Imago Machinae

We have acknowledged our kinship with the animals. Now we need to concede that some machines are closer to us than are most animals, and perhaps than all animals.[50] We have come to the point at which we can say that man is an animal without having to deny characteristics that make him unique among animals. Now we need to be able to say, in a similar way, that man is a machine without having to deny characteristics that make him unique among machines. Although man at first fought the suggestion that he could be categorized with the animals, he gained a deeper understanding of himself when he could make this concession. Emil Brunner's *Man in Revolt* and Reinhold Niebuhr's *The Nature and Destiny of Man* both recognize the insights of the naturalist view of man, but they also provide keen criticism of its shortcomings. In the age of cybernetics we need to incorporate and transcend the concept of man as a machine, albeit a unique one, within our theological perspective. We have been willing to recognize machines as able to outperform man in some functions, such as locomotion. And yet we are so hesitant to grant that machines can outperform us in certain aspects of thinking that we almost define thinking as that which machines cannot do. This reaction has been referred to as the "machines can't" psychosis.[51] Although there is a strong element of defensiveness in this attitude, there is also a basic wisdom that underlies our tenacious clinging to the uniqueness of man. But instead of fearing the way in which machines take over what we do, we should welcome this as the liberation of man to do what machines cannot do, which in the final analysis is a liberation to be human rather than a means to some other end. Although he

---

[50] Cf. Wiener, *The Human Use of Human Beings*, chap. 3, on the contrast between the rigidity of ants and the learning capacity of machines, and chap. 4 on the exclusion of ants (and even of chimpanzees, who are among "man's closest relatives and his most active imitators") from the field of language and the admission of machines to the field of linguistic capability.

[51] Steinbuch, *Automat und Mensch*, p. 387.

is writing in the context of the socioeconomic implications of the cybernetic revolution, Robert Theobald captures the theological import for our understanding of the nature of man.

> Man will no longer need to toil: he must find a new role in the cybernetics era which must emerge from a new goal of self-fulfillment. He can no longer view himself as a superanimal at the center of the physical universe, nor as a superefficient maker of decisions self-fashioned in the model of the computer. He must now view himself as a truly creative being in the image of a creative God.[52]

In earlier discussion of the two histories of man, we defended the thesis that freedom and determinism increase concomitantly in both man and machine. Now we have reached the point where we can assert that the understanding of man as the *imago machinae* and as the *imago dei* also increase concomitantly. The human mind is unquestionably dependent upon the 10^{10} electrical circuits in its system of nerve fibers, but to talk in these terms is to describe the mind from only one perspective. A tremendous, but not impossible, feat of electrical engineering is required to create artificially a system which reaches the magic number of 10^{10}. There are also chemical components of the mind, but again we do not re-create the mind simply by synthesizing the chemical constituents. We have to talk about the mind not only in both electrical and chemical terms, but also in the nonscientific terms developed in art, religion, and philosophy. Advance in one area of discourse will influence other perspectives, but we cannot solve all the problems by concentrating upon progress of understanding in any one dimension.

Our need is not for a rehearsal of the old debate between mechanists and vitalists, but for a quest for some means of

---

[52] Theobald, "Cybernetics and the Problems of Social Reorganization," in Charles R. Dechert, ed., *The Social Impact of Cybernetics* (Notre Dame: University of Notre Dame Press, 1966), pp. 68-69.

transcending it. Cybernetics could provide, as did evolution before it, an occasion for the former; but it also provides a means
for the latter. As Marshall McLuhan constantly points out, new
developments bring about new ways of thought, although at
first they seem to provide nothing more than extensions of the
old order. It will be tragic if we move into the age of cybernetics
without transforming earlier categories for the scientific, philosophical, and theological understanding of man. It has been suggested that our age may be "witnessing the birth of a new kind
of mechanistic explanation and at the same time a new kind of
vitalism each more appropriate and more embracing than the
old kinds." [53] Norbert Wiener puts the import more bluntly:
"The whole mechanist-vitalist controversy has been relegated to
the limbo of badly posed questions." [54] Pan-mechanism is not
adequate because the individual cannot be explained in terms of
quantitative analyses that yield exact prediction. Pan-vitalism
is not adequate because important facets of life in general and
human life in particular have yielded to quantitative, as opposed
to qualitative, analysis.

Cybernetics has brought us to a problem which supersedes
the question of whether material substance or vital force is the
primary category. Cybernetics has subordinated the issue of the
nature of the parts to the issue of their arrangement in a system.
Parts are now to be seen as operating within a system, whether
it be a mechanical, biological, or sociological system. In other

[53] W. H. Thorpe, *Science, Man and Morals* (London: Methuen & Co., 1956),
p. 6.

[54] *Cybernetics*, p. 44. "Vitalism has won to the extent that even mechanisms
correspond to the time-structure of vitalism; but . . . this victory is a complete
defeat, for from every point of view which has the slightest relation to morality
or religion, the new mechanics is fully as mechanistic as the old. Whether we
should call the new point of view materialistic is largely a question of words:
the ascendancy of matter characterizes a phase of nineteenth-century physics
far more than the present age, and 'materialism' has come to be but little more
than a loose synonym for 'mechanism.' "—*Ibid.* For a critique of Wiener as overly
harsh on vitalism and overly soft on mechanism see Robert McClintock,
"Machines and Vitalists," *The American Scholar*, XXV (Spring, 1966), 249-57.

words, whether we are dealing with a machine, an organism, or a group, it is the system which organizes and relates the component parts that is more important than the nature of the component parts themselves. The emphasis shifts from things and items to contexts and relations.[55] This is especially significant in light of the fact that the history of philosophy abounds with efforts to play off one part against another—body vs. soul, freedom vs. determinism, heredity vs. environment, nature vs. history, and so forth. Cybernetics does not mean that only one of the former contending factions can be right, but rather it suggests that the debate between them ought not to be settled for as a stalemate. Cybernetics enables us to get the previously stalled dialogue back into motion so that we can attempt to discover what is shared commonly by both sides.

The emphasis of cybernetics upon unity and totality reinforces the dissatisfaction with those theologies which draw sharp dichotomies. In current theological activities, Kierkegaard's insistence upon "either/or" is losing ground to Hegel's insistence upon "both/and." Brunner's theology is clearly oriented to the dichotomist pole. My earlier book, *Encountering Truth,* was an attempt to moderate Buber's and Brunner's dichotomy between I-It and I-Thou. My concern there was to argue that elements of both are involved in any encounter with God. In this book, we have noted that cybernetics provides further impetus and support for such a modification of Brunner's stance.

---

[55] Leon Bagrit, *The Age of Automation* (New York: New American Library; Mentor Books, 1965) , pp. xviii-xix.

Part Three

The Cybernetic Revolution and Social Responsibility

7 | The Resurgence of Utopianism

I concluded Part Two with an observation that cybernetics calls for a moderation of Brunner's tendency toward the drawing of dichotomies. It is perhaps only fitting that Part Three should open with an observation that the emphasis on communication in cybernetics is compatible with Brunner's emphasis upon dialogue.

The Imago Dei and Society

Faith apprehends that man's true being is love in response to the creative love of God. We are not our own creators, and we even depend upon others for becoming and knowing who we are. The human I-thou relation is constitutive of our humanity, and in fulfilling the command to love our neighbor we express the image of God, just as we do in loving him. The image is not simply a reflection of the divine. It is a possession or characteristic of man. Man is not simply to reflect, but to realize the image of God. And man has significance and dignity, not simply in relation to God, but also in relation to the human community. Such an interpretation of theology highlights the responsibility of each member of the system, and this sensitivity to one's responsibility is a significant form of feedback.

Paul Ricoeur contends that the dichotomy that has vitiated our doctrine of the image of God is the dichotomy between man as an individual and man as mankind.[1] Having separated these two elements, which were united in the theology of the church Fathers, we have lost the historical and the cosmic dimensions of the image of God. It is theological considerations that lead Ricoeur to insist that we must recapture the unity of man as an individual and as a social being. The cybernetic understanding of man gives further support to this plea. In Part Three we will examine the nature of man as it is illumined by his response to the challenges and opportunities of the cybernetic revolution in society.

Brunner's concept of the natural orders of society, as we noted in chapter two, is a prominent feature of his social ethic. This concept is still helpful, but it does pertain to and grow out of a period characterized by more stable social conditions than those which are possible today. Indeed, flux has so replaced fixity that Bagrit suggests that we need to create a new federal cabinet post in order to guide society smoothly through accelerated change.[2]

The cybernetic revolution increases both the possibility and the necessity for planning social function and organization. Cybernetics emphasizes communication and control, but our tendency has been to let things happen as they will and only under exceptional circumstances to seek to direct the course of events. Social planning is inevitably going to increase, just as planning has and will continue to increase in business.[3]

Cybernetics not only necessitates, but also facilitates social planning. Indeed the very etymology of "cybernetics" manifests

---

[1] " 'The Image of God' and the Epic of Man," trans. George Gingras, *Cross Currents*, XI (Winter, 1961), pp. 37-50.

[2] *The Age of Automation*, pp. 85-88.

[3] For a discussion of planning in business, see John Kenneth Galbraith, *The New Industrial State* (Boston: Houghton Mifflin, 1967). Galbraith argues, for example, that businessmen in America have shifted from the competitive system of free enterprise to a socialist philosophy of creating markets, administering prices, and so forth on the basis of a plan of action for the next several years.

a strong affinity to political application. *Kubernetes* is used in the Septuagint (Prov. 23:34; Ezek. 27:8, 27, 28) and in Acts 27:11 and Rev. 18:17 to refer to the master of a ship. The image of the helmsman or steersman has long been applied to the politician, who guides the course of the "ship of state." *Kubernesis* is found in I Cor. 12:28 to refer to administrators as appointed by God for the government of the church. *Kubernetes* was carried into Latin as *gubernator,* whence our word "governor," which is used both in engineering and political science. In the nineteenth century, André Ampère coined the term *cybernétique* to refer to the effect of feedback on the art of politics. So the term has had definite links with politics prior to the renewed use of the term under the influence of Norbert Wiener.

The Development of Utopianism

The possibility of applying cybernetics to social planning as well as to production has given rise to a resurgence of utopianism. We need some historical background to evaluate this new development. The expectation of a future state in which all is well and good is anticipated in Thomas More's (a Renaissance Catholic) *Utopia* (1516). It spawned other Utopianisms— Campanella's (a Dominican) *City of the Sun,* and Valentin Andreae's (a Lutheran) *Christianapolis.* Utopian writings continued to appear from time to time until well into the nineteenth century. The Enlightenment was marked by an extreme optimism. One of the major contributing factors was the Renaissance emphasis on the goodness of man. Another was the confidence that science provided a new method which was applicable to all areas of life. Man felt that it was simply a matter of getting around to applying science for all of life to be rendered good. And the successes of science to that date made such an expectation reasonable. But evil proved to be a little more intractable than was anticipated. This led to the transformation from a static to a dynamic optimism. In other words, men recognized the evils and injustices of the present, but they still had a strong confidence that all would be well in the not too distant future. Their hope was in progress. It was Voltaire's belief in progress that supported his optimism, although his *Candide* mercilessly lampooned those whose optimism led them to affirm that the present world was the best of all possible worlds. This belief in progress flourished into the nineteenth century. In science it contributed to the elaboration of the theory of evolution. And the idea of progress flourished also in the antiscientific mood of the Romanticist movement, although its emphasis upon history as the bearer of the unique encouraged it to look backwards as much as forwards through history. In liberal theology the continuity between the divine and the human was a pervasive underlying theme.

The optimistic mood of the nineteenth century and the early decades of this century led to certain claims that were later the objects of ridicule. In ethics it was felt that men would eventually be so altruistic that one individual would refrain from performing an altruistic act so that another might have the satisfaction of performing it. Wars were thought to have been caused by religious superstition and dogmatism, and were thus thought to be a thing of the past. It was not anticipated that nationalism would spawn wars. When World War I raged across Europe the mood of the people was changed abruptly. America was more removed from the war, and the optimistic mood survived through a depression and a second world war before it was shaken. Eventually, phrases such as "a war to end all wars" began to sound very hollow. Originally they prompted feelings of patriotism and humanitarianism; now they prompted feelings of cynicism. Emile Coué's autosuggestive phrase, "Every day in every way I am getting better and better," had been seriously practiced by multitudes, but with the shift in mood it was lampooned as a platitude.

The possibility that the future might be a decline rather than an ascent was broached before the turn of the century in *The Time Machine* (1895) by the basically optimistic H. G. Wells. Another early expression of the possibility of retrogression as well as progression was Jack London's *The Iron Heel* (1907), which ends with a golden age, but only after a period of oppressive totalitarianism. After the two world wars and the introduction of Communist as well as fascist totalitarianism, we have a vision of the future as a nightmare rather than as a dream. Examples of this are Aldous Huxley's *Brave New World*, Yevgeny Zamyatin's *We,* George Orwell's *1984,* and Anthony Burgess's *A Clockwork Orange.* I think that it is important to see, as Erich Fromm points out in the "Afterword" of the New American Library edition of *1984,* that these contemporary anti-utopias are not exclusively concerned with the future nor are they completely devoid of hope. They are projections into the future of what we can expect if there is not a reversal of the trend toward dehumanization and alienation. Fromm also points out clearly that this trend is not restricted to Communist societies, but is found also in the "managerial industrialism" of capitalism. He gives some examples of "doublethink" in the West, such as our use of the phrase "free world" to include any country that is anti-Communist, no matter how dictatorial and oppressive it may be. Fromm sees the hope of these negative utopias in their belief that it is possible for man to reverse the horrible trend that is now under way. They are not prophesying disaster, but are rather expressing their hope, though it is not an easy but a desperate hope.

The New Optimism

One would hardly have thought, however, that utopianism could be taken seriously again, and yet we have been evaluating utopian and anti-utopian interpretations of cybernetics. The optimism that had submerged in the laboratories for so long is now clamoring for adherents in the public forum. The newly emerging optimism may be of a chastened form, but it marks a definite shift of opinion. This can be seen at many levels and in many facets of contemporary life. For example, the earlier generation of beatniks was marked by cynicism and despair for society. The present generation of hippies, although equally determined not to conform to society, is marked by a much more optimistic view of man and society and is determined to replace war with love. The shift in mood can also be illustrated in the change in name of a CBS-TV network program from *The Twentieth Century* to *The Twenty-first Century,* even though the final third of the twentieth century has not yet elapsed. Men are again looking ahead with enthusiasm and excitement. Whereas, for example, Walter Cronkite formerly narrated scenes of the bombing of cities during various wars, he now narrates plans and procedures for building the cities of the future. The emphasis is no longer upon the events that led us to the condition we are now in but is rather on the tremendous accomplishments that lie ahead.

Theology has always had a strong element of hope, and some forms of theology readily embrace the new optimism. For example, William Hamilton wrote an essay, "The New Optimism— from Prufrock to Ringo," in which he called for an acceptance and affirmation of modern technology. He wrote in reaction to the negative attitude of neo-orthodox theology toward scientific advancement. And yet, there is a note of optimism in Brunner that incorporates and exceeds the optimism of scientific progress. For example, Brunner makes this kind of statement about the despair that science in his day was occasioning in those who believed in man, but not in the God who created man in his image—and who were infecting theology with their pessimistic interpretation:

Truth as encounter contains the evolutionism of science within it, but leaves it infinitely far behind, as it discloses itself as a Christological

theanthropology, which broadens out into the doctrine of the consumma-
tion of man in the coming Kingdom of God. Therefore the truth that
encounters us is a criticism of the contemporary theology that surrenders
to the skepticism of the *Zeitgeist* the hope for the future that is an
essential ingredient of the New Testament witness of faith.[4]

We can also contrast Brunner's *Faith, Hope and Love* with
Jürgen Moltmann's *Theology of Hope.* In Brunner, hope expresses the Christian gospel in its future mode, but this hope is
built upon the foundation of faith and love. In Moltmann, hope
becomes not the consequence or extension of faith and love, but
rather the very foundation on which all other aspects of theology
depend.

Can hope maintain the weight that it has recently come to
bear? Cybernetics is such a powerful influence in the new utopian hope that it necessitates a reappraisal of this hope. To begin
with, it should be clear by now that machines are quite able to
deal with social problems. They were first applied to such things
as games of checkers and chess, which present well-defined problems, in contrast with the problems of a social and economic
nature. The capability for dealing with more complicated problems was developed only gradually, but it was in the purview
from the beginning. Cybernetics emphasizes the similarity between men and machines namely, as systems of control and communication. Cybernetics is a comprehensive science, and many
scientists and engineers, especially in America, tend to break it
down into specific areas of application, such as bionics, control
systems, and computer engineering. Cybernetics also brings society into its purview along with men and machines, and on the
same terms.[5] Society is another type of organism, and thus fits
into the framework of cybernetics. Many governments have employed cybernetics in dealing with specific problems. Thus far,

---

[4] Brunner, *Truth as Encounter,* p. 40.
[5] "Cybernetics stands to the real machine—electronic, mechanical, neural,
or economic—much as geometry stands to the real object in our terrestrial
space."—Ashby, *An Introduction to Cybernetics,* p. 2.

the most extensive use of cybernetics for the implementation of a planned and controlled society is in the Soviet Union. In Marxist philosophy empirical theories are dependent upon the philosophy of dialectical materialism. The first reaction of the Marxists was that cybernetics and dialectical materialism are incompatible. They considered cybernetics a pseudoscience, doomed to perish along with the imperialism that gave it birth. If I may be allowed a pun in Russian, their first response was, "cyber*nyet*ics." But soon the Communist Party commissioned one of their senior theoreticians, trained in mathematics and philosophy of science, to effect an acceptance of cybernetics as a major means of accomplishing the transition from socialism to Communism.[6] In Red China computer capability is still marginal, but all indications are that the next decade will see significant developments in this area.[7]

It is not at all surprising that the first major steps toward a cybernetically planned and controlled society have been taken in the context of totalitarian traditions. The assumption of the Utopian is not merely that a perfect society can be realized, but that it can be implemented by human planning and effort. Since it is difficult, if not impossible, to plan for the exercise of human free will, social planners are consequently tempted to ignore it. They thus presuppose the old mechanistic philosophy that men behave like machines and that we can plan accordingly.[8] This

----

[6] Lee R. Kerschner, "Cybernetics and Soviet Philosophy," *International Philosophical Quarterly*, VI (June, 1966), pp. 270-85. The article is a distillation of the forthcoming book, *Cybernetics in the Soviet Union*, and distinguishes the attitude toward cybernetics of Communist traditionalists, moderates, and ultras. For a historical survey of shifting Soviet attitudes to cybernetics, see Maxim W. Mikulak, "Cybernetics and Marxism-Leninism," *The Social Impact of Cybernetics*, pp. 129-59. For a survey of developments in the Russian experiment in the application of cybernetics to the entire range of social engineering, see John J. Ford, "Soviet Cybernetics and International Development," *ibid.*, pp. 161-92.

[7] Donald G. Audette, "Computer Technology in Communist China, 1956-1965," *Communications of the ACM*, IX (Sept., 1966), 655-61.

[8] Cf. Weizsäcker, *The Relevance of Science*, p. 20.

is why there is an affinity between utopianism and totalitarianism.

Sometimes this movement toward an authoritarian imposition of the perfect society is present at the purely theoretical or planning stage. A classic example of this belief that stern measures will be required is Plato's *Republic*. At other times the movement toward totalitarianism results from an exasperated desire to speed up the progress toward the ideal, with the conviction that sometimes people have to be forced, for their own good, to do what they do not like to do at the time.

The question that is raised by this impatience is whether the frustrations are accidental or necessary. For example, in the eighteenth century it was believed that kings were the sources of all social evil. It was thought that if we could rid the world of monarchy, we would usher in a golden age. Then the Communists decided that the source of all social evil was capitalism, and they set about to establish a classless society. They recognized that it would take a long time to accomplish this goal. Thus we do not refute them by pointing out that they really have state capitalism, because they recognized that they would necessarily have to pass through such stages. The real question for our day is raised by the split between Russia and China. If these two Communist societies are in conflict, then it would seem that antagonism would not necessarily be eliminated if all the world should become Communist.

The newest hope of utopians is the behavioral sciences and technology. Probably the chief spokesman of this group is B. F. Skinner, especially in his book *Walden Two*. Utopianism is, of course, not universal among behavioral scientists. For example, Carl Rogers is critical of Skinner's utopianism. Rogers is fully cognizant of the tremendous advances in our capacity to predict and control behavior.[9] But how is this power to be used? Rogers

---

[9] "The Growing Power of the Behavioral Sciences," *On Becoming a Person* (Boston: Houghton Mifflin, 1961), pp. 363-83.

finds three different answers in B. F. Skinner's *Walden Two,* Aldous Huxley's *Brave New World,* and George Orwell's *1984.* Skinner recognizes the danger of misuse, but basically foresees the use of the power to manipulate men as benevolent in intent and in fact; Huxley foresees its use as benevolent in intent but malignant in fact; and Orwell foresees its use as malignant in intent and in fact.[10] In stating his personal reaction to Skinner's program, Rogers states:

> If the good life of the future consists in so conditioning individuals through the control of their environment, and through the control of the rewards they receive, that they will be inexorably productive, well-behaved, happy or whatever, then I want none of it. To me this is a pseudo-form of the good life which includes everything save that which makes it good.[11]

Because of this conviction, Rogers undertakes a critical evaluation of Skinner's position,[12] which he describes as resting "upon a faulty perception of the relationship of goals and values to the enterprise of science." Basically, Skinner has failed to realize that scientific endeavor serves a goal which is freely and personally chosen prior to that endeavor. Thus, Skinner has chosen to make man "productive" and "well-behaved" and has set himself to accomplish that end. But he has eliminated any way of evaluating this choice of goals and selecting alternate goals. Rogers finds Skinner's goals too static and stultifying. Instead, he suggests a radically different kind of goal which values free development and dynamic self-transcendence.[13] Such an approach would lead to an open rather than a closed society, in the sense that we would cultivate individuals who are responsible for the free choice of their own values.

---

[10] Rogers, "The Place of the Individual in the New World of the Behavioral Sciences," *ibid.,* p. 386.

[11] *Ibid.,* p. 391.   [12] *Ibid.,* pp. 391-95.   [13] *Ibid.,* pp. 395-99.

The Threat of Depersonalization

There is something that seems unnatural when we consider the powers that have been unleashed by modern automation and cybernetics. But is the awe that we feel in the presence of machines an appropriate response to forces that lure us seductively until we are slaves to that which we thought would serve us creatively? Or is the negative attitude that is evoked by machines simply an expression of man's uneasiness in the presence of powers that are new and unfamiliar? This dilemma has been a common theme in religion and literature.[14]

The Romanticist critique of science has often been re-echoed in recent literature. In *The Secular City*, Harvey Cox describes existentialism as a form of the Romanticist yearning for the simplicities and values of an earlier pastoral age. He contends that its repudiation of technology is guilty of a failure to see the possibilities for development of the personal in a technopolitan civilization. I would agree that some existentialists have overstated their case, but not that existentialism is an anachronism in a technological age.[15] Any appraisal of the social impact of technology must take into account its ability to overcome obstacles to human fulfillment and to create leisure which, in sharp contrast with the earlier necessity of tedious drudgery, can be used in fulfilling ways. But it is still true that the possibility of depersonalization is with us. Technology increases the potential for this, too. Since the existentialist protest is against depersonalization and not against technology, it is still very much needed. The portrayal of depersonalization is a prominent element in much modern literature.

---

[14] For a brief survey dealing with such things as the Black Mass, simony, *The Sorcerer's Apprentice*, "The Monkey's Paw," and the "failsafe" devices of modern warfare see Wiener, *God and Golem, Inc.*, chap. 5. Cf. Brunner, *Man in Revolt*, pp. 182-83.

[15] Cf. *Encountering Truth*, pp. 16-18, 26-27, 53-59.

One literary device is to write of man as an animal and hence as one who has lost that which is uniquely human. In this device we see a contrast between modern man and pre-literate man, who feels a kinship with animals and sometimes thinks of them as gods. The Greeks held animals in high respect, as seen in the number and popularity of names with *hippos*, e.g. Phillip—lover of horses; Hippocrates—trainer of horses; Hippolytus; Hippomenes; and so forth. However, such an identification today suggests man's debasement.

In Franz Kafka's "The Metamorphosis," a man is turned into an insect. Gregor Samsa awoke one morning to find himself transformed into a bug. His job as a traveling salesman had been a depersonalizing influence, but had enabled him to support his parents and sister. When he failed to follow the old daily grind of getting up at four in the morning and going down to the office, his family urged him to hurry so that he would not lose his job. But when he appeared as a bug, they first shooed him, and then drove him back into his room, injuring him in the process. They were now ashamed of Gregor, even though it was their oppressive dependence upon him that produced the metamorphosis. Kafka expressed this with various details, one of which is the feeding. His sister put out a bowl of milk, but he wanted something else. When she checked back and found that Gregor has not eaten it,

she lifted it immediately, not with her bare hands, true, but with a cloth and carried it away. Gregor was wildly curious to know what she would bring instead, and made various speculations about it. Yet what she actually did next, in the goodness of her heart, he could never have guessed at. To find out what he liked she brought him a whole selection of food, all set out on an old newspaper. There were old, half-decayed vegetables, bones from last night's supper covered with a white sauce that had thickened; some raisins and almonds; a piece of cheese that Gregor would have called uneatable two days ago; a dry roll of bread, a buttered roll, and a roll both buttered and salted. Besides all that, she set down again the same basin, into which she had poured some water, and which was apparently to be reserved for his exclusive use.[16]

Eventually, his supposedly helpless father got a job, and later the two ladies got jobs, now that they no longer had Gregor's support. Indeed, his formerly invalid father was now hale. One day, his father returned from work and found Gregor out of his room. He began to bombard him with apples. One of the apples injured him seriously, and it was allowed to remain in his back, because no one wanted to remove it. The apple rotting in the sore probably contributed to his early death. Also, the inflammation was probably aggravated by the dirt of the room, which they became too busy to clean. He was also weakened because they did not give him sufficient food. But perhaps the most damaging of all was the personal ostracism. They had never accepted him as a person, but only as a means of financial support. As a result he could not become a person, and when he could no longer provide support, he had no reason for existence.

In Eugene Ionesco's play *Rhinoceros*, the process of men becoming animals is carried on until there is only one survivor. Everyone has given up his humanity and become a rhinoceros, except Berenger; and he does not really resist depersonalization, but finds it impossible for him. Whereas in Kafka, one man was unwillingly metamorphosed into an animal, in Ionesco the symbol is intensified to the extent that one man unwillingly retains his personality.

In "A Report to an Academy," [17] Kafka reverses the process. An ape describes his relatively easy assumption of the role of a human. He had to learn to spit in other people's faces, to smoke a pipe, to drink schnapps and to fling the empty bottle away. He thus, in his own words, "managed to reach the cultural level of an average European." Charles I. Glicksberg's interpretation of

---

[16] In *The Penal Colony*, trans. Willa and Edwin Muir (New York: Schocken Books, 1961), p. 91.

[17] *Ibid.*, pp. 173-84.

Kafka's use of animal imagery is very germane to our contention that we must see man as a whole comprising both determinism and freedom, so that anything less than this is less than human.

The use of these metaphysical dogs and inquiring apes and humiliated, catatonic cockroaches heightens the force of the ironic contrast. The animal metaphor widens the gulf that separates two levels of existence: the biological and the spiritual, the natural and the human. Man is an animal who attempts not only to speak but to sing; he spells out the secrets of the stars; he walks upright; but he is oppressed by the cruel necessity of his physical being. He hears music that seems to promise a loftier life of the spirit and he reaches out eagerly for this new life, only to be thrust back ignobly on his animal self. He feels guilty if he keeps silent and seeks safety and security in becoming like the others; he feels equally guilty if he turns against his animal origin.[18]

Franz Kafka's short story "In the Penal Colony" is an interesting example of an attack upon the depersonalizing influence of the machine, which also illustrates the romanticist-existentialist emphasis on the horrible and the gruesome. It concerns an officer in the colony explaining the method of justice in the colony to a foreign visitor. The officer continues the ideals of the old commandant, which he is now the only one to advocate openly and which the new commandant wants to eliminate. The officer has in mind winning the support of the visitor, so he is presenting his case in the most winning way.

The visitor is to witness the execution of a man by an ingenious device invented by the old commandant. The execution is drawn out for twelve hours, and the machine cuts into the flesh the prisoner's sentence. In this case it will read: "HONOR THY SUPERIORS!" because the prisoner had failed to carry out his duty to get up every hour and salute the captain's door. The captain reported that he had checked once at two in the morning and the man was asleep. The man had not been in-

---

[18] *The Self in Modern Literature* (University Park: Pennsylvania State University Press, 1963), pp. 46-47.

formed of the charge because he would only answer with lies, and that would complicate things.

Before the execution the officer is explaining the machine to the visitor. It is of three parts: the "Bed," to which the prisoner is strapped; the "Designer," which is the device controlling the inscription to be cut in the prisoner; and the "Harrow," which is the cutting instrument. The officer shows the visitor the two kinds of needles in the Harrow. There are long ones that barely cut into the skin and shorter ones that spray a jet of water so that the blood does not obscure the inscription. While the visitor is examining the machine the prisoner raises a commotion, and the officer calls to his guard.

"Set him on his feet!" yelled the officer, for he noticed that the explorer's attention was being too much distracted by the prisoner. In fact he was even leaning right across the Harrow, without taking any notice of it, intent only on finding out what was happening to the prisoner.[19]

Imagine! In the presence of an ingenious machine, the visitor was being distracted by a mere man! The machine, in Kafka's story and in general, stands for depersonalization in two senses. It expresses a reduction of human qualities and powers and also expresses a force that impinges upon man beyond his ability to control it.

But the machine has also enhanced life for man. Indeed, we name the stone, bronze, and iron ages by the level of technology that had been attained. The significance of this development should make us aware of the freeing and personalizing, as well as of the enslaving and depersonalizing power of the machine. This ambiguity of the machine is a common theme in Lewis Mumford's discussions of the history of technology. The limitations of the machine do give some ground for the fears of depersonalization and mass control; but they should be fears which issue in concern and caution rather than in a Luddite condemnation of

---

[19] *The Penal Colony*, p. 201.

each revolutionary development in technology. On the other hand, the creativity of machines does give some ground for the hope that they will usher in a new and better society, but it should be a hope which issues in careful planning and deliberate judgment, rather than in a joyous following of the machine wherever it leads.

The Relation of Science and Technology

Perhaps the distinction between science and technology has contributed in a small measure to the tendency of some to view the latter solely in negative terms. It is easy to move from this distinction to the view that pure science comes first, and that when it is applied to technology it tends to become perverse and corrupt. But I doubt that science has ever been as severed from technology as such a view assumes. And certainly, with the rapidity of developments in the contemporary period, the distinction between science and technology represents little more than a difference in orientation.

Because we are now facing what is aptly called an "ecologic backlash," we easily overlook "the historical roots of our ecological crisis." [20] Indeed, not only man has constantly transformed his environment, but so have all forms of life. Just as man builds his cities, so the coral polyp builds its reefs. Just as man builds his dams, so does the beaver. And yet, there is no question that man's influence on nature has been more pervasive and noticeable than that of any other creature. Moreover, the changes have grown exponentially and are now proceeding at a staggering rate. Change that once had to be assimilated by generations, or even centuries, now occurs within a lifetime. And in these days of pollution of the air we breathe and of the water we drink the problem confronts us on the fundamental level of existence. But

---

[20] Lynn White, Jr., "The Historical Roots of Our Ecological Crisis," *Science*, Mar. 10, 1967, pp. 1203-7.

our solutions to the problem of "ecologic backlash" have not been fundamental, and their shortcomings have been satirically pointed out:

> There are many calls to action, but specific proposals, however worthy as individual items, seem too partial, palliative, negative: ban the bomb, tear down the billboards, give the Hindus contraceptives and tell them to eat their sacred cows. The simplest solution to any suspect change is, of course, to stop it, or, better yet, to revert to a romanticized past: make those ugly gasoline stations look like Anne Hathaway's cottage or (in the Far West) like ghost-town saloons. The "wilderness area" mentality invariably advocates deep-freezing an ecology, whether San Gimignano or the High Sierra, as it was before the first Kleenex was dropped. But neither atavism nor prettification will cope with the ecologic crisis of our time.[21]

White feels that we need historical depth in order to clarify our thinking. He feels that modern science is an extrapolation of natural theology and that technology is an expression of the exhortation of man to exercise dominion over nature. Science and technology both developed in the Christian middle ages but remained separate—science being more aristocratic, speculative, and intellectual; technology being more lower-class, empirical, and activistic. The democratic revolution led to a fusion of these two forces in the middle of the nineteenth century, and this has precipitated the crisis we face a century later. Because of the religious rootage of science and technology, White is skeptical about any solution that would advocate more application of science and technology to our problems. White feels that the problem and the solution are religious. The major culprit is the Christian teaching that nature has only one purpose—namely, to serve man, whose rule over nature is to be exercised without any limitations. White sees the concept of the *imago dei* feeding into this problem by saying that though man's body is of earth, he is not really part of nature but a Godlike transcender of and ruler over nature. Although Zen Buddhism is popular in the

---

[21] *Ibid.*, p. 1204.

West and gives an opposite picture of the relation of man and nature, White is dubious about its viability because it is so deeply conditioned by Asian history. Rather, he points to St. Francis of Assisi's teaching that there is an equality of all God's creatures. White feels that his emphasis on humility, in accord with the cosmic humility of the Creator who assumed flesh and was born as a helpless infant, is the antidote to human arrogance. Because of man's proud disdain for all other creatures in nature, White proposes St. Francis of Assisi as the patron saint for ecologists.

The Two Cultures

As a further step toward a view which avoids on one hand the overzealous welcoming of all technological developments and on the other hand the overzealous repudiation of all such developments, we can consider some of the issues raised in C. P. Snow's provocative essay *The Two Cultures*. Snow laments the polarization of scientists and literary intellectuals (whom he chastises for abrogating the last half of this phrase as applicable only to themselves) . Because there is no understanding of the opposite pole, these groups regard each other with indifference at best, but more often with hostility. Each side caricatures the other, and Snow seeks to expose the misunderstanding that underlies some of the specific elements of these caricatures.

The scientist is accused of shallow optimism, but Snow argues that scientific optimism refers to social experience rather than to individual life. Scientists are aware of human loneliness and the inevitability of death. But they do not conclude from this that it is futile to improve the conditions of human life. Indeed, they have tended to brand the literary intellectuals as fatalistic and inactive in the face of such tragedies. Snow contrasts the concern for the future among scientists with the retreat from the future among literary intellectuals. He cites the contrast between J. D. Bernal's *World Without War* and George Orwell's *1984* as illustrative. It is true that modern literary intellectuals have tended to be negative about the future, and we have already cited several examples of literary anti-utopianism. But are the optimism of the scientist and the pessimism of the literary intellectual concerned with the same thing, so that they are able to be compared without some qualification of the terms involved? I would suggest that a more instructive comparison would be B. F. Skinner's *Walden Two* and Aldous Huxley's *Brave New World.* I suggest Huxley rather than Orwell for such a comparison, because Orwell's society is based on punishment and coercion, while Huxley's is based on reward and seduction. Skinner and Huxley both picture a society in which men will be so conditioned that they will feel more comfortable when conforming than when they are not. They will think they are free because they will not really miss their lack of freedom. In this sense, both writers are "optimistic" about the technological accomplishments and the degree of social control which produce a society that provides pleasurable sensations in abundance and avoids painful frustrations and decisions. But they sharply disagree when they move from the social to the individual dimension. Huxley feels that the price that must be paid in terms of humanness is too great, whereas Skinner feels that there is nothing but gain in such a social order.

Actually, in order to make this point, we do not have to go beyond what Snow himself has said. As we have noted, he responded to the charge that scientists are shallow optimists by drawing a distinction between social and individual experience. In *A Second Look* Snow reaffirms this distinction, although it has worried people who otherwise concurred in his presentation. He further notes that his own literary works have emphasized the solitariness and tragedy of individual life. And it is just this feature of life in future "utopias" that is so easily overlooked or denied by those whose focus is on the structuring of society and the management of human behavior in the future. Because this aspect is so easily overlooked, literary intellectuals have wanted to express the tragedy and suffering that cannot be expelled from any society, and that is even more menacing and devastating when it cannot be acknowledged or named. Snow does not want us to label the scientists "optimists" unless we specify that they are social optimists but recognize individual tragedy. Snow does add in passing that the scientist is "too facile" when he tags the literary intellectuals with the label of "pessimist" without any additional qualifications or specifications. But Snow spends more time compiling support for the charge that the literary intellectuals are socially complacent and inactive. Despite the imbalance in presentation, *The Two Cultures* is a forceful challenge to the common assumption of literary intellectuals that they alone have any sensitivity to values. They may not be as reactionary as Snow's emphasis in *The Two Cultures* and *A Second Look* would suggest, but he has effectively made the point that they can use dignified and learned concepts to defend social injustice. And while it may be an overstatement to say that "there is a moral component right in the grain of science itself," [22] Snow has effectively shown that there is undoubtedly a creative and significant contribution to the betterment of human life that is primarily, if not solely, due to the very nature of science.

The scientist's devotion to truth and his interest in the material world may easily prompt an unassuming, but most practical, expression of service to his fellowmen. And with the influence of the formula that science deals with facts while the humanities deal with values, we need Snow's reminder. To take a specific example, he points out that the community of scientific learning crosses racial and cultural lines and produces the kind of outlook that can work with the nationals in a technologically underdeveloped nation with a focus solely on the problem at hand, free of overtones of paternalism. But without any attempt to deny that there is a relation between scientific ideals and human values, I would want to add that they do not follow automatically

---

[22] C. P. Snow, *The Two Cultures and The Scientific Revolution* (New York: Cambridge University Press, 1959), p. 14.

in science, nor anywhere else for that matter. Snow overlooks the condescension that can result from a purely scientific outlook. An engineer assisting an underdeveloped country may judge its society on technical criteria alone and fail utterly to appreciate that society's advanced sensitivity to other human values. One of the mottoes of scientific endeavor since the time of Francis Bacon has been "Knowledge is power." This power can undoubtedly be used for the welfare of all mankind, and, as such, it is consistent with the affirmation of the goodness of all creation. But power can also be sought for purposes of serving one's own pride, and this vanity can lead to the denigration of some aspects of creation, contrary to the affirmation of the goodness of all creation. Because of the inadequacy of either optimism or pessimism, Weizsäcker uses the word "ambiguity" to describe the future promise of science.[23]

On the surface, *The Two Cultures* is appealing for intercommunication between the sciences and the humanities. In this regard it is, as Harry Levin remarks, "about as blandly unexceptionable as a commencement speech." [24] Who would cavil at the plea for such cross-disciplinary understanding? I would dare say that even those who never intend to read a book or an article in the opposite field would never object to a call for mutual understanding. But Levin suggests that beneath this proposal there may be a most significant and debatable assumption; namely, that science is an independent "culture" that can insist on standing by itself even though it ought to know something about the humanities.[25] At a later point, Levin distinguishes the structure of scientific and humanistic knowledge. Scientific knowledge has a vertical structure, so that one builds on the work of predecessors and forges ahead into new stages. Humanistic knowledge is horizontal, in the sense that it is the broad foun-

---

[23] *The Relevance of Science*, p. 21.

[24] "Semantics of Culture," *Refractions* (New York: Oxford University Press, 1966) , p. 5.

[25] *Ibid.*, p. 6.

dation of knowledge that cannot be left behind as one moves into new stages. Levin concludes: "To think of the two modes of knowledge as existing on the same plane may . . . verge upon fallacy." [26]

If there is truly a category mistake or type-trespass in Snow's discussion, it is one which is all too common in our culture. In *Encountering Truth* I remarked that the relation of science and theology is oversimplified when it is treated as a problem of reconciling two different people with different outlooks rather than as a problem of integrating the one person who is a man of faith and a man of science.[27] This same principle holds true for the relation of science and the humanities. Perhaps our sense of uncertainty about ourselves and our proper role in a constantly expanding universe and constantly changing society causes us to have a strong inclination to seize upon partial perspectives as not only the latest, but also the full and final word about the nature of man. Because we are so anxious to know who we are, modern men are eager to hear anyone say, "this is what you really are." Norman Mailer has caught the uncertainty and the desperateness of our age in this poem:

> How can you
>   say
>   you're
>   only
>   three-quarters
>   a man,
>   why you're
>   completely
>   a man
>   said the
>   lady
>   in a
>   three-quarter voice.[28]

---

[26] *Ibid.*, p. 15.   [27] *Encountering Truth,* p. 143.

[28] Norman Mailer, *Deaths for the Ladies (and Other Disasters)* (New York: G. P. Putnam's Sons, 1962), in section entitled "Cannibals."

It is this mood which makes men prone to accept the scientific explanation of life as the full and only explanation of life.

Even the sciences dealing with the nature of man, such as psychotherapy, deal with him on a reduced basis. Leslie H. Farber remarks that the creatures described in psychiatric writings, though they

> may bear some resemblance to animals or to steam engines or robots or electric brains, they do not sound like people. They are, in fact, constructs of theory, more humanoid than human; and, whether they are based on the libido theory or on one of the new interpersonal theories of relationships, it is just those qualities most distinctively human that seem to have been omitted. It is a matter of some irony, if one turns from psychology to one of Dostoyevsky's novels, to find that, no matter how wretched, how puerile, or how dilapidated his characters may be, they all possess more humanity than the ideal man who lives in the pages of psychiatry.[29]

Farber is not objecting to the specialization of the therapeutic method, nor even to its special limitations. But he does think that it needs to be set within the context of a general framework, such as that provided by Martin Buber.[30] In addition to the reductionism of therapeutic reports, Farber calls attention to the "obsessive anecdotalism" of therapists. "The trouble with these anecdotes," Farber remarks, "is not that they are boring or pointless; on the contrary, they have too much point." He explains that they are too "compact, oversimplified, and contrived in their denouement." [31] The outcome is usually successful, although occasion-

---

[29] *The Ways of the Will*, p. 133. Cf. Rollo May, who speaks of the "odd discovery" that more was learned about man in courses in literature than was learned in courses in psychology. He advises those who wish to become psychoanalysts to major in literature and the humanities rather than in biology, psychology, and premedical courses. In this way, the student can first grasp the symbols and myths of human self-interpretation, and then in his graduate study he can develop a method for dealing with these data. But the method itself, May warns, will not enable the student to grasp the data concerning man.—"The Significance of Symbols," *Symbolism in Religion and Literature*, ed. Rollo May (New York: George Braziller, 1960), p. 13 n.

[30] *The Ways of the Will*, pp. 147-54. [31] *Ibid.*, p. 177.

ally they stress the failure of the therapist and the patient's correction of the situation, lest things become too immodest.

Science and the humanities are not completely isolated from one another, so the fundamental problem is not one of relating literary intellectuals and scientists. It is not external, but within. How am I to be both scientist and humanist? And each of us is both. It is a matter of learning to live with ourselves. Any intellectualism that fails to treat science seriously and appreciatively is both unrealistic and ungrateful, and any science which neglects its dependence upon and participation in the tradition of the humanities is similarly guilty.

There have always been changes in the world, throughout its historical and prehistorical periods. And, as Marshall McLuhan points out, the revolutionary nature of the changes was usually not recognized at the outset. For example, many people thought that the invention of the automobile provided a new play toy for the rich, but expected it to have no impact upon the life of the masses. Now, cybernetics has transformed the automobile industry. It is reported that an official of the Ford Motor Company asked the president of the CIO, Walter Reuther: "How are you going to collect Union dues from these machines?" Reuther's retort was "How are *you* going to get them to buy Fords?" [32] The point behind the jest is that mass production requires mass consumption. The revolutionary impact of cybernetics is felt throughout society. We have not simply mechanized our old way of life, we have transformed it. But the changes have rapidly accelerated in modern times. Generations were born and died in the stone age, but people born in the horse-and-buggy age have lived into the space age. Science has played a major role in this acceleration. On the other hand, the accomplishments of science and every other advance of civiliza-

---

[32] R. H. Macmillan, *Automation: Friend or Foe* (Cambridge: University Press, 1956), p. 78; Magnus Pyke, *Automation: Its Purpose and Future* (New York: Philosophical Library, 1957), p. 179.

tion, are threatened by people who cannot discuss the meaning of the present situation, or even operate the elements of our social order with any degree of understanding.

We cannot return to the Kantian dichotomy between science, which deals with the "is" (fact), and religion, which deals with the "ought" (value). We are now in need of statements that are more fine and precise. In *Science and Human Values*, J. Bronowski distinguishes between the findings of science and the activity of science. He concedes that the findings of science are ethically neutral, but insists that the activity of science cannot be described as value-free. At the very least, we need to make such a distinction between the findings and the activities of science. But can we exclude all values even from the sphere of scientific findings?

Rather than say that value is not the concern of scientific findings, which deal solely with fact, I would consider it more accurate to say that scientific findings can deal with both facts and values, but they can never deal exhaustively with values. In other words, there is always an assumption of value which is prior to the element of value in the findings of the scientist. To use an example suggested by Carl Rogers,[33] scientific method can enable us to evaluate the relative merit of education in the three R's and in problem-solving. But, it can do so only in the light of another value not subject to scientific investigation— for example, success in college, integration of personality, success in one's vocation, or responsible citizenship. In the light of the acceptance of one of these goals, or some other goal, it is then possible to evaluate scientifically the values that will lead to the most successful attainment of the chosen value. So values can be included within the findings of scientific investigation, but they always rest on the basis of a goal or value that is prior to scientific investigation.

Our choice of the person to whom we will take a problem

---

[33] *On Becoming a Person*, p. 393.

often involves a prior choice. For example, if a businessman takes a problem to an architect he will get an architectural solution. No matter how objective and detached the architect may be in his procedure, he is operating within the framework of a decision made prior to his investigation.

Not only do we decide on the specialist to whom we will turn, but sometimes we take into account differences of opinion, so that our choice of a particular specialist is a prior determination of the answer we will receive. For example, if a young person is seeking advice on the subject of premarital sexual relations, he decides in advance on the kind of advice he will receive by his decision to seek such advice from Ann Landers or from *Playboy*.

Cybernetics and Human Values

Cybernetics is often accused of abetting the depersonalization of man by producing an inescapable force toward conformity. But there is something to be said on the other side. John McCarthy suggests that "the command of information made possible by the computer should also make it possible to reverse the trends toward mass-produced uniformity started by the industrial revolution." [34] He illustrates with a practical example. In the future, in each individual case of a car entering an intersection, it will be possible for a computer to decide whether it is safe for the car to proceed or necessary for it to stop.[35] This decision on an individual basis is contrasted with the present situation in which a law applies generally.

For another example, consider recent developments in reading machines for the blind, such as the Visotactor,[36] a portable machine that can translate any printed material in which the symbols are not more than one half inch in height into tactile

---

[34] "Information," *Scientific American,* CCXV (Sept., 1966), p. 65.
[35] *Ibid.,* p. 67.
[36] Patricia McBroom, "Blind Read by Machine," *Science News Letter,* Feb. 12, 1966, p. 99. See also *ibid.,* July 1, 1967, pp. 5-6, 12.

vibrations received through the fingertips. This means that the blind person will not be dependent upon braille, but can read any book, labels on cans and boxes, and so forth. Surely the very development of such a device, made possible through the development of miniature transistors, is to be recognized as a creation of value. Indeed, it is a creation of very personal value, and not at all a move in the direction of depersonalization that we are often led to believe is inevitable with each onward stride of technology.

Bagrit distinguishes between mechanization and automation.[37] Mechanization, such as the assembly line, does necessitate subhuman work. But automation does the opposite, for the worker remains himself but extends his faculties. I am not convinced that the consequences can be this neatly divided, but this emphasis is a helpful corrective against those views which see nothing but threat to man in technological advance.

Thus far we have seen that technologies can enhance as well as diminish personal value. In some cases, the values of technology may not be realized because they are not tried. Such things as pollution of the atmosphere and of our water supply can be attributed to the rapid advance of technology, but in another sense they can be attributed to the inadequate application of technology. Technology may cause such problems, but further application of technology can also solve them.[38] Indeed, the more we can accomplish by our technology, the more we are faced with the ethical dilemma of what we should accomplish. The matter of values and priorities confronts us not simply as an intellectual dilemma, but as a practical matter of decision and policy.

Let us focus on a crucial value that is currently the subject

---

[37] *The Age of Automation,* pp. 38-40.

[38] For a list of some social problems currently posed by technological developments and a list of some problems that are now capable of technological solution, see Lee A. DuBridge, "Educational and Social Consequences," *Automation and Technological Change,* pp. 33-34.

of heated debate. The cry of "Freedom now!" has re-echoed through our land in the second half of the twentieth century. Does this demand make sense? Is freedom a value that can be demanded or even requested? I think that everyone would agree that freedom is something that can be infringed and that it occasionally has to be protected from encroachments. But the cry "freedom now" is not simply a call for the protection of freedom, but a plea for its very creation.

Though the difference in wording may be slight, there is a wide divergence of attitude that hinges upon this issue. Those who feel that freedom needs simply to be protected assume that there are natural and inalienable rights that are enjoyed by all men. From this point of view, it is quite adequate to take a few relatively simple measures from time to time to make sure that this natural state of affairs is not being obstructed. But if freedom is something that has to be created, then men have no rights at all until the rights are brought into being. Talk about freedom and liberty is hollow unless there are strong measures taken to establish them.

Consequently, both sides talk about freedom but have very different attitudes toward what is being done and what has to be done. This is why one side accuses the other of impatience and lack of appreciation for what has already been done; and why, from the other side of the fence, there are accusations of tokenism and insincerity.

Moreover, as we have mentioned earlier, freedom is one of the more slippery words of our language. And when a word is difficult to clarify, it is even more difficult to organize people with a view to achieving its implementation.

An incident recorded in Scripture sheds some light on the dynamics of the situation. Jeremiah 34:8-17 has some interesting parallels to, though some important differences from, our own situation of involvement in war in Vietnam. Jerusalem was at war, but it was not waging war in some distant part of the globe; it was being besieged by the Babylonians. For various reasons, not the least of which was to get more men into the army, Zedekiah proclaimed release for all slaves. Again, a noteworthy parallel, except that in our case the proclamation of emancipation had been issued over a hundred years ago, so that we were able to have in the army, from the very beginning of the Vietnam conflict and not as a later addition when the need for additional troops became acute, those who formerly would have been slaves.

But after the call-up of the slaves in Jerusalem an interesting thing occurred. As we learn a couple of chapters later (37:6-15), the Egyptian army approached and diverted the Babylonians from their siege. And so there is a significant shift that takes place between verses 10 and 11 (ch. 34). The proclamation of liberty is announced, and verse 10 records: "And they obeyed, all the princes and all the people who had entered into the covenant that every one would set free his slave, male or female, so that they would not be enslaved again; they obeyed and set them free." The interesting phrase in this verse is the one which reads: "so that they would not be enslaved again." But verse 11 follows immediately with this report. "But afterward they turned around and took back the male and female slaves they had set free, and brought them into subjection as slaves." The prophet announced that the people did right when they proclaimed the covenant of liberty and that they profaned the name of the Lord when they reversed their action. Because of their disobedience, they are to hear this divine word: "Behold, I proclaim to you liberty to the sword, to pestilence, and to famine says the Lord. I will make you a horror to all the kingdoms of the earth." Because of their faithlessness, the Lord announced the ironic concept of "liberty to the sword, to pestilence, and to famine." Liberty is something that we have to create. The slaves had no natural and inalienable rights. And the freedom created for them by the noblemen was as quickly taken away as it was given, though not without a word of the Lord which says that liberty is not only something we have to create, but it is also precisely the kind of liberty that we make it to be.

Although freedom is a creation of man, with all the imperfection of workmanship which that implies even under the best of circumstances, it is nonetheless a creation of great value. This is illustrated in the attitudes and actions of Paul the Apostle. Paul made it abundantly clear that his primary allegiance was to the kingdom of God and that his citizenship was in heaven and not in earth. Indeed, in our day he sometimes seems exasperatingly otherworldly. But nonetheless, Paul was able to use his Roman citizenship to full advantage when he wanted to. In the instance recorded in Acts 22:25-29, Paul avoided a scourging by invoking the law that a Roman citizen should not be scourged as long as he was uncondemned.

Granted, this law had its weakness. Why, for example, should the proud Romans have proclaimed this as a right for Roman citizens alone, instead of for all people? Moreover, it did not always protect Paul from scourging. Perhaps the turbulence of some situations, or perhaps the understandable cynicism of officials, prevented his claim from being heard; or perhaps Paul did not assert his right in circumstances in which his co-workers could not be protected under the same provisions. But whatever the explanation may be we do know that under certain circumstances Paul made effective use of the rights of Roman citizenship.

From the incident narrated in Jeremiah we noted that freedom has to be created by man. But we must further note that even when freedom is poorly created we can make use of the good that is in it, though perhaps not without consideration for the situation of others who do not enjoy the values of its provisions.

Now, with these insights we can come back to the views that freedom is an inalienable right and that freedom is a creation of man. The individual is given a freedom of choice, and this is the insight of the view that freedom is a natural right. But because it operates within a context, this freedom of choice is not described most accurately as a natural and inalienable right. It is a freedom that can be severely limited by others. And it is little comfort to say that man is free in choosing how he will respond to a situation when he is trapped in a condition that deprives him of opportunity to enjoy the good life. The freedom that all men naturally have for determining their choice must be used in such a way as to create a context of decision which asserts the rights of man. The natural freedom of choice does not entail this freedom. Here there is no freedom until it is created. This explains the paradox that Rousseau noted in *The Social Contract:* "Man is born free—and everywhere he is in irons." But the solution is more complex than Rousseau expected. There is no state of natural freedom, and there is no turning the clock back even if there were.

Let me illustrate by showing how one of the problems in protecting the rights of citizens in a technological society is being inadequately dealt with because of an outmoded concept of the source of freedom. People think that they have always had certain freedoms, and they write laws as if they were designed to prevent the infringement of rights. John McCarthy makes this point with regard to the debate concerning the use of computers to establish a centralized national data bank. This proposed system would have a record for each citizen, containing tax, legal, security, credit, educational, medical, and employment information. Controversy has erupted over whether or not this is an invasion of privacy. A variant form of the problem is raised by time sharing. If certain information is not to be made available to all subscribers, then costly time is consumed while the computer goes through a routine to determine whether a request for information is authorized. Even if there is a willingness to pay this price for the principle involved, there is always the possibility of wire-tapping on lines connecting computers with remote consoles. The problem of invasion of privacy is facing us, whether or not a national data bank is established. McCarthy notes that even the files we have now are open to abuse; for example, security information has been used for political perse-

cutions and credit information for purposes that have nothing
to do with the decision as to whether or not to extend credit.
How then can we expect anything except greater abuse if we
adopt a new, centralized, and more wide-ranging system?

McCarthy's answer is that we have to scrap the fraud that
we have rights and that laws are necessary only to preserve them.
Rather, he insists, we must create the rights. For example, we
may need to specify that access to credit information must be
authorized by the person concerned and must be restricted to
only the type of credit that is under consideration. In other
words, the full file is not necessary for a decision as to whether
a person can be allowed time payments on a television set. The
law must also state such provisions as the right of the individual
to see his own file, as well as to limit the access of others to it.
There must be provision for the individual to challenge entries
in his file if he desires to, and so forth. The important thing is
that these are not existing rights that have to be protected, but
nonexistent rights that have to be created. Nothing less will do in
the face of the rapid developments of technology in the present
age.[39]

Technological developments create moral problems not
only by introducing new institutions, but also by introducing
new complexities into older institutions. An example of this
is the development of moral issues revolving around public
transportation. Roger L. Shinn has a succinct statement of the
issue.

Transportation has rarely been listed as one of the urgent moral issues
of mankind, but in our world it is exactly that. Movement is characteristic
of human life. But the institutions of transportation have often been
regarded as part of the given circumstances of life. Now we are increasingly
aware that those institutions are the results of human decisions involving
major value choices.

A recent study from the Committee for Economic Development points

---

[39] "Information," p. 72.

out that decisions about transportation in growing metropolitan areas "will largely determine . . . the character of the community—how space is used and how people live and work" ("Developing Metropolitan Transportation Policies," p. 14). In such situations transportation becomes an instrument for justice or injustice, a means of opportunity or frustration, a mechanism for confining or releasing those who live in ghettos.[40]

This incisive statement of "the moral meaning of transportation" is representative of the kind of sensitivity that we must develop in a rapidly increasing number of areas of human life.

As science develops its ability to determine the behavior of man and his environment, it simultaneously enlarges the possibilities and magnifies their consequences. Scientists have not been unaware of the ethical dilemmas they have generated, but they have been too inclined to think blithely that scientific knowledge is good, no matter how it is used, and that the ethical dilemmas raised by science are easily resolved by others. However, those whom the scientists expect to cope with the ethical dilemmas have, on their part, been too inclined to lament the growth of science rather than to deal with its growing pains. They have seen the scientific concern with determinism as a restriction of alternatives and as a threat to responsibility, rather than as a creation of possibilities with the resultant increase of the importance of responsible decision. A biologist attributes the gulf between the "two cultures" to this disparity of attitude, rather than to ignorance of and lack of interest in what is going on in the other camp. As a scientist, he laments that philosophy of science rarely inquires beyond the structure of science and its logic, and that history of science is seldom related to the study of social change.[41] It does seem to me that there is more interest of nonscientists in science than vice versa, but even when the importance of science for the study of the arts and

[40] "The Moral Meaning of Transportation," *Christianity and Crisis*, Oct. 3, 1966, p. 209.

[41] Bentley Glass, *Science and Ethical Values* (Chapel Hill: University of North Carolina Press, 1965), pp. ix-x.

humanities is emphasized, it is often given little substance in the ensuing discussion. I do not think that this state of alienation can be attributed primarily to jealousy or pride. The source of the disparity can be seen in terms of the aforementioned utopian and anti-utopian outlooks.

Utopian hopes and anti-utopian sentiments both represent half-truths. We can call these, respectively, the Aladdin and the Frankenstein images. Some combine the two in a Dr. Jekyll and Mr. Hyde image. In combining, we tend to use what each camp affirms and neglect what it attacks. But any combination which does not recognize the truth which validates the ardent concern of each camp about the dangers of the other is doomed to failure. Both camps do have blind spots as well as vital insights. Optimistic utopianism neglects the power of the machine to enslave man, and the complexity of the situation thwarts efforts to avoid such depersonalizing consequences. Pessimistic anti-utopianism neglects the potential of technology for enriching and enhancing life. Creative use of developments in technology in general and cybernetics in particular is neither inevitable nor impossible. Nonetheless, it seems more accurate to call utopianism and anti-utopianism "half-truths" than to brand them as "errors."

The cybernetic revolution has tremendously increased the potential for good or for ill.[42] For example, the stupendous developments in the area of communications make possible both a far greater depth of understanding than was formerly possible and also a far greater degree of manipulation and control. In the light of the extension of man that has been accomplished through cybernetics, the notion of responsibility has taken on a

---

[42] Cf.: "We do not make men automatically good and virtuous by making them rich and powerful; indeed the truth frequently seems to be the opposite. Nevertheless we must not fall into the other trap of equating innocence with ignorance or of thinking that impotence is the same thing as virtue. An increase in power increases the potential both for good and for evil."—Boulding, *The Meaning of the Twentieth Century*, p. 22.

cosmic dimension. We noted at the beginning of this chapter that such a cosmic dimension is present in the historical tradition out of which the doctrine of the image of God comes to us. Human action and the values that are expressed in it are greatly amplified in our world, whether for good or for ill. This means that the complexity of life in our age necessitates an approach to problems in which the solution of them is attempted through all the possible devices of intelligence amplification. Previous methods of responsible attention to many problems have been rendered archaic—indeed, even irresponsible—by the development of cybernetics.

In our world man faces the threat of global destruction, and so man's responsibility has taken on a global dimension. A concept of limited freedom is particularly appropriate for the cybernetic age. Such an understanding of freedom is mentioned in the discussion of Brunner in chapter two and is developed in subsequent chapters as a theory in which freedom and determinism are understood as concomitant. Freedom cannot be understood as an unlimited freedom for the individual. It must rather be seen within the context of a given situation, and responsibility is the concept which expresses the impact that our exercise of freedom within the context of our historical situation has upon other people. Above all, responsibility today is related to the basic Christian notion of reconciliation. There must be communication between persons which enables them to become reconciled to one another. This communication leading to reconciliation and realization of community is of vital importance in the world of today.

In the final chapter we will examine the role of education in equipping us to realize the beneficial and avoid the pernicious possibilities that now demand our response. But first we must look at another source of utopianism. Thus far we have considered only the control of environment, but now we must turn to examine the possibility of the control of heredity.

8 | The Control of Heredity

Much of the intellectual ferment in scientific circles today is concerned with molecular biology. By a study of the processes of genetics, scientists are confident that they can remake man, and some speak of actually creating the kind of person we choose. The more modest claim of remaking man involves initially a system of genetic detection, so that prospective parents may be informed of the probability that their offspring will be afflicted by hereditary disorders, and so that inherited weaknesses can be spotted soon after birth and steps prescribed to prevent the actualization of any potential weaknesses. Eventually, genetic surgery is contemplated, in which undesirable genes will be replaced with desirable genes. This kind of talk has occasioned little reaction from the anti-utopians, for it is, after all, nothing more than an extension of present diagnostic and surgical capabilities.

However, the claim that we can not only remake man but can also create the kind of man we desire has evoked glowing accounts of the coming golden age from utopians and shudders of apprehension from their critics. One form of hereditary control is little more than an extension of earlier programs of eugenics. The new possibility for "scientific pairing" of mates is presented by the establishment of sperm banks. With this possibility, the decision as to a person's desirability as a progenitor can be decided by a committee after his death.

There are some technical difficulties with the sperm bank theories. For example, there are some who doubt that sperm cells can be preserved without deterioration. Glenn W. Salisbury, of the University of Illinois at Urbana, reports that sex cells mutate even when stored at $-320°$ F.[1] Whereas we have commonly thought of the freezing of sperm cells in connection with the process of birth, Salisbury suggests that we might find significant information for developing our understanding of the process of aging. If the attempt to preserve sperm cells eventually produces mutations and defective RNA, then fertilization will not occur, or the embryo will be aborted early in pregnancy in most cases. Such technical difficulties may be overcome through development of the ability to provide a laboratory supply of germ cells from cultures of pieces of the testis of a male donor or of the ovary of a female donor.

The Program of Heredity

Some of the most spectacular achievements in molecular biology revolve around the study of DNA molecules (deoxyribonucleic acid) and the closely related RNA molecules (ribonucleic acid). The problem of how one cell could contain the information and power of control necessary to develop and then in its turn to reproduce its own kind—whether green beans, fruit flies, horses, or humans,—was illuminated by the discovery of DNA and RNA. Research into these molecules is opening up further possibilities for controlling life, and the consequent responsibilities. The principle that life comes only from life has been rejected, although there has as yet been no significant case of artificial creation of a living organism from inorganic materials. But even so there is no unattainable vital substance or force to thwart man's efforts, and it is quite likely that in the not too

---

[1] Barbara J. Culliton, "Sperm Banks Debated," *Science News,* Aug. 26, 1967, pp. 208-9.

distant future man will be able to duplicate the physiochemical process of generating living organisms.

DNA molecules are found in each cell and are located exclusively within the nucleus. They are constructed of two strands of atoms in a helix or spiral form. At regular intervals along each strand there is a projection that is linked by hydrogen bonds to a similar projection on the other strand. These projections are called "nucleotides." The nucleotides are composed of phosphate, deoxyribose (a kind of sugar), and a base for which the nucleotide is named. The four bases are adenine and guanine (both purines) and cytosine and thymine (both pyrimidines). These four bases are known respectively as A, G, C, and T, and these four letters form the entire genetic alphabet.[2] Words of three letters, or triplets, have been related to specific amino acids. This genetic language has startling possibilities. "A single human chromosome (a string of thousands of genes) contains on the order of 100 million nucleotide triplets—which is several times the number of words in a set of the *Encyclopaedia Britannica.*"[3]

DNA molecules are the controlling factor in heredity and morphology. They provide the means by which hereditary information is communicated from one generation to another. Scientists have found that when they extract the DNA molecules from one type of bacteria and put them in another type, the latter are transformed into the type from which the DNA molecules were taken.

---

[2] For a diagram, see Theodosius Dobzhansky, *Mankind Evolving* (New Haven: Yale University Press, 1962), p. 36. On the use of the genetic alphabet to form words and sentences, see *ibid.*, pp. 37-38. The entire second chapter is a brief survey of the historical antecedents and contemporary status of the science of heredity. Dobzhansky's earlier work, *Genetics and the Origin of Species,* is still a classic in the field, but even in the revised editions the information is not as up-to-date.

[3] Ian G. Barbour, *Issues in Science and Religion* (Englewood Cliffs, N.J.: Prentice-Hall, 1966), p. 321; cf. Bruce Wallace and Adrian M. Srb, *Adaptation* (Prentice-Hall, 1961), p. 16.

RNA molecules are composed of a single helical strand and are found primarily in the cytoplasm, although they can also be found in the nucleus. The relationship between DNA and RNA is not yet fully clarified, but DNA seems to provide the "blueprint" or pattern, and RNA is like the engineer or foreman who directs its implementation. RNA can also be thought of as the messenger that communicates the information stored in the DNA molecules in order to guide the cells in the production of amino acids, proteins, and enzymes, so that the organism grows in accord with its genetic heritage. The fertilized egg cells of parents of different species or of different parents of the same species may seem indistinguishable, but if we probe further into the genetic code the differences that will later become so obvious are already there, but simply latent. It is because the elements involved and the principles of operation are so similar that we can gain insights for understanding human heredity from studies of such things as sweet peas or drosophila.

DNA and RNA work together to communicate with and control the chemistry of life. This element of communication and control relates molecular biology to cybernetics. If we understand this process, to what extent can we bring about the genetic structures we desire for man, instead of depending upon random reproduction?

The possibility of affecting human life with this knowledge is suggested by work with rats, who are thought to have the same basic memory system as human beings. In experimentation, brain material has been taken from rats that have been trained to recognize a light or sound signal of food and has been injected into rats that have not been so trained. These rats were able to "remember" the signal on the basis of the injection. It is believed that this is due to the transfer of either DNA or RNA or both.[4]

Molecular biology has inquired into the physical basis of

---

[4] *Science News Letter*, Aug. 21, 1965, p. 114.

life, but at the same time there has been investigation into the physiological basis of mind.[5] The study of brain neurons and connecting nerve fibers has produced some results that may eventually link closely with the studies of DNA and RNA. For example, according to one theory the memory of the individual organism, like its genetic inheritance, may involve a molecular code structure which can achieve tremendous complexity.[6] What if we learn to read the memory code? We have already learned how to stimulate the brain artificially. By the insertion of electrodes through the human skull scientists have produced sensations of sight, sound, or taste, and have even brought about vivid recall of forgotten memories. It has been possible to create moods of happiness, anxiety, or anger by electrical stimulation of the brain. It is presently pure conjecture, but perhaps it will become possible to "plant" human memories.

But even without any assistance from other fields, DNA and RNA research holds promise of tremendous capabilities. Already scientists working with DNA and RNA have discovered means of untwisting the complicated helix, of sorting the elements for analysis, and of synthesizing these building blocks of life.[7] This is an important step in the direction of controlling the heredity of people. Once we can read the genetic code, it will not be long until we can write it.[8] But if we can remake human beings, then we are responsible for deciding what we want to create.

Genetic Control and Utopianism

Is it possible to attain anything resembling the genetic control of society that is pictured in Aldous Huxley's *Brave New World?*

---

[5] For a survey, see Barbour, *Issues in Science and Religion*, pp. 322-24.

[6] For a discussion of genetics as a form of memory and its relation to other forms of memory, see von Neumann, *The Computer and the Brain*, pp. 64-69.

[7] *Science News Letter*, June 19, 1965, p. 391; July 17, 1965, p. 37; July 24, 1965, p. 53; *Science News*, Oct. 21, 1967, p. 394; Dec. 30, 1967, pp. 629-30.

[8] For a discussion of "cracking the genetic code," see Barbour, *Issues in Science and Religion*, pp. 320-21.

In this society infants are created in the laboratory and are nourished so that they will develop into persons who are capable of and satisfied with the particular tasks society has in mind for them. This is a systematic plan not only of eugenics, but also of dysgenics, for unskilled laborers are as carefully prepared and nurtured as are the superior individuals. The only way in which things go wrong is through a mistake in the handling of the chemical materials. In *Brave New World Revisited* Huxley appraises the extent to which his fable of freedom and its enemies has been actualized in the developments of the first quarter of a century after its publication. In the second and by far the most brief chapter, Huxley comments that breeding of humans has been quite unregulated and unsystematic. The result is that we are not only overpopulating, but also lowering the quality. People of inferior genetic quality are kept alive beyond puberty and are allowed to pass on their hereditary defects to their off-spring. Paradoxically, contemporary man is less healthy than his predecessors, but will live longer. The decline in the average level of health is accompanied by a decline in the average level of intelligence. Huxley sees this decline as a threat to the maintenance of individual liberty and democratic government. But in the decade since Huxley's essay, the focus has shifted from the problem of dysgenics to the new possibilities for eugenics. Can we bring in a utopian realm by controlling heredity itself?

There is a definite genetic basis for human society,[9] although this is often overlooked because there is no genetic basis for

---

[9] For example: "Man has become the most successful of all biological species not because he acquired genes for cooking, for hygiene, for prenatal care, or for trade. His success has been due to genes which made him able to develop and to retain any of these and many other cultural traits. . . . Human genes have accomplished what no other genes succeeded in doing. They formed the biological basis for a superorganic culture, which proved to be the most powerful method of adaptation to the environment ever developed by any species." Theodosius Dobzhansky, *The Biological Basis of Human Freedom* (New York: Columbia University Press, 1956), p. 121.

specific cultural traits. But the presence of a genetic basis for society does not answer the question of the extent to which control of the genetic basis can extend to control of the structures of society and to the behavior of individuals within them. Assuming that man can control biological evolution, can man thereby control cultural evolution? Theodosius Dobzhansky answers in the negative.

Cultural history is not biological history, in the sense that, given the genetic constitution which the human species actually has, human history could not have taken a variety of courses different from the course it actually took. The most important agents which propel human history are contained in that history itself, not in the stuff of which human genes are made. Historical events of the past could not be deduced, nor could future ones be predicted with any precision, only from a knowledge of the human genotype, no matter how complete.[10]

Again we see that the recognition of scientific determinism does not, as many people fear, necessarily entail denial of freedom and responsibility. The cause-effect sequence involved is much too complex to permit the rigid enforcement of social conformity by means of tampering with the genetic structure. This is not to say that hereditary control could not be used as a significant contributory factor, but mishandling of chemical elements would not be the only cause of expressions of volition which run counter to those intended by the genetic planners. We also see again that there is a sound basis for the utopian's optimism and also for the anti-utopian's pessimism. There is a power of control that can be used for good or for ill, but there is not such an automatic connection between the intention and the outcome as is presupposed in both of the extreme positions.

Even if we shift from society to attend to the relatively less complex subject of the individual in society, we find much the same situation. There is a genetic foundation, but also a variety

---

[10] *Ibid.*, pp. 118-19.

of possibilities for expression of the genetic constitution. For example:

> The biological fact of heterosexuality is not so much a determining fact of life as a condition upon which different people build radically different life facts. The sexually expressive, the asexual, the apathetic, the hostile—all have built their characteristics upon the biological and cultural substructure of a two-sex order, but they have done it so differently that they are strangers to one another in this important regard, however close may be their affinities on political, recreational, or aesthetic matters.[11]

There is a determination in the sense that we cannot deny the decisive and significant influence of the human genetic constitution, but not in the sense that this factor automatically controls the outcome. Man is able to incorporate the forces and factors within a self-determinism. The nature of the self which is self-determined is briefly, but adequately, described in this statement:

> The self is not merely the passive resultant of inherited constitution plus environmental influences; it builds up an internal unity of its own which enters actively as well as passively into interplay with the surrounding world and other persons. Yet the character-structure being what it is at a given moment, the thoughts, feelings and actions of that moment follow necessarily. This does not imply that the character-structure cannot change, radically and fundamentally; but does imply that such changes are "law-abiding" in the sense that they come about in response to specific conditions.[12]

Determinism and freedom are not essentially opposed, but are rather concomitant. Even so, can genetic determinism be used as an instrument for curtailing human freedom? This is the nub of the question of genetic control in society.

Genetic surgery will be available some day, although we need to remember that it will require not only major breakthroughs in knowledge but also tremendous developments in

---

[11] Cuber and Harroff, *The Significant Americans*, p. 193.
[12] David E. Roberts, *Psychotherapy and a Christian View of Man* (New York: Charles Scribner's Sons, 1951), p. 94.

the skills by which this knowledge is applied. It may be that we cannot restrict ourselves to the cell nucleus, but will have to deal also with the cytoplasm in genetic surgery. Even though the first uses of them will be to remedy physical defects, it seems inevitable that genetic studies will eventually provide occasions for changes in character structure as well as in physical structure.

Some may object that certain things, such as attitudes, are environmental rather than hereditary. This is true insofar as there is no genetic foundation for specific attitudes, but it oversimplifies the relationship between heredity and environment. Some things are primarily influenced by one or the other, but very few things are attributable exclusively to one or the other. Rejecting the dichotomy of heredity and environment, Dobzhansky states: "In principle any trait is modifiable by changes in the genes and by manipulation of the environment." [13]

In some cases of genetic manipulation, the consequent change in character will be accepted as the price to be paid for the sake of other gains, as lobotomy has been accepted in the past. But what about character control for the sake of society? We may welcome genetic manipulation as an addition to our medical capabilities, but is it a means for implementing a plan for the betterment of the entire human race?

Teilhard de Chardin speaks of man as evolution become conscious of itself. Man has become not only a locus but also an agent of evolution. Man has gained sufficient knowledge to enable him to exert a major influence in shaping his future development. With this new sphere for the exercise of human freedom there is a heightened responsibility. This new responsibility of man for shaping his future development is generally recognized, but the Christian contribution grows out of the Christian emphasis that man is fundamentally responsible to

[13] *Mankind Evolving*, p. 42.

God. But we must move from this fundamental recognition of responsibility to its application to the specific issues which confront man today. For example, how does our responsibility to God influence our decisions concerning the practice of genetic surgery?

The Imago Dei and Genetic Manipulation

There are theological resources in our discussion of Brunner in chapter two, both for our acceptance of genetic surgery and also for a question as to the extent to which it may properly be pursued. Brunner welcomed the scientific investigation of chromosomes, which was the high point of genetic studies at the time he was writing. He also warned against the identification of man's present nature with the nature intended for man by God. This distinction between the present situation of physical existence and the divine intention gives clear and ample warrant for the improvement of man through genetic surgery.

However, the qualifying phrase, "for the improvement of man," needs further consideration. When does surgical manipulation of the genetic structure of man go beyond this limit? The question becomes even more acute if we project ourselves into the not so distant future when synthetic DNA and RNA become available for the genetic surgeon. Here the primary theological resource of Brunner's interpretation of the *imago dei* as responsibility seems to me to be his emphasis upon the uniqueness of each individual and of each relation. The implication of this emphasis for all genetic manipulation is that we must preserve, fulfill, and enhance individual differences. Conversely, we must withstand the cultivation of uniformity and similarity, however desirable the universal reproduction of a certain characteristic might seem to be. To encroach upon the freedom of each individual to be his own unique self is to flaunt the conviction that each man is created in the *imago dei*. The imminent possibilities for the manipulation of human nature present fully as awesome a threat to man as did the development of the atomic bomb in Brunner's day—for each in its own way could destroy man. It is this destructive potential, which goes along with the creative, that gives point to Theodosius Dobzhansky's questions: "Are we to have, in place of Plato's philosopher-king, a geneticist-king? And who will be the president of the National Sperm Bank and of the National DNA Bank? What checks and balances are to be imposed on the genetic legislative and the genetic executive powers? Who will guard the guardians?" [14]

It is important to note that when we speak of applying genetic control we raise an order of problems that genetic studies alone cannot answer. In our ever-increasing *ability* to make human life what we want it to be, we are increasing the importance of our *decision* as to what man ought to be. For example, it is one thing to apply our scientific knowledge to dairy stock, for all are agreed that our goal is maximum milk production per unit cost. But what is the goal for man? How are we to use our knowledge of DNA and RNA to change man? Here there is no universally accepted goal.[15] Should we make all men more intelligent, or only a few, with the rest programmed to be their followers? When we cultivate intelligence, how should we dis-

---

[14] "Changing Man," *Science*, Jan. 27, 1967, p. 413.

[15] "Beside the genetic problem of detecting the bearers of detrimental genes and ethical problem of what to do then, we must place the weighty problem of selecting the goals of any program of positive selection upon which we may embark. Clearly, this is no matter for science alone—we are concerned with social values, and which of these is preeminent? In a former essay on this subject I suggested as goals 'freedom from gross physical or mental defects, sound health, high intelligence, general adaptability, integrity of character, and nobility of spirit.' H. J. Muller selects a somewhat different list: 'Genuine warmth of fellow feeling and a cooperative disposition, a depth and breadth of intellectual capacity, moral courage and integrity, an appreciation of nature and of art, and an aptness of expression and of communication'; and on the physical side, 'to better the genetic foundations of health, vigor, and longevity; to reduce the need for sleep; to bring the induction of sedation and stimulation under more effective voluntary control; and to develop increasing physical tolerances and aptitudes in general.' Now we cannot select for these without having ways and means of defining them precisely and measuring them at least in a roughly quantitative way. Obviously, the psychologist and sociologist will need to do a great deal of preliminary work before genetic analysis and understanding of these traits become possible."—Glass, *Science and Ethical Values*, pp. 59-60.

tribute the various types? Should we cultivate or weed out artistic and aesthetic interests? Should we make man more submissive to social control or more individualistic? These are typical of many such questions that would reveal sharply divergent ends, even if we could determine the means to them.

A Philosophy of Birth and Heredity

Obviously, these are not new questions. But we make a mistake if we think that genetic research simply provides a new set of data for the consideration of hoary questions. We face a situation in which we are not merely confronted with the incorporation of new data into our philosophical perspective, but are also faced with the demand for developing a new dimension to the philosophical background with which we approach questions concerning the chief ends of human life. We need a philosophy of birth and heredity. Little enough has been done to work out a philosophy of death, although we do have significant discussions of this theme as early as Plato and the Stoics. Major contemporary treatments of this theme are found in Heidegger and others influenced by existentialism. Plato does deal with birth in his theory of the pre-existence of the soul and its passage at birth through the river of forgetfulness, so we can claim an early discussion of this theme. We can also point to a modern treatment in the work of Otto Rank, one of the more philosophical of the early Freudians, who developed the theory of the birth trauma. But even when we have said all this, it still remains that the beginning of life has not received attention comparable to that devoted to the end of life.

Paul Ricoeur, who has given some systematic consideration to life as birth[16] (as well as life as structure and life as growth), suggests that birth has not received much attention because it is accomplished and does not lie menacingly in the future. But

---

[16] *Freedom and Nature: The Voluntary and the Involuntary,* pp. 433-43.

Ricoeur notes that "it is precisely because it (birth) is accomplished that it holds the germ of the full growth of necessity which casts a shadow on my freedom." [17] Ricoeur's way of grappling with this issue is most relevant to our discussion of genetics in the context of an examination of the nature of man in the light of cybernetics.

In reflection upon the concept of birth, Ricoeur analyzes three basic ideas. First, birth expresses that my life had a beginning in time. Because this crucial event leaves no memory in my own consciousness I feel compelled to consider it objectively as a spectator rather than as a participant. Second, birth expresses the dependence of my life on two other lives. I do not will my own existence, but depend on others. "What is worse, they did not exactly will it, since I know very well that a responsibility was undertaken which is never measured because it functions in the region of possibilities impossible to calculate—a monstrous collusion of chance, instinct, and another's freedom cast me up on this shore." [18] My sense of filiation or dependence on others is experienced as something that is increasingly being abolished each moment from the severing of the umbilical cord onward. Again, I seem to be forced to think in terms of detachment, rather than in terms of participation. Third, birth expresses my inheritance of a nature. Both my physical makeup and my personality have developed on the basis of that which I have been given by another. Here, again, the mood of objectivity seems to be the only way in which I can reflect upon my birth.

Ricoeur then examines what happens in an objectification of birth, such as in the approach of genetic science. From the objective point of view, the notion of a beginning disappears. The moment of birth is simply a transition from intrauterine to

---

[17] *Ibid.*, p. 433.

[18] *Ibid.*, p. 434. Cf. Pascal in his "Discourses on the Conditions of the Great": "Your birth depends on a marriage, or rather on the marriages of all those from whom you descend. But upon what do these marriages depend? A visit made by chance, an idle word, a thousand unforeseen occasions."

external existence. Nor does the biologist consider the fertilization of the egg cell to be a beginning of individual existence.
Rather, this is understood as an event in the self-perpetuation of
the species, and the species becomes absorbed within the sequence of evolutionary development. The sense of a beginning
of our life seemed to drive us to an objective point of view
which paradoxically dissolved any significance or sharpness to
the concept of an individual beginning.

The second element of birth, the notion of filiation, is clarified by biology only by means of a reversal of perspective. I was
driven by my own sense of contingency to look to my ancestors.
But biological science proceeds not from descendents to ancestors, but just the reverse. From the perspective of biology,
"I explain my filiation not as *my* ancestry, but as my ancestor's
posterity." [19] Ricoeur points out that this seemingly innocent
change of perspective actually contains a decisive element of
alienation. "I leave myself in order to place myself in a being
outside my control, my ancestor, and follow out a chain of
effects down to myself." [20] And yet this introduces the element
of chance. I happen to be the product of two people because a
particular sperm reached a particular ovum. But that sperm and
that ovum represent a chromosomic reduction, and what if the
egg had been of a different makeup or what if it had been
reached by a different sperm? [21] The attempt to provide an
objective explanation of my dependence on others has paradoxically made me appear to be an effect of chance and has alienated
me from myself.

The third element in the analysis of birth, my inheritance
not only of existence but of a particular nature, also leads to
alienation when an objective stance is adopted. The attempt to
understand our heredity leads us to the scientific examination of

[19] *Ibid.*, p. 435.   [20] *Ibid.*
[21] For a similar expression of the element of chance in heredity, from a
geneticist, see Dobzhansky, *Mankind Evolving*, pp. 27-28. For a difference in
emphasis, however, see *ibid.*, pp. 29-32 on the genetic basis of individuality.

our genetic structure. But once we speak in such terms, all else becomes subordinated, and the individual is thought of as only the bearer of the seed by means of which it serves the species. The attempt to explain objectively my own particular nature has paradoxically rendered my own particular nature an insignificant and ephemeral expression of the species.

Ricoeur fully recognizes both the self-sufficiency of explanation on the level of genetics, once we have chosen to operate on that level, and also the necessity of receiving guidance from this level of explanation for any effort of man to achieve self-understanding. Indeed, its elimination of subjectivity enables us to clarify aspects of birth that would otherwise remain vague and obscure. Nonetheless, Ricoeur insists: "I must at the same time break through the nascent dogmatism which follows from genetics and convert genetics philosophically into an index of my birth." [22] But if we have no experience of our birth, how can we possibly supplement an objective consideration of it? Ricoeur's description of his approach in the light of this objection deserves development in his own words.

But if the idea of heredity is to have a subjective meaning, the ultimate level of necessity must be characterized for the consciousness which is subject to it as a limit level, as a point of necessity which we always approach and never reach. Thus here is the theme which we shall attempt to elucidate at least faintly: my birth in the first person is not an experience but the necessary presupposition of all experience. This necessity of being born in order to exist remains a horizon of consciousness but it is demanded as a horizon by consciousness itself. The Cogito implies the anteriority of its beginning apart from its own perception. How shall we engender this sense of beginning as limit in the womb of consciousness, failing a memory of my birth? There is no other means than to follow the objective scientific knowledge which constitutes our knowledge of birth, and to attempt to apply it to ourselves, to interiorize it in some way. This effort at the limits of possibility of objective knowledge is in a sense an obstacle to knowledge, but as that knowledge vanishes, something will be suggested as necessity in the first person of *my* beginning.[23]

---

[22] Ricoeur, *Freedom and Nature*, p. 437.   [23] *Ibid.*

It is important to note that Ricoeur reverses the direction pursued by genetic science. What the objective approach sought to explain in terms of the other, Ricoeur seeks to understand in himself. Instead of absorbing the beginning of an individual life as an aspect of heredity, Ricoeur incorporates heredity as only one aspect of *my* beginning. In this light he reexamines the meaning of heredity, the ancestor, and the beginning of my life.

Heredity, genetically thought of as something given to me by others, can now be recognized as my own character, unconsciously received from another. Ricoeur gives an interesting statement of the translation involved.

The geneticist in me says that existence is capital received from the other and that this capital is a collection of genetic properties inscribed in a chromosomic structure; thus this capital is a diversity which, while possessing some functional unity, remains fundamentally multiple. The philosopher in me translates this: this multiple capital is the indivisible unity of my life, of my sheer existence; this capital received from the other is not the burden of an external nature, it is my self given to myself.[24]

Even with such a translation, the ancestor can exert tremendous force over the individual. Conceived biologically, filiation renders me an effect of my ancestor, the necessary outcome of a cause-effect sequence. Now we must subjectivize this relationship and understand the necessity not objectively, but in ourselves. But how can we make the transition from thinking of the ancestor who is the cause of myself to thinking of myself as the one who has come from my ancestors? Ricoeur draws upon the concept of embodiment to help us at this point. Indeed, he says: "Being born of definite parents and being united to this definite body is one and the same mystery: these beings are my parents as my body is my body." [25] To begin living is to participate in a lineage. Thus, the genetic inheritance and the ancestral bond which were objectivized in genetics have been interpreted as two

---

[24] *Ibid.*, p. 438.   [25] *Ibid.*, p. 439.

aspects of *my* beginning in Ricoeur's philosophy of birth. But how can Ricoeur establish "my beginning" as the center of his philosophy of birth, since it is unavailable to memory or to consciousness? Ricoeur claims that the very flight from his birth illuminates the nature of man. "I experience life as having begun *before* I began anything whatever." [26] It might be helpful at this point to call attention to the analogous unavailability of death to human consciousness, which Ricoeur commented upon when initiating his discussion. "I am always *after* my birth—in a sense analogous to that of being always *before* my death." [27] I cannot grasp in my consciousness the beginning of my life nor its ending. My consciousness is restricted to the interval between these events (indeed, not even all this interval is available to my recall). But this consciousness is the basis for the subjective method of reflecting on "my beginning," which it presupposes. My free decision to begin anything whatever occurs in a time which is after my beginning and before my ending. The beginning of freedom is always imminent. But the beginning of my existence is not an act, but a state, and it necessarily precedes any process of acting freely.

The basic thrust of Ricoeur's philosophy of heredity is away from the distortions that are supposedly avoided by an objective approach and toward a subjective appropriation of the human condition of born-ness. I am of the opinion that any adequate philosophy of heredity must include some subjective element. However, we must be cautious in developing such an approach, lest we succumb to the anthropocentrism that has characterized idealist philosophy in the nineteenth century and existentialism and existential phenomenology in the twentieth century. The reaction of these schools of thought to the opposite excesses of scientific materialism is certainly understandable. But the fact that cyberneticists have tended to succumb to a reductionist behaviorism in their incorporation of living organisms and

---

[26] *Ibid.,* p. 441.   [27] *Ibid.,* p. 433.

machines without distinction into one theoretical system does not justify an overly sharp separation. In the particular case of heredity, for example, the elements and the processes are extremely similar, not only for man and animal but also for plants as well. I certainly would not want to advocate that any philosophy of heredity must purge itself of all that is peculiarly human, for it is man alone who seeks to develop a philosophy of heredity. But the uniqueness of man is dulled, rather than enhanced, by a consideration which neglects man's relation to the rest of creation. That which man, in his philosophizing, has tended to separate is united in man the philosopher. The animate and the inanimate, the organic and the inorganic, the ideal and the material, the self and the world, the subjective and objective, determinism and freedom, and all such things that tend to be opposed to one another in philosophies are united in man. Indeed, the Teilhardians and Whiteheadians, among others, claim that this is true in rudimentary fashion for all of creation, although this claim is hard to refute or to substantiate. Tillich, in a most apt phrase, speaks of "the multidimensional unity of life." This phrase not only points out the basic and organic unity of that which becomes divided in schools of thought and also the distortion involved in any reductionism, but also points out that the dimensions of life are many and are oversimplified even by talking about a combination of the organic and inorganic.[28]

Man is not simply a combination of mechanical elements, let alone a combination of mechanism and vitalism. Hence, it is important to follow Ricoeur's emphasis (in which he is far from alone) on the unity of man which transcends the various components. Put from another perspective, any dealing with components is an abstraction. This is in conflict with the scientific tendency to hold that science is dealing with reality and that

[28] Tillich, *Systematic Theology* (Chicago: University of Chicago Press, 1963), III, 11-30.

anything that transcends the dimension of the mechanical-material is at best abstraction and at worst superstition.

As we noted in chapter two, Brunner does not merely object to the claim of science to have the *sole* truth about man, but he further insists that science does not have the *first* truth about man. The first truth about man, for Brunner, is that he is responsible to God. This order is important for Brunner. We must first see man in relation to God, and then we can understand his reason and his physical body as avenues through which man expresses his responsibility.[29]

Dealing with components is not merely permissible, however, but is of positive value. Partial investigations ought neither to be neglected in appraising man as a totality, nor to masquerade as the totality of man. The physical, chemical, and biological components are influential on each response of the person. They can be studied separately from the total person, but they should then be recognized as abstractions from the totality of man.

But neither should the person be thought of in abstraction from the component parts, as if some strange fate attached him to this mechanistically determined housing but without vital interrelation to it. In other words, we are not dealing with a Cartesian dualism of a free mind attached to a mechanically determined body. Rather, we are dealing with a total person, who incorporates mechanical determinism and freedom-responsibility in a context of values, meanings loyalties, affections, memories, and so forth. Consequently, the individual is an abstraction from the relationships that make up his life as a social

---

[29] For a similar statement, but without the theological emphasis on man's relation to God, cf.: "For no matter how interesting or theoretically true is the fact that I am composed of such and such chemicals or act by such and such mechanisms or patterns, the crucial question always is that I happen to exist at this given moment in time and space, and my problem is how I am to be aware of that fact and what I shall do about it."—Rollo May, "The Origins and Significance of the Existential Movement in Psychology," *Existence*, ed. Rollo May, Ernest Angel, and Henri F. Ellenberger (New York: Basic Books, 1958), p. 12.

being.[30] Man's freedom can be influenced by the mechanisms of life because man is not a dichotomy but a unity; but the free person cannot be exhaustively described in mechanistic terms because this would be a reductionism rather than a recognition of the unity of man.

Part Two of this book explored several of the impasses that need to be overcome, taking the issue of freedom and determinism as the key. When we overcome the mind-set that conceives of these as contrary if not actually contradictory concepts, then we can gain a new understanding of man and machine and their relation in the building of a new social order. By seeing freedom and determinism as concomitants, we can recognize the potential contribution of cybernetics without becoming calloused, and we can recognize the potential dangers without becoming paralyzed.

---

[30] See my discussion of the concept of "betweenness" (*Zwischenmenschliche*) in *Encountering Truth*, pp. 30-40, esp. pp. 30-31.

9 | The Challenge to Education

The cybernetic revolution is not only guided by, but is furthermore closely related to the process of education, and there are some valuable insights to be gained from an examination of its impact upon this specific area. There are at least two major reasons for the close relation of cybernetics and education. In the first place, an age that magnifies not merely the muscle power of man but also his brain power has reduced the margin for error. In the second place, the concern of cybernetics for communication and control closely parallels the interests of education.

The cybernetic revolution has increased the importance of education and has thus provided an apologetic for education. Much effort has been expended to persuade school dropouts to resume their education and to prevent potential dropouts from becoming actual dropouts. Already, human beings spend a much larger portion of their lifetime in education than do any of the other living beings, and the cybernetic revolution is placing an even higher premium upon education. The amount of time spent in education is being extended at both ends. Continuing education, postgraduate, and preschool programs are multiplying. Such devices as television have widened the range of experiences for children to a remarkable degree, so that learning is greatly accelerated. In such circumstances an expanded program of education is both inevitable and desirable.

Sometimes, however, the apology for education becomes a little misleading. We do need to develop people to their full capacity, both for their own sakes and for the needs of society. But on the other hand, we are not developing a society in which only those with tremendous ability and training can survive.[1] We will need geniuses to guide the use of present developments and to initiate new developments in the age of cybernetics. But as devices become common, they will be taken in stride by everyone. For example, the telephone system is quite complicated, but the use of it is simple. Television is another complicated development that is now taken for granted. Radio repairmen did have to learn to repair the more complicated television sets, but a general increase in electronic knowledge was not called for. The majority of people had merely to learn how to turn the set off and on and to make a few adjustments. Sometimes less skill is required. As McLuhan observes, more mechanical knowledge was demanded to operate a model T than a car of today. So the cybernetic revolution will not continue to seem as imposing after we become accustomed to it, but it will nonetheless bring about a significant increase in education. This expanding market also plays a part in the second facet, to which we now turn.

Computerized Teaching and the Role of the Teacher

The concern of cybernetics for communication and control has enabled it to supply devices that are useful to teachers. This is reflected economically in the mergers, now numbering over one hundred, of electronic and publishing companies, such as R.C.A. and Random House.[2] The existence of a network of television transmitters and the presence of a television set in almost every

---

[1] Cf. Walter Buckingham, *Automation* (New York: Harper & Row, 1961), pp. 96-100; Herbert A. Simon, *The Shape of Automation* (Harper & Row, 1965), pp. 48-49.

[2] Carl Behrens, "Publishing Goes Electronic," *Science News*, July 8, 1967, pp. 44-45.

home provides a foundation for the development of home printers to receive verbal, pictorial, and diagrammatic material. However, the more immediate concern behind the merging of electronic firms and textbook publishers is the development of computerized teaching. The manufacturers of computers are interested in securing the services of those who are experienced in the preparation of textbooks. Present systems of computerized teaching are rather pedestrian. They are useful for repetitive drills, especially for the average student, but are rather expensive if this is the limit of their capacity. Hence there is a concern to develop input that allows for complexity and adaptability in computerized teaching programs.

Three levels of computerized teaching have been analyzed.[3] On the level of drill and practice, the computer has a strictly supplementary role. On the tutorial level, the computer assumes primary responsibility for teaching. This kind of program is available for well structured subjects, such as reading and mathematics. It is able to accept a constructed rather than a multiple-choice response. For example, it may accept any valid proof of a math theorem. The third level is still in the exploratory and prototype stage. This level is dialogical—the computer interacts with the learner and responds to his contributions. This presents a number of technical and theoretical problems. For example, a serious technical problem is presented by the undeveloped speech patterns of children in the lower grades. It is difficult enough to enable a computer to recognize relatively clear and precise patterns of speech, but this is not adequate for the primary grades. An example of a theoretical problem is the possibility of unanticipated responses. Can a computer be equipped to take advantage of unusual, but potentially creative, exchanges?

The fixed teaching program of most computers now in use

---

[3] Patrick Suppes, "The Uses of Computers in Education," *Scientific American*, CCXV (Sept., 1966), pp. 207-20.

is based on averages and thus has a static or stationary character, whereas the individual learner is, by virtue of his learning, non-stationary. The need for development of new approaches is seen when we consider that the programming is based on a sequence, and usually an invariant sequence, of stationary states.[4] One of the major drawbacks of computerized teaching now is that the student's role is entirely passive. Even if the machine is able to remember the student's earlier performance and guide the instruction accordingly, it is completely insensitive to the student's present state of mind.[5] However, although they do not yet allow variation from the programmed sequence, compu-terized teaching programs do allow the individual to advance at his own pace, and this is an advantage for both the slow and the fast learner.

Until the automatic teaching devices become more sophisti-cated it is more accurate to speak of computerized drilling, rather than computerized teaching. More sophisticated devices will need to take into account the rapidity as well as the correct-ness of the student's response and will probably have to de-emphasize the right-or-wrong approach. The hardware for com-puterized teaching is already available, and, as we have seeen, there is now a concern for the development of software that can handle advanced and complex assignments. With the expanding market as a strong incentive, we can expect significant accom-plishments in the development of computerized teaching. On the theoretical level, this concern has shifted attention away from methods of teaching and has focused it rather on theories of learning. Theories of learning include such issues as the most effective methods of psychological reinforcement (e.g., should the student be informed immediately upon making a mistake, or later), the effect of differences in personality types on learning, and the question of whether there are different patterns of learn-

---

[4] Pask, *An Approach to Cybernetics*, p. 89.
[5] McCarthy, "Information," p. 72; cf. p. 67.

ing (e.g., the impulsive vs. the reflective type of learner). But learning theory is not yet well articulated, and we must still consider computerized teaching from the perspective of the aims of the teacher.

There are variations in the understanding of the role of the teacher within different philosophies of education, and corresponding variations in the attitude toward computerized teaching. Three common philosophies of education are realism, idealism, and pragmatism (progressive education). Realism sees the teacher as an imparter of knowledge. This is a role that can be filled adequately by a computerized teacher, and the realist would be likely to have the least qualms about accepting computerized teaching. Idealism sees the teacher as an example. The teacher's role is to be the ideal of an educated person, which the students will want to emulate. In this view computerized teaching would certainly be incomplete. However, the computer could perform certain tasks that would free the teacher for the more creative and significant aspects of teaching. The pragmatist (progressive educationist) views the teacher as a supervisor and resource person. Both teacher and computer provide resources for learning. But the computer would provide resources in the form of information, while the pragmatist places more importance on social adaptation. The pragmatist's attitude toward computerized teaching would be influenced by his strong emphasis on the value of social grouping, which the teacher catalyzes and which is not realized by a student facing a computer rather than a peer group.

But what about existentialism? This philosophy has been considered antiscientific and anti-technological, and we have earlier considered ways of modifying its more radical expressions of this attitude. What attitude toward computerized teaching would be possible from the existentialist perspective? Existentialism is not as pervasive an influence on education as the above mentioned views, but it does make a very significant contribution.[6] The existentialist teacher seeks primarily neither to impart knowledge (a la realism), nor to present himself as a model to be imitated (a la idealism), nor yet to serve as a resource person guiding the student through a social process of learning (a la pragmatism). Rather, he sees his role as a teacher to be that of a participant in the individual quest for truth of each of his students. He seeks to establish an intensely personal (I-Thou) relation with each of his students, in order that each may search freely for truth. And they are to be motivated to learn, not because the teacher is a mine of information, nor because the teacher's personality is inspiring and overwhelming, nor because they want to be smoothly functioning members of the group project. Rather, the existentialist teacher will handle subject matter in such a way that the student will openly and freely examine the resources of learning and the vital options in order to come to his own free decision. This is an educational application of Brunner's theological emphasis upon establishing a rhythm of individual self-discovery and communal relation.

Now, how does computerized teaching accord with such goals? Insofar as it tended to mass-produce students by giving them all the same information and the same categories for organizing it, the existentialist would be horrified. In Brunner's terms, both that which is common to all men and that which is unique to individuals come from God, and both must be accorded the same dignity. Nonetheless, computerized teaching needs to be supplemented according to other philosophies of education, and not solely according to existentialism. Moreover, the computer itself is able to meet some of the existentialist ideals that would be impossible of attainment for the human teacher. The individual teacher has neither the time nor the patience to deal at length with each individual student. But the computer can proceed at the pace, and perhaps eventually in the style, of

---

[6] See George F. Kneller, *Existentialism and Education* (New York: Philosophical Library, 1958). On the role of the teacher, see esp. pp. 114-22.

the individual student. The student can stay at each stage until he has come to his own convictions concerning what is being taught to him. In group teaching, with a human teacher, it is impossible to proceed at the exact pace needed by each individual student. This means that the teacher must move the *group* along through the subject matter. Yet it is the emphasis upon the individual rather than upon the social group that is one of the major differences, if not the most significant difference, between the existentialist and pragmatist philosophies of education. Here the computer can serve the aims of the teacher as interpreted from the existentialist perspective. But another word must be said. The existentialist also emphasizes the need for inclusion of teaching content that is not easily handled by a computer—what is the meaning of life, the appropriate attitude toward death, what value (s) is worth dying for, how is creative nonconformity to be encouraged.

There is no graduation from these issues. Such an education is a process which continues through life. There is an increasing need for cultivating an *attitude* of learning, so that it continues after graduation because it has become part of a person. We are all too often bedeviled by the attitude that the teacher is making the students jump over hurdles. This attitude creates a vicious circle because the obvious alternatives are stepping up the pace, which confirms the suspicion and hardens the resistance, or relaxing the pace, which weakens the students' grasp of fundamentals so that they have little to build on later if their attitudes should change. Either way there is a serious loss both to the individual and to society.

The Education of Man in the Age of Cybernetics

An expanding society requires an expanding "knowledge industry." [7] The individual must gain new knowledge to keep up

---

[7] Kenneth E. Boulding, *The Meaning of the Twentieth Century* chap. 2.

with change and to replace the knowledge he has forgotten. Society must replace the knowledge that is lost to it with the death of each individual. If the society is not to regress or remain stationary it must take the necessary steps to see that it gains more knowledge than it loses. Much knowledge, of course, is gained informally, but society must give an increasingly greater amount of time and money to the process of formal education.

In the cybernetic age more is needed than an increase in the quantity of education. The rapid changes that are occurring at an ever-increasing rate necessitate the cultivation of the ability to think creatively and to adapt to the new and unexpected. Increasingly man finds himself in unstructured situations.[8] The factual information that we learn in school becomes outdated at an increasingly accelerated pace. Consequently, the value of education will more and more come to depend on the development of the ability to reason and the capacity to assimilate new facts and to adjust continually one's perspective. Old answers will not be adequate to the new society. There has always been a need for continuing education, but it is becoming increasingly important.

Robert Theobald considers that the most pressing need in education is to change from a discipline-oriented to a problem-oriented educational process. But he cautions that "we must do this in such a way as to avoid the 'new education' emphasis on means, the smoothly interacting group or seminar, and concentrate on ends, the kind of problems that will be studied." [9] He goes on to recommend a "two-dimensional seminar technique," in which a person can choose to pursue one problem area through an increasingly complex level of seminars, or to move horizontally so that he extends his knowledge by dealing with seminars on a variety of problems.

---

[8] Cf. Dietrich von Oppen, "Der Mensch in der offenen Situation," *Zeitschrift für Theologie und Kirche*, LIX, Heft 3 (1962), 315-45.

[9] "Cybernetics and the Problems of Social Reorganization," *The Social Impact of Cybernetics*, p. 64.

Marshall McLuhan suggests that the immense flow of data in the electronic age has rendered our educational processes outdated. Traditional educational procedures keep the flow of data minimal and also fragmented; that is, the subjects are unrelated.[10] Although most school systems still fall into the traditional mold, educators must be given credit for taking this kind of complaint seriously, even though much of the impetus has come from the impact of progressive education rather than of the cybernetic revolution. There have been experiments with several methods. Subjects such as history and literature have been correlated. Sometimes they are taught by one teacher, and sometimes by a team. Study has also been focused upon a particular era with inquiry into all the facets of its cultural expression. Some subjects, such as history and geography, have been fused—not merely correlated but actually merged into one subject. Another method is the development of broad field courses, such as general science or fine arts. McLuhan also contends that our education is planned on the pre-feedback age. Education provides data as products for students to consume, and allows them little role in the creative process of education.[11] Again, progressive education provided a head start for dealing with such complaints, and forms of team-teaching that generate a dialogue also help to break through a rigid structuring of courses.

The relation of education to the worlds of business and economics has been a hotly debated issue, and the cybernetic revolution fires it up even more. Those emphasizing vocational and professional preparation point to the need for specialization. Those emphasizing liberal arts counter that a highly specialized world is also a rapidly changing one, so that a broad education is the best preparation for participation in it. With increasing specialization the various sciences and their subdivisions have been increasingly closed to outsiders, even to close neighbors.

---

[10] "Cybernation and Culture," *The Social Impact of Cybernetics*, p. 105.
[11] *Ibid.*, pp. 105-6.

But the cybernetic emphasis on the system rather than on the components is calling us to a reappraisal of the unity of the sciences, in terms of the regulatory process involved.

Hyman G. Rickover contends that democracy can no longer survive with a concentration on education to prepare us to meet job requirements. The issues are now so complex that education is essential if citizens are to attain sound opinions on public issues in order to vote intelligently. He comments:

> Paradoxically, liberal education, which at one time we tended to regard as "aristocratic," is the very kind of education we now need most to preserve our "democratic" way of life. Since it seeks to develop all the potentialities of the individual, not merely those he needs to earn a living, liberal or humanistic education shapes or forms him into a more capable, a more observant, a more discriminating human being. This he needs to be if he is to cope with the huge public and private power conglomerates that now dominate our society and interpose themselves between the American people and the men elected to public office, making it increasingly difficult for the popular will to assert itself whenever it goes counter to the interests of large organizations.[12]

He notes that this need is especially significant in situations where there is a misuse of technology by powerful organizations. Only the government can then provide protection for the public, and yet the self-interest of organizations can easily be exerted to block efforts designed to prevent or curtail harmful practices. Marshall McLuhan has perhaps a more job-oriented approach to the need for liberal education, but he still comes out with an emphasis on the liberal arts. He refers to the need of businessmen to anticipate new environments and their hiring of people to predict the situation ten years ahead. But, says McLuhan, the persons most sensitive to environments are artists.

If, in fact, the businessman had perceptions trained to read the language of the arts, he would be able to foresee not 10, but 50 years ahead in all

---

[12] "A Humanistic Technology," *The Social Impact of Cybernetics*, pp. 126-27.

fields of education, government, and merchandising. It is one of the ironies of the electronic age that the businessman must become alert and highly trained in the world of the arts.[13]

The very complexity of national and international politics, plus the increasing vocational specialization of our political leaders, poses a threat to democracy which education must prepare us to handle. The scientific, industrial, and cybernetic revolutions have slowly whittled away an unnecessary assumption that many Americans had about democracy—namely, that ordinary voters can make technical decisions. It is not necessary to democratic process at all that the general electorate have a say-so in every decision, and when they do democracy is likely to strangle itself with ineptness. It is necessary to democracy only that those who are qualified and assigned to these specialized roles be responsible to the people and subject to the people's approval or disapproval. But this "only" is a very big "only" and must be guarded jealously. The danger is that we the electorate will be so overwhelmed with the information and training necessary for making such decisions that we will disavow any responsibility for passing judgment on the way we are being governed. During the various stages of escalation of the Vietnam war, I heard intellectual colleagues argue seriously not only pro and con but also non—that is, that no nongovernment official could possibly know whether United States policy was justified or not, and that all we could do was trust our leaders. There is, of course, some truth in this, but such a categorical surrender of responsibility threatens the essence of democracy, since it has no built-in theoretical limitation of scope. As the role of computers in policy decisions becomes more prominent and more a matter of common knowledge, the temptation to opt out of the decision-making process will become stronger. How can you argue with the computer when you are not only ignorant of the facts it is

---

[13] "Cybernation and Culture," *ibid.*, p. 101.

taking into consideration, but do not even know how it was programmed to handle them? And yet it is most demoralizing for men to feel that they have no part in that which vitally concerns them. This concern takes on heightened gravity in the light of our discussion in chapter two of Brunner's interpretation of responsibility as a relationship of community or love between men, and our mention in chapter seven of Ricoeur's plea for the interpretation of the image in social and cosmic, as well as in individual terms. Although I recognize the force of the pressures to opt out, I recognize also that a decision not to decide is, in the terms of the doctrine of the image of God, a response that is not responsible.

Perhaps, as Jacques Barzun claims, although specialists may be competent in their specialty they suffer from a misunderstanding of specialization itself. Specialization is seen as a barrier between one man and the next, because we wrongly equate understanding with professional skill. "The universal formula is: 'You cannot understand or appreciate my art (science) (trade) unless you yourself practice it.' " [14] Barzun objects that it is a fallacy to make no distinction between knowing a subject and knowing its craft. In most fields the nonspecialist can understand the accepted truths, the disputed problems, the rival schools, and the methods currently in favor, and Barzun sees this kind of appreciation and exchange essential to the preservation (or the rebuilding) of our "House of Intellect." He indicts the schools for propagating this error, and so we come again to the inadequacy of job-oriented education, at least in this atmosphere of fragmentation. To apply this situation specifically to the political challenges of the cybernetic age, we must charge the schools with the task of educating us to understand fundamental political issues and to demand that those

---

[14] Jacques Barzun, *The House of Intellect* (New York: Harper & Row, 1961), p. 11.

specialists who act in our names keep us apprised of their rationale.

Cybernetics does not take politics out of our hands unless we default. "Since social action normally involves a feedback loop, the socially controlled in some sense also control the controller." [15] From this perspective it is possible to see cybernetically controlled politics as potentially able to broaden the base of democracy as well as potentially able to destroy it. The organization of political campaigns is no longer the responsibility of the old-style political "machine" operated by political bosses and ward heelers, but it is now becoming the highly statistical professional business of social scientists and computers. This is the theme of *The 480,* a novel by Eugene Burdick (co-author of *Fail-safe,* another novel dealing with a cybernetic device). "Voter profile analysis" and "managed campaigns" are just two of the many new phrases that have come into our language through computerized politics. There are now several large corporations whose business it is to win elections for any candidates who will employ their services. Dedicated to no political view themselves, these corporations have done equally well for candidates whose views are diametrically opposed. The cybernetic age is ushering in tremendous power for both analyzing and manipulating the voter. If this power is wielded unethically on a lethargic and unsuspecting electorate, democracy will be no more. But if education can respond to this challenge with such programs as an enlarged and continually more sophisticated attention to the role of propaganda in our society, with serious exploration of new ways to utilize the feedback potential of these analysis techniques, it is possible that democratic processes may be facilitated. Mass media may now bring the faces and words of national candidates to many more individuals than the most rigorous whistle-stop campaign of the past, and the many

---

[15] Charles R. Dechert, "The Development of Cybernetics," *The Social Impact of Cybernetics,* p. 31.

surveys of voter opinion provide a feedback mechanism that could be a powerful tool in the hands of alert voters.

Cybernetics also challenges the adequacy of job-oriented education from an economic perspective. As more and more work becomes automated it becomes increasingly hard to maintain full employment. But we are caught in a bind because we need consumers for the vast numbers of goods produced by automation. Our inheritance of the puritan ethic of work as a moral necessity pressures us to create jobs, on the principle that only he who works (produces) shall eat (consume). Now that production is facilitated by automation, the problem is not to provide sufficient incentive to productivity, but to stimulate consumption. With our ethical values pulling us one way, and economic necessity another, there is much schizophrenia. Certainly one of the keys for relieving this pressure and for making a smooth adjustment to both the economic threats and blessings of the cybernetic age will be education for leisure. And when we have created a sense of the value of leisure, there can then be a feedback into the cybernetic revolution. Once leisure activities are valued, then there will be interest in improving and enhancing them through the application of cybernetics, as there is now interest in improving and enhancing production by such means. In this way cybernetics can be brought into better balance between production and leisure activities,[16] and thus serve the person more than the system by enabling him to respond to authentic values rather than to react to manipulation to consume.

Cybernetics is often viewed as a threat to individualism, but it could also be its servant as well. Either outcome is possible and neither is inevitable. Scattered throughout Marshall McLuhan's

---

[16] For a discussion of the detrimental effect of maintaining production as an overriding national goal, see John Kenneth Galbraith, *The Affluent Society* (Boston: Houghton Mifflin, 1958). Cf. Paul Tillich, *Systematic Theology*, III, 259: "The gadget itself is not evil, but gearing a whole economy to it and repressing the question of an ultimate end of all production of technical goods is."

writings there are some observations which suggest to me, at least, that the issue of individuality-conformity in the contemporary scene is more complex than many statements of the trend have recognized. McLuhan suggests that the industrial revolution issued in a mechanical context in which specialists coped with fragmented elements, and that cybernetics has reestablished the awareness of integral and inclusive patterns that had been dominant in the age of hunting and farming. He describes our age as a "cool" period, demanding involvement by the increase of speed in communication and general availability of information. We are now living in what McLuhan terms a "global village." And yet, with all this emphasis on the trend away from individual isolation, McLuhan also insists that the fear of centralism is misguided. It misconceives of cybernetics and automation as extensions of the mechanical age, rather than as harbingers of a new age. For example, the wide availability of information will break down monopolistic control of the media of communication, and the wealth of possibilities will necessitate an autonomy of learning.

But there is, as Wiener notes,[17] an opposite tendency toward secrecy. Items of knowledge are classified, and to communicate them to the enemy is to be guilty of both treason and theft. And yet the biggest secret of all about the atom bomb was broadcast without the least hesitation—namely, the secret that it could be made. Once this was known, the scientists of any country could duplicate the feat. Also, on the American scene at least, information is considered a commodity which can be bought or sold; and thus there are various regulations, such as patent and copyright laws, to protect the "ownership rights" of the possessor of information, and which do so by means of regulating and limiting the flow of information. And yet, the newest and most revolutionary information is so different from the common stock

---

[17] *The Human Use of Human Beings,* chap. 7.

of information available to the public that it is either not valued
or is actually opposed. Some of the dynamics of the resistance to
new truths is captured in this quotation:

> Reasonable persons may well differ over what is the major menace
> to our way of life in our time. There is Communism and also those who
> hold that it can be best extirpated by universal annihilation. The men
> who picture the American family poised in prayer around a Thanksgiving
> turkey with a word for life insurance, light beer, or Coca-Cola worked
> gracefully into the text have a claim. So do the increasing numbers who
> defend low pecuniary interest on grounds of high moral principle—the
> industrial statesmen who selflessly resist wage increases to protect the
> community from inflation, and the large fruit and vegetable farmers who
> argue that minimum wages and working standards for migrant labor would
> be an interference with our treasured traditions of human liberty. Not for
> years, we should note, has anyone complained with candor that some
> reform would cost him money.
>
> However, it is possible that our greatest danger, in these days of
> massive introspection, is from our terrible solemnity. For this is a serious
> source of inflexibility. Change and new evidence have a way of making
> previous convictions seem odd, even ridiculous. The reasonably relaxed
> man can accept correction without too grievous loss of dignity. But the
> solemn man cannot. He may have heard that the truth will set him free.
> But he rightly senses that it might also make him seem silly.[18]

But there is also a foolishness in our attempts to accept the truth
only after it becomes inevitable, although this foolishness is more
readily overlooked by others and evaded by ourselves. The process runs about like this. Each new development is first scorned as
visionary and impractical. When it becomes economically advan-
tageous it is adopted by business and commended as good common sense. Finally it is incorporated into the general way of life,
with abundant comment to the effect that it was nothing really
new, after all.[19]

---

[18] John Kenneth Galbraith, *The Liberal Hour* (Boston: Houghton Mifflin,
1960), pp. 1-2.

[19] Diebold, *Beyond Automation*, p. 114.

The Rhythm of Imagination and Doubt

Education, by its very nature and desire, has sought out the complex issues of life and has approached them with a rhythm of imagination and doubt. Cybernetics provides no occasion to change this basic approach. Today, as always, we need men who can use their imagination to project themselves into new situations and devise new concepts and techniques; and, equally, we need men of critical acumen who will test, examine, verify, and doublecheck before they proceed. The cultivation of imagination is especially crucial. In the past we have been suspicious of it, and now in the cybernetic age reality has outrun the imagination of most of us.

One of the reasons for depreciating imagination is our use of it to refer to something which we thought in the past and now recognize as mistaken. For example, "I had imagined that he was a member of a conspiracy." Perhaps it is seen more clearly in the statement: "The assumed conspiracy was purely imaginary."

But we do have other uses of the term. For example, we prefer an imaginative story, painting, or term paper to its unimaginative counterpart. Here we refer to the creativity and ingenuity expressed in some actual production of man.

Another use combines elements of both of these. It refers (as in #1) to something which is "purely" imaginary, but without any suggestion that we have been mistaken. Rather, it is an expression of creativity (as in #2), but without being concretized in an artifact or product. This is illustrated in the exhortation: "Imagine what it would be like if all illness were eliminated." There can also be a past reference—for example, "Imagine what it would have been like to live in Rome at the time of Julius or Augustus Caesar."

Basically, imagination is the ability of the mind to form pictures (images), especially the ability to do so with a wealth of detail, even when prompted by the most meager stimulus. As W. Macneile Dixon imaginatively describes it, the human mind is not a debating hall, but a picture gallery.[20] The memory also has the capacity to form pictures, and has often preempted all other meanings of imagination. For example, Thomas Hobbes described imagination as "decaying sense." He said that it is identical with memory, but that the use of the term "memory" emphasized the *decaying* of the sense and the term "imagination" emphasized the *object* itself which is fading from the senses.[21] But there is a more significant difference than this. Memory is restricted to the re-creation of past events and experiences. Memory images are re-produced, rather than invented. Memory speaks of the imitative and perceptive capacities of the mind, imagination of its creative and generative capacities. The imagination is unlimited, except by our own failure to cultivate it. The new and exciting possibilities opened up by the cybernetic revolution are both an expression of and a demand for an unbridled exercise of imagination.

Imagination has always been a vital element of good education. In the cybernetic age the need is intensified for the cultivation of imagination in the process of education and for the application of imagination to the challenges and problems posed by education.

There has always been change in the world, but in the cybernetic revolution the rapidity of change and the novelty of the outcome are greatly increased. This means that education must basically be education for change.[22] It will still be necessary to learn blocks of material, but it will be more important to cultivate the ability to relate materials, often of a seemingly disparate nature. It will still be necessary to memorize lists and tables, but it will be more important to understand the why's and wherefore's. It will still be necessary to achieve technical competence, but it will be more important to be able to adapt to change.

Much confusion is engendered by a failure to distinguish be-

---

[20] *The Human Situation*, p. 65.   [21] *Leviathan*, Part I, chap. 2.

[22] Diebold, *Beyond Automation*, chap. 5. Diebold characterizes education as "at once the core of the problem and the seed of the solution" (p. 11).

tween a student who is well-adapted and one who is adaptable. The situation of rapid change is often interpreted as calling for an emphasis on education that produces a well-adapted student. But in a rapidly changing world, it is detrimental to the future life and work of the student to have him feel that he is adapted, or even that adaptation is to be valued, even if not necessarily attained. In other words, adaptation can be in tension with adaptability, and the conflict between the two is heightened in an age of rapid transition. Consequently, the danger of confusing the two is heightened.

There is an interesting tension that is raised in this connection. The type of education that is needed in the cybernetic age is not the kind that can be recorded in a true-false or multiple-choice exam, and yet this is the kind of exam that can most easily be turned over to the machine for grading. Those who are interested in the application of cybernetics to education will have to choose between attending primarily to the gadgetry it offers or to the new situation and new world view that cybernetic machinery creates.

Another problem for education in the cybernetic age is the means whereby talent can be discovered at an early age. The educational deprivation of talented people becomes more and more serious in the cybernetic age. Already, too many people of ability are being lost to higher education. This is especially true in minority groups. The small number of Negroes and women in graduate school, for example, is testimony to the capacities that are not being cultivated.[23] It is going to take imagination to solve this problem.

Our tendency to view imagination as an inferior form of sense perception has led to some distorted views of the relation of art and science, and of the nature of science itself. We have tended to look upon artists as something of a luxury. Such a view

---

[23] DuBridge, "Educational and Social Consequences," *Automation and Technological Change*, pp. 37-39.

is commented on by the narrator in Lawrence Durrell's *Justine*. He remarks that although art is useless it has value in the solace it provides. The consolation of art operates through its capacity for achieving significance through reordering. As he artistically expresses it:

> Our common actions in reality are simply the sackcloth covering which hides the cloth-of-gold—the meaning of the pattern. For us artists there waits the joyous compromise through art with all that wounded or defeated us in daily life; in this way, not to evade destiny, as the ordinary people try to do, but to fulfil it in its true potential—the imagination.[24]

Later, he comments on Balthazar, whom he considers to be exerting such a control over life. Balthazar was "using himself up" in living, unlike most people who "lie and let life play upon them like the tepid discharges of a douche-bag." Instead of the Cartesian *cogito,* Balthazar's philosophy was "I imagine, therefore I belong and am free." [25] Later, in *Clea,* reflecting upon an incident in which Balthazar hunted for the lost key to a watch his father had given him because it "belonged" [26] to the watch and could not simply be replaced, the narrator recalls these thoughts of Balthazar: "We become what we dream. . . . We achieve in reality, in substance, only the picture of the imagination." [27] This is a forceful apologia for the artistic imagination.

Indeed, H. D. Lewis argues that the artist "looks at the world more squarely than the scientist." He is referring to the fact that the scientist looks for universal truths, whereas the artist looks at the specific and individual aspects, and also to the fact that the scientist strives for detachment while the artist strives for involvement. Lewis also goes on to note that this more direct

---

[24] *The Alexandria Quartet* (New York: E. P. Dutton, 1962), p. 20.

[25] *Ibid.,* pp. 79-80.

[26] Cf. Gabriel Marcel's notion of "participation."

[27] *The Alexandria Quartet,* p. 701. We also find this view expressed by the diplomat and writer, Ludwig Pursewarden, e.g.: "The so-called act of living is really an act of the imagination" (p. 772).

confrontation with reality places severe limits upon the artist's work, especially in the area of rational analysis and prediction. He has an excellent statement of the paradox of the artist's confrontation with reality.

> The more the artist invests the commonplace reality of ordinary experience with the significance of his peculiar individual impression of them, the more starkly do they also present to him an alien irreducible nature. The finer his appreciation of objects the more is their distinctiveness stressed; there are no essential grips, no claims to be staked, but only a relationship which, in becoming more intimate, is in that measure also more precarious and fortuitous; the closer the artist moves to reality the more it is alarmingly aloof, and so, paradoxically but unmistakably, in art there is an unveiling which is at the same time a concealment; in the very process of clarification there is also a deepening of mystery, not in the sense that there is a mystery at the end of every scientific truth, the sense, that is, that the solution of problems sets us *ad infinitum* new problems to solve, but in a more absolute immediate sense that that which is made peculiarly plain to us is itself proportionately more enigmatic. Mystery and illumination are one in art.[28]

Such appreciations of the artistic imagination are very much needed to overcome the rather grudging tolerance that society affords the artists in its midst.[29]

But we need to recognize the role that imagination plays in science itself. Creative imagination and scientific objectivity are not simply in need of a willingness to coexist; they are in need of a more vital relation. It is at this point that Jacob Bronowski's work has made such a valuable contribution. In *Science and Human Values* he argues that imagination is as truly involved in scientific discovery as it is in artistic creation. He considers the use of imagination in scientific discovery to be essential not only to the original insight, but also to later appropriation of it.

---

[28] *Morals and Revelation* (London: George Allen & Unwin, 1951), pp. 212-13.
[29] Galbraith's essay, "Economics and Art," refutes the rationalization that artists are more creative when they are poverty-stricken.—*The Liberal Hour*, pp. 44-62

In *The Identity of Man*[30] Bronowski insists that science is different from poetry, not in its execution but in its endeavor. Paradoxically, the endeavor to which science puts imagination has as its aim the impoverishment of imagination, in the sense that it wants to weed out the proliferation of new ideas. It is in this particular application, rather than in the use of imagination as such, that we discern the difference between the artist and the scientist. The artist manifests a more unbridled exercise of imagination, but the imagination is an essential element in the scientist's as well as in the artist's attempt to understand the world around him.

Responsibility and the Quest for Order

It is the closer tie of the scientist to what we commonly term "the natural order" that necessitates a greater bridling of imagination by the scientist than by the artist, and that makes the scientist seem to be more disciplined in his quest. But in another sense the scientist has less need for discipline because of the nature of his quest. Norbert Wiener employs the theological distinction between Manichaean and Augustinian interpretations of nature to clarify the approach of the scientist in his attempts to bring about order.[31] In seeking to discover the organization within nature, what kind of opponent is the scientist confronting? Is it a positive force dedicated to the frustration and overthrow of order, a la Manichaeism? Or is it rather the absence of order, a la Augustinianism? The decision on this question determines which of sharply opposed alternatives is chosen as a tactic. The Manichaean believes that nature will try to deceive us, and we can never be certain that we are not being taken in by a bluff. Moreover, nature will alter its policy if we begin to catch on to it. The Augustinian believes that

---

[30] (Garden City, N.Y.: The Natural History Press, 1965), pp. 49-50.
[31] *The Human Use of Human Beings*, pp. 11, 34-36, 190-93; cf. Coulson, *Christianity in an Age of Science*, pp. 11 ff.

nature is not an autonomous and opposing power. It may challenge our utmost resources and energies of mind and body to overcome the resistance of disorder, but this resistance is passive rather than active. If the human situation becomes disordered it is not because nature is too powerful and too deceptive for man to cope with, but because man is too weak for his own good. But the weakness of man only delays scientific advance and does not cause a loss of ground, as may result from a weak move in chess, for example. Wiener feels that the Manichaean attitude may be appropriate for the chess player or the detective or the military commander, but that it is disastrous for the scientist.

But where do we go from here? To take a specific example, the genetic code may not frustrate efforts to crack it, but what attitude do we employ when we seek to apply this code to the genetic betterment of the human race? Do we now shed our scientific confidence and assume an attitude of wariness and suspicion? If we have to surrender our Augustinianism, must we then move to a Manichaean outlook? We need a theological perspective not only on scientific discovery, but also on the social application of science.

Wiener's emphasis upon malevolence as resulting from man's inner weakness and failure recalls our discussion, in chapter two, of the *imago dei* as man's freedom and responsibility. If man responds in faith, he fulfills his relation with God; sin perverts this relation. But in both cases man is equally a responsible being. Through sin, man is in opposition to the image of God, and his whole existence is affected by this revolt. It perverts, but does not annihilate, the *imago dei*. Man, for Brunner, must be understood in terms of the contradiction between his origin and his opposition to it. In other words, the contradiction between creation and sin is not *in* man, it *is* man. The word of God is, however, not basically *demand*, but rather *gift*, since the word is the way in which God communicates himself to man and thereby gives him life. The word is also the source of our fellow human beings, with whom we are called to live in responsible community.

The burden of our investigation has been to support the contention that the cybernetic understanding of man as being in the image of the machine is compatible with the view that man is free and responsible as the image of God. This capacity for free response involves the possibility of both creative and destructive response. Consequently, we have considered the beneficial and detrimental possibilities that are latent in the social application of cybernetics. Wiener's emphasis upon the importance of an Augustinian perspective for the scientist implies a decisive element of freedom and responsibility for man in the cybernetic age.

But there is something unusual about Wiener's reference to Augustine that merits our consideration. Wiener is contrasting him with the Manichaeans, and thus he places Augustine at the pole of optimism regarding the problem of evil. But Augustine has often been branded as overly pessimistic about man's nature and potential, teaching that man is guilty of original sin and unable to free himself from bondage to sin. In other contexts, Wiener himself has expressed grave doubts that man will make beneficial use of the power released by cybernetics, and his justification for continuing to develop this science is that failure to do so would, by default, hand this power to those who scheme without scruple.[32] Wiener is quite sound in his contention that Augustine thought of evil as privative, rather than positive. But we need to carry the theological development further if it is also to illumine what Wiener terms "excessive optimism." [33] If we look further into Augustine's concept of creation as good and examine his understanding of man in this wider context, there are valuable lessons for those who seek to cultivate the fruits of the cybernetic revolution without harvesting its destructive possibilities.

---

[32] Wiener, *Cybernetics*, pp. 27-29. [33] *Ibid.*, p. 162.

For Augustine, creation is *ex nihilo*, and all creation is good because it is created out of nothing and therefore solely due to God's purposive and loving activity.[34] This is in contrast with the Manichaean view, which saw creation as being out of matter and therefore essentially evil. Augustine, by saying that we are created out of nothing and not out of God, also denied pantheism. Further, we are created out of nothing, not out of necessity. Since creation is a voluntary and not a forced act, God's purpose for creation is good and loving. All created beings are good because they are created by God, and not out of some evil substance. There is nothing that is essentially, and hence irredeemably, evil in creation.[35] Evil is *privatio boni*.[36] Evil depends on the good of which it is the perversion.[37] Therefore evil is not necessary. It does not come from nature. There is no efficient cause of evil, only a deficient cause.[38] This means that evil comes from freedom. It is not metaphysical but historical. It cannot be defined in terms of external acts, but only in terms of inward lust.[39] As a creature, man is good. He sins, not because he is a creature of God, but in spite of it. "The devil did not take man by force, but caught him by persuasion." [40] Although evil has arisen out of nature, it is not essentially of nature. Things are not to be blamed, but the evil use of them.[41] Because evil is not an essential aspect of creatureliness, all evil is redeemable, however pervasive and destructive it may be. Evil is not natural, but is the perversion of nature. It is the vitiation of nature, not the fulfillment of nature.

It is important to note that the assertion that creation is essentially good is not, for the Augustinian tradition, a denial of the reality of evil. It is a denial that evil is essentially real, but not in the same sense as the claim that in the light of the

---

[34] For a forceful contemporary restatement of this doctrine of creation and its ramifications, see Gilkey, *Maker of Heaven and Earth.*

[35] *Civ. dei,* XII, 3.   [36] *Enchir.* 11.   [37] *Conf. VII,* 12 (18) .

[38] *Civ. dei,* XII, 6-8.   [39] *De lib. arb.* I, iii (14-21) .

[40] *De lib. arb.* III, x (112) .   [41] *De lib. arb.* I, xv (113) .

total system evil is not real, as is urged by those who seek an intellectual solution to the problem of evil. For the Augustinian tradition, the problem of evil is not theoretical, but practical. Augustinianism denies that evil is ultimately real, but not in order to conclude that it is only apparently real. Rather, it denies that evil is ultimately real in order to assert that evil is redeemable because it is not essential in the nature of things. The description of evil as a perversion of the good involves a recognition of the destructive power of evil, combined with a determination to take hold of what seems radically evil and, to the utmost of our ability, turn it into good. In making an affirmation that creation is essentially good, we dare not deny the baffling and tragic nature of life by means of pious platitudes. If we indulge in these, we are untrue both to life and to the context of the doctrine, actually negating it by our manner of expressing it.

Because of his recognition of the pervasiveness of evil and its power to blind and corrupt man, Augustine engaged in controversy not only with Manichaeism, but also with Pelagianism. Paul Tillich is a contemporary theologian who expresses this same balance in his concept of man. He contends that both the Manichaean and Pelagian perspectives have serious lacunae in their understanding of man. The Manichaean view disregards man's moral freedom and responsibility; the Pelagian view disregards man's tragic predicament and bondage. Tillich discusses this in connection with his consideration of "the fall" of man, or as he prefers to call it, "the transition from essence to existence." [42] Man's "finite freedom" makes the fall possible. Nature, though finite, lacks the freedom which is necessary to the possibility of a fall. But it is not freedom alone that accounts for the possibility of the fall, for God is infinite freedom. It is "finite freedom" that makes the fall possible. Man is not only finite, but is also aware of his finitude; therefore, he experiences

---

[42] Tillich, *Systematic Theology*, II, 29-44.

anxiety. This drives man beyond his state of "dreaming innocence." Man cannot avoid temptation. Lest he lose himself by
lack of actualization, man loses himself by actualization. Since
the previous chapter closed with a plea for an understanding of
man in the light of cybernetics which transcends the old dualisms,
it is important to note that Tillich is presenting a monistic view
of man. Tillich himself stresses this feature of his discussion.

> The analysis of temptation, as given here, makes no reference to a
> conflict between the bodily and the spiritual side of man as a possible
> cause. The doctrine of man indicated here implies a "monistic" under-
> standing of man's nature in contrast to a dualistic one. Man is a whole
> man, whose essential being has the character of dreaming innocence, whose
> finite freedom makes possible the transition from essence to existence,
> whose aroused freedom puts him between two anxieties which threaten
> the loss of self, whose decision is against the preservation of dreaming
> innocence and for self-actualization. Mythologically speaking, the fruit of
> the tree of temptation is both sensuous and spiritual.[43]

The transition from essence to existence contains both a moral
and a tragic element. Man's situation is a result both of his own
responsible decision and of the universal tragic destiny of man.
    The tension involved in this situation leads to denials of one
side or the other, and it is in this light that we can understand the
dynamics of Manichaeism and Pelagianism. The Pelagian view
disregards the tragic element and retains the element of responsible decision, holding that man can just as freely respond not
to contradict as to contradict his nature. But Tillich points
out, in contrast to such a view, that there are limits to responsibility, even in the mature man, and that some of these are of
such a drastic nature as to be readily recognized in moral and
legal decisions. In terms of our discussion at the end of Part Two,
man is dependent upon the machinery of his physical and
nervous system. Conversely, the Manichaean disregards the free

---

[43] *Ibid.*, p. 36.

response of the total person, in which all the determining factors are incorporated. Again, there is a denial of the integral unity of man, but from the opposite extreme. Tillich sums up his critique of the extremes of Pelagianism and Manichaeism in this formula: "Moral freedom becomes 'Pelagian' only if it is separated from tragic destiny; and tragic destiny becomes 'Manichaean' only if it is separated from moral freedom."

At times, Tillich sounds very negative and pessimistic in his references to technology. Consider this quotation, for example:

> History is the sphere in which man *determines himself* in freedom. And history, at the same time, is the sphere in which man *is determined* by fate against his freedom. Very often the creations of his freedom are the tools used by fate against him; as, for instance, today the technical powers created by him turn against him with irresistible force.[44]

On the other hand, it is possible to point to an interesting parallel between Francis Bacon and Tillich. Bacon is often considered the father of technology because of his insistence that "knowledge is power." But Bacon recognized some degree of human limitation when he asserted that "nature to be commanded must be obeyed." [45] Similar elements seem to be included in Tillich's interpretation of the Cross as the symbol of subjection to existence and of the Resurrection as the symbol of the conquest of existence.[46] Obedience and subjection form a close parallel, and so do commanding and conquering. But it is significant that Tillich is talking about existence and Bacon about nature. In an earlier age, when man was fighting against the forces of nature, technology was almost inevitably a means of progress. Today, in our crowded cities, far removed from direct contact with nature, the situation is far more complex and technology is much more a mixture of bane and blessing. In his attempt to

---

[44] *The Protestant Era*, p. 186.
[45] *Novum Organum* (First Book), Aphorism 3.
[46] *Systematic Theology*, II, 152-53.

influence and control his environment man has slowly made such progress that the natural environment is no longer the decisive influence on his life. With the cybernetic revolution, man has made such a breakthrough that he is now threatened by his artificially created environment, which was originally intended to protect him from his natural environment. About this ironical situation, it has been well said: "The interesting question seems to be whether man, having succeeded after all these years in bringing so much of the natural environment under his control, can now manage the imposing system he has created for the specific purpose of enabling him to manage his natural environment." [47] In such a situation technology needs to be appraised with a critical eye, but this so easily becomes a jaundiced view.

Neither the rose-colored nor the jaundiced view of affairs expresses the Christian tradition. The Christian doctrine of creation is not only a basis for recognizing the bondage of man and his liability to perverse and destructive use of the created order. It is also the basis for soundly affirming the possibility of redemption. Thus the Christian tradition has attempted to combine a realistic appraisal of the destructive outcome of human misuse of power with a realistic hope that man's power can be more often and more effectively exerted toward efforts at reconciliation and creative change. Nature is seen both as fallen and as sacramental. Neither progress nor regress are inevitable. Consequently, neither complacency nor fatalism are appropriate. This flexibility of the Christian heritage needs to be brought to bear upon its appraisal of the actualities and potentialities of the cybernetic revolution. The development of cybernetics has not created the possibility of widespread destruction, but it has intensified it. Man is still free and responsible in his use of cybernetic developments, but the consequences for good and for ill are increased.

---

[47] Elting E. Morison, *Men, Machines, and Modern Times* (Cambridge: M. I. T. Press, 1966), p. 16.

This is not simply a fifty-fifty proposition, however, since the increase in potential lowers the possibility of recovering from misuse.

A carefully balanced statement of Tillich's appraisal of technological advancement is found in his discussion of the three ambiguities of all technological development, including the most primitive tools and the most sophisticated productions of the cybernetic age. The "ambiguity of freedom and limitation" expresses the combination of creative and destructive possibilities of technical production. "It opens up a road along which no limit can be seen, but it does so through a limited, finite being." The "ambiguity of means and ends" refers to the problem of the purpose of technical production. This problem is obscured when technology is geared to the satisfaction of basic needs, but it looms large when new needs are being artificially created. "The production of means—of gadgets—becomes an end in itself, since no superior end is visible." The "ambiguity of self and thing" refers to man's ability to transform natural objects into things and the reflexive influence of this act. "The transforming subject himself is transformed." By transforming natural objects into things, man loses his own selfhood to thinghood. Hence, "the liberation given to man by technical possibilities turns into enslavement to technical actuality." Tillich may at times seem anti-technological, but his discussion at this point is clearly balanced between the possibilities and the danger, and explicitly disavows any romanticist solutions that involve a return to the "so-called natural" state of primitivism or pretechnology.[48]

The dual possibility of technology as that which is able to free man and also to enslave him is expressed for me in a most felicitous phrase found in the writings of William Burroughs— "antibiotic handcuffs." I am far from confident that I can properly interpret the imagery of this febrile writer, but his phrase

---

[48] Tillich, *Systematic Theology*, III, 73-74.

suggests to me the combination of the callous indifference with which we enslave men, and the solicitous attention we give to the provision of the niceties of our polite society while doing so. Burroughs is rightly in a rage against antibiotic handcuffs, for they are a graver peril than germ-laden ones. In other words, a society that is as developed as ours in combating the baneful effects of germs upon man is not only without excuse for enslaving man, but stands under the severest condemnation for its grossly inadequate standard of values. The age of antibiotics is the time for releasing man. It is the time for the fullest range of freedom and responsibility. The cybernetic age provides unprecedented opportunities for freedom and responsibility, and also for bondage and enslavement, albeit antibiotic. The development of the *imago machinae* has not diminished the *imago dei*. The enlargement of man in the cybernetic revolution is tremendously exciting and confronts us with the necessity to respond to responsibility itself, which is the very essence of the image of man. To this new human situation, brought about by the cybernetic revolution, the church has the good news that it is God's call to man and God's grace for man that enables him to respond.

Index

Abstracting machine, 190-91, 193

Acts, Book of, 71, 211, 238

Adams, E. M., 105

Adaptation, and adaptability, 282; in machines, 156-58

African Genesis (Ardrey), 16

ALGOL, 189, 194

Alice in Wonderland (Carroll), 123-24

Alienation, 17, 61, 257

Allee, Warner Clyde, 103

Ambiguity, of future of science, 229; of machines, 223; in technology, 291-94

Ampère, André, 211

Analogy of Religion (Butler), 34

Anderson, Alan Ross, 170

Andreae, Valentin, 211

Android, 49-50, 164-65, 182, 198

Anshen, Melvin, 176

"Antibiotic handcuffs," 293-94

Anti-civil-libertarian arguments, 181, 182

Anti-utopianism, 213, 227, 242, 250

Anxiety, 117-18, 119, 290

Ardrey, Robert, 16

Aristotle, 81

Artist, attitude toward, 282-83; imagination in, 283-84; and scientist, 285; sensitivity of, to environment, 273-74

Ashby, W. Ross, 155, 156

Atomism, 38, 40

Augustine, 72, 285-89

Austin, John, 137, 144-45, 193

Authority, overt and anonymous, 110

Automatic abstracting and translating, 190-92, 193

Automatic factory, 157

Automatic teaching, 265-70

Automation, 9, 235, 277

Autonomy, 67, 90, 278

Bacon, Francis, 291

Bagrit, Leon, 210, 235

Barbour, Ian G., 246

Barrett, William, 100

Barth, Karl, 52, 53-54, 61-62, 66

Barzun, Jacques, 275

Beatniks, 214

Beginning, notion of, 256-60

Behaviorism, 198, 217-18

Beloff, John, 147 n.

Bernal, J. D., 226

Bertocci, Peter A., 108, 132-33

Biblical view of man, 76-77, 84

Binary system, 43-44

Biology, 10, 164, 244

Birth and heredity, philosophy of, 255-63

Black power, 17

Blanshard, Brand, 99-100

Bohr, Niels, 39

Boorstin, Daniel J., 195

Born, Max, 41

Boulding, Kenneth E., 16

Brain, electronic, 23, 170 (*see also* Computer); human, 46, 156; and memory, 248

Brave New World (Huxley), 213, 218, 227, 248-49

Brave New World Revisited (Huxley), 249

Brightman, Edgar S., 119-21

Bronowski, Jacob, 127, 233, 284, 285

Brunner, Emil, 12-14, 51-91, 152-53, 168-69, 189, 202, 205, 210, 214-15, 243, 253, 262, 269, 275, 286

Buber, Martin, 74 n., 149, 205, 231

Burdick, Eugene, 276

Burgess, Anthony, 213

Burroughs, William, 293-94

Butler, Joseph, 34, 35

295

Date

Demco 38-297